AN INTRODUCTION TO X-RAY
METALLOGRAPHY

AN INTRODUCTION TO
X-RAY
METALLOGRAPHY

By

A. TAYLOR

M.Sc., Ph.D., F.Inst.P.

*Sometime Darbishire Research Fellow
in the Victoria University of Manchester*

WITH A FOREWORD

by

SIR LAWRENCE BRAGG

O.B.E., F.R.S.

Cavendish Professor of Physics, Cambridge

LONDON

CHAPMAN & HALL LTD.

11 HENRIETTA STREET W.C.2

1945

First published . . . 1945

BOOK
PRODUCTION
WAR ECONOMY
STANDARD

THIS BOOK IS PRODUCED
IN COMPLETE CONFORMITY
WITH THE AUTHORIZED
ECONOMY STANDARDS

PRINTED IN GREAT BRITAIN BY BUTLER AND TANNER LTD., FROME AND LONDON
BOUND BY G. AND J. KITCAT LTD., LONDON. FLEXIBACK BINDING.

FOREWORD

X-Ray metallography, as Dr. Taylor says in his Preface, is proving itself to be an essential tool in metallurgical research. It is taking its place beside the classical thermal and microscopic methods which have proved to be so valuable to the study of metals and alloys. It supplements these methods rather than replaces them, the combination of all being the ideal at which to aim. X-ray analysis has almost entirely been developed by physicists, who have been handicapped by their lack of metallurgical experience. The metallurgist's wide knowledge of the behaviour and characteristics of alloys is beyond the reach of the physicist, and he must look to his colleagues to appreciate the uses to which the new tool he has developed can be put.

This book should be valuable in bringing the two sciences together. While the subject has been rapidly expanding, there is a dearth of books of reference and reviews owing to the war. Dr. Taylor has collected and arranged much of the material which has appeared as scattered original papers in recent years, and it may be confidently hoped that the present volume will be very useful to the student, whether physicist or metallurgist, who is using X-ray methods of examination.

W. L. BRAGG.

Cavendish Laboratory,
August, 1944.

PREFACE

X-Ray analysis is now playing a leading part in the physical examination of metals. Until quite recently, the technique was in the hands of a few specialists who served their apprenticeship in university research departments and research institutions. As their methods permeated into the more enlightened industrial organizations, the demand for skilled personnel and improved equipment steadily grew.

The stress of war has suddenly accentuated the increasing demand for physicists and metallurgists with a knowledge of X-ray crystallography and for crystallographers skilled in metallurgy. Few have had the necessary experience in both fields, and the research worker is often faced with the unenviable task of sorting out the relevant information from a vast literature written by experts for experts. I have tried to fill the need for an introductory book which affords a guide to the literature and which, at the same time, possesses the character of a work of reference. It should therefore be of service to the student reading for a degree and the research worker in college or in industry.

Ever widening in its scope, X-ray analysis is rapidly extending far beyond the original aim of determining atomic arrangements in crystals. It is now proving itself an essential tool in metallurgical research. For this highly specialized field of application, I have used the name X-ray Metallography.

Among the many problems which confront the metallurgist are those of thermal equilibrium, internal stress and strain, crystal texture and phase identification. The practical solution of these problems does not require the elegant methods of Fourier Synthesis, the theory of Space Groups, or the use of the Reciprocal Lattice, so invaluable in Structure Analysis. For this reason, I have not dealt with these more theoretical aspects of structure theory, giving only the barest essentials necessary to cover known simple structures. Should the reader require detailed information on the technique of structure analysis, he will find it fully treated in *The Crystalline State*, by W. H. Bragg and W. L. Bragg, and in other works in English by R. W. G. Wyckoff, G. L. Clark, M. J. Buerger, W. P. Davey, J. T. Randall and R. W. James.

To my wife I owe a special debt of gratitude for her assistance in preparing the book for publication. I also wish to record my thanks to the many learned societies and industrial organizations who have given permission to reproduce illustrations from their publications. My grateful thanks are also due to my former chief, Dr. A. J. Bradley, F.R.S., for Figs. 36 and 134, and to the following who supplied photographs or blocks: The American Society for Testing Materials, Messrs. G. Bell & Sons, Ltd., The British Ceramic Society, *The Electrical Times*, The Institute of Metals, The Iron and Steel Institute, *The Journal of Scientific Instruments*, The Metropolitan-Vickers Electrical Co., Ltd., *Nature* (Messrs. Macmillan & Co., Ltd.), Messrs. Philips Lamps, Ltd., The Royal Society, The Royal Society of Arts, Messrs. Siemens-Schuckert, Ltd., The Society of Glass Technology, the English Electric Co., Ltd., and the Victor X-Ray Corporation, Ltd.

Finally, I should like to thank Sir Lawrence Bragg for the Foreword which he has kindly written, and for the interest he has taken in this work.

MANCHESTER,
  October, 1944.

CONTENTS

CHAPTER I

INTRODUCTORY—THE SCOPE OF X-RAY ANALYSIS

THE improvement of the microscope in the seventeenth century was destined to open up new fields of biological and metallurgical discovery only paralleled by the great advances made in astronomy by Galileo's telescope. Robert Hooke, in his *Micrographia*, not only described the appearance of various insects, plants and seeds which he observed under the microscope, thereby helping to lay the foundations of the theory of evolution, but by his researches on metals he could lay claim to being the first metallographer. In the opening chapters of his book, he describes the rough, truncated appearance of the point of a small sharp needle and the apparently blunted jagged edge of a sharpened razor, both important tests of the quality of his instrument, and later he goes on to discuss the nature of colour films on steel and to describe the appearance of lead crystallizing from its alloy with silver. Very little subsequent work seems to have been done until Sorby, by his classical investigations on steel in the second half of the nineteenth century, securely laid the foundations of modern microscopical metallography. To-day, the microscope still remains the most important instrument of investigation at the metallurgists' disposal.

The most powerful microscope is limited by one important factor, namely, its resolving power. This is entirely dependent upon the effective aperture of the lens system and the wavelength of the light used for making the observations. There is thus a limit set to the scale of the phenomena which are capable of microscopical observation, and erroneous conclusions may be drawn from the misinterpretation of diffraction effects produced by structures just beyond the limits of resolution. During the last few years, interest has been centring about a new type of microscope which uses the principles of electron optics. Although the electron microscope has a resolving power approximately 50 times greater than the finest metallurgical microscopes, it still has several drawbacks which have to be overcome. Nevertheless, it holds great promise for the not too distant future, when it will certainly take its place as standard equipment for the metallurgical laboratory.

The discovery of X-rays by W. C. Röntgen [1] in the year 1895 had immediate and far-reaching consequences in medicine and many

branches of science.   The true nature of the rays was not fully understood for some time, and when, in 1912, crucial experiments were
carried out to test the nature of the radiation, there was at once created
a new branch of physical-chemistry which enabled the molecular
architecture of matter to be revealed.   Many considerations led
physicists to the opinion that X-rays were electro-magnetic waves with
an extremely short wavelength of about 10^{-9} cm. and this accounted
for the failure of all early experimental efforts to demonstrate diffraction effects with the rays by using ordinary optical gratings, because
the intervals between the rulings must not be much larger than the
wavelength of the light investigated.

Now long before the discovery of X-rays, a considerable body of
experimental evidence had accumulated which justified the belief that
the atoms or molecules in matter were arranged in an orderly fashion.
The atoms were conceived to be arranged in groups governed by
well-defined rules of symmetry which fixed their positions in space
by the constant repetition of a unit of pattern.   Furthermore, since
the number of atoms per gram-atom was known, it was not difficult to deduce from simple assumed atomic configurations that the
distances between the atoms in a solid body were of the order of
10^{-8} cm.   In 1912, Max von Laue [2], developing ideas put forward by
P. P. Ewald on the passage of light through a crystal, conceived the
idea of trying to use crystals instead of artificial gratings to diffract
the X-rays.   For if the atoms could behave as diffraction centres, then
a crystal built up from regularly spaced rows of atoms would form
a naturally ruled three-dimensional grating with just the right order
of distance between the rulings to ensure diffraction of the rays.

Friedrich and Knipping, at Laue's suggestion, placed a crystal
of copper sulphate in the X-ray beam so that the rays traversing the
crystal fell upon a photographic plate held in a position to record
any diffracted rays which made a small angle with the transmitted
beam.   The experiment was brilliantly successful, for they obtained
the now familiar "Laue photograph" consisting of arcs of spots
surrounding a central spot produced by the undeviated primary
beam.   X-rays were thus shown to behave in very much the same
manner as waves of visible light, and, simultaneously, the principle
that crystals were founded upon a regularly ordered array of atomic
groups or "space lattice", was firmly established.

Copper sulphate with its low symmetry yields a complex Laue
pattern.   Because of this, Friedrich and Knipping repeated the
experiment using zinc blende, ZnS, which is a crystal with cubic
symmetry, and thereby obtained a relatively simple arrangement of

spots. Laue was able to show that the four-fold symmetry of the pattern was due to the diffraction of electromagnetic waves by a cubic space lattice, but he held the erroneous view that the peculiarities of the X-ray pattern were due, in part, to a number of discrete wave-lengths in the X-ray spectrum. W. L. Bragg [3] made a study of the Laue phenomena and showed that the patterns could be regarded as being produced by a mirror-like reflexion of the electromagnetic waves by regularly spaced plane sheets of atoms in the crystal. He showed that the spectrum of the X-rays used by Friedrich and Knipping was really continuous and that the distribution of the spots in the photographs was entirely due to the cubic character of the crystal. Using the ionization chamber designed by his father, W. H. Bragg, and simplifying the experimental conditions by using monochromatic radiation, he was able to determine the actual arrangements of the atoms in crystals of sylvine (KCl) and rock-salt (NaCl).

From these experiments, a whole new science has sprung. Many new methods of studying crystals by means of X-rays have been developed, and to-day X-rays offer a new versatile tool which can be used side by side with the microscope for the investigation of metallurgical problems. Having a resolving power several hundred times greater than the finest microscope, X-ray diffraction methods can be used to study phenomena dependent on the grouping of the atoms themselves, and because of this, the metallurgist can now avail himself of fundamental knowledge which the microscope is absolutely incapable of giving.

Among the early pioneers of the new technique, special mention should be made of A. Westgren, E. A. Owen and A. J. Bradley, who applied the new methods to the study of metal structures and the thermal equilibrium diagrams of alloys. Mention should also be made of M. Polanyi, who was among the first to study crystal orientation textures in worked metals by means of X-rays.

The metallurgist has evolved a technique of microscopical investigation based on many years of experience, and has learnt to interpret, in an empirical sort of way, the mechanical properties of his material in terms of the microstructures. The newer X-ray technique is unfamiliar to him, and because of inexperience and lack of training in the application of its methods, he is apt to look upon it with some suspicion or to dismiss the X-ray approach as too academic. It must be admitted that over-enthusiasm among some X-ray workers has led them to overlook the fact that many of the results they have obtained could have been achieved almost as readily by the more conventional methods of metallographical practice. Both microscopic and X-ray methods have their limitations, and, while having a great deal of ground in common, each method has problems to which it is peculiarly adapted. X-ray metallography is complementary to microscopical metallography.

At this stage, it will be helpful to get some idea of the scale of magnitude of the structures which can be observed by X-ray and microscopical methods. Structures larger than 10^{-4} cm. become visible under the microscope in polished and etched specimens. Such structures may also be studied by X-ray methods. In the size range 10^{-4} to 10^{-6} cm. X-ray methods have been successfully used to study the mechanism of age hardening, the coercive force in magnets and problems connected with resistance to deformation. The structure of martensite is upon this scale. In the 10^{-7} cm. range, the segregation which leads to one type of age hardening occurs. Finally, and perhaps most important of all, X-rays can be used to investigate structures on the scale of 10^{-8} cm. This is the order of magnitude of the unit of atomic pattern in the crystalline structure of alloy phases.

In the course of a typical metallographical investigation, the alloy is sectioned, carefully polished and etched and then examined under the microscope. In order to see as many of the relevant details as possible, a suitable etching reagent must be selected which will discriminate between the various constituents in the micro-section, and the microscope must be correctly adjusted both with regard to illumination and to magnification. Discrimination between constituents is not always possible microscopically even under the most favourable conditions, yet with very few exceptions this may be accomplished with the greatest of ease by X-ray methods which do not depend on the etching characteristics of the material. On the other hand, while the microscope reveals the manner in which the constituents are distributed, as in a eutectic, for example, an X-ray diffraction photograph merely indicates the co-existence of two phases but reveals nothing at all about the state of aggregation.

During the preliminary period in the investigation of an equilibrium diagram, X-rays are invaluable, yielding as they do a very rapid, certain means of phase identification. Indeed, rapid surveys of complicated ternary systems have already been carried out in a fraction of the time required by microscopic methods, but these investigations must be regarded only as a beginning, necessitating the use of the microscope in future work in order to increase the accuracy of the phase boundary determinations.

The application of X-rays has made fundamental contributions to our understanding of age-hardening phenomena. It has revealed subtle changes in the ordering of the atomic lattice as a result of long periods of annealing, changes which profoundly affect magnetic properties and electrical conductivity. Grain sizes beyond the limits of resolution of the microscope have been measured and the grain orientation in rolled sheet and drawn wire which gives the finished material its anisotropic properties has been made the subject of several fruitful investigations. In the case of rolled sheet, X-rays will reveal grain fragmentation and directionality long before the elongation of grains in the rolling direction becomes evident under the microscope.

Special cameras have been devised for studying alloys at elevated temperatures, one of the early triumphs of this mode of investigation being the elucidation of the true nature of the change points in iron, shown to be caused by the transition from one cubic arrangement of atoms to another. The thermal expansion of the crystal lattice can be studied with great accuracy by means of high-temperature X-ray cameras, and the results compared with those obtained by other methods which can only yield average values representative of the material in bulk. Cameras for studying alloys at very low temperatures have also been constructed. Interesting phase changes in iron-nickel alloys at the temperature of liquid air have been investigated, but so far very little has been published about this aspect of X-ray technique.

Among the more interesting achievements of X-ray crystallography is the discovery that the atomic pattern in a vast number of alloys is a function of the electron concentration. Such an occurrence had been anticipated by Hume-Rothery [4] and was explained afterwards by Jones [5] on the basis of wave-mechanics. In addition to the older substitutional and interstitial types of solid solution already known to exist, a new type of defect lattice has been discovered, in which there is a large percentage of empty places which would normally be occupied by atoms of the parent lattice.

The above is but a very brief summary of the metallographic applications of the new X-ray diffraction methods which, as we can see, are immensely powerful and versatile. The scope of X-ray technique already covers an immense field of enquiry and is rapidly growing. The object of this book is to give the metallurgist an introduction to the applications of X-rays. It does not claim to be comprehensive, for such a book would run into several large volumes. The methods of deducing crystal structures and the theory of space groups are only touched upon, for the metallurgist has neither the time nor the interest to concern himself with the time-consuming task of determining complicated atomic arrangements, although he is interested in the final results. The book falls naturally into two parts, one dealing with the physics of X-rays, and the other with their application to certain aspects of metallurgy. However, despite the large amount of theory underlying the subject, its application has a character essentially practical, and the inclusion of X-ray apparatus in the laboratory will undoubtedly form a worthy and useful complement to the already existing metallographical equipment.

CHAPTER II

X-RAY GENERATING APPARATUS

The Production of X-rays. The sudden stoppage of rapidly
moving electrons by the atoms of matter is accompanied by the
generation of X-rays. The apparatus for the production of the
radiation consists of an evacuated vessel containing two electrodes,
the cathode, which acts as a source of electrons, and an anode, or
target. A high potential difference is applied between the two
electrodes by means of an external circuit, and, under the influence
of the electrostatic field, electrons leave the cathode and strike the
anode with a high velocity. The character of the X-rays thus
generated depends in part upon the velocity of the electrons and
therefore on the tube potential, and partly upon the element composing the target which arrests the motion of the electron stream.
In the early days of X-ray investigation, the radiation was termed
"hard" or "soft" according to whether it penetrated matter or was
easily absorbed. The harder radiations are produced by the higher
tube potentials.

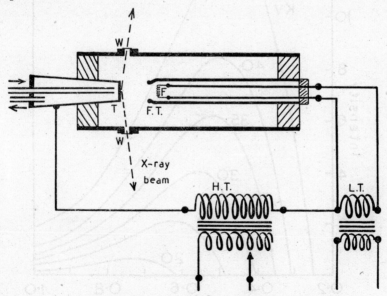

FIG. 1.—Diagrammatic view of X-ray tube and electric circuit.

T. Water-cooled target. *F.* Incandescent tungsten filament. *F.T.* Focusing tube. *W.W.*
Windows covered with thin Al foil, beryllium or Lindemann glass. *H.T.* High-tension transformer.
L.T. Low-tension transformer.

The residual gases in the early types of X-ray tubes were ionized by the electrons extracted from the cold cathode by the field of the applied potential, and the electrons generated in the ionization process also contributed to the stream which bombarded the anti-cathode.   In the more recent Coolidge tube, a spiral of heated tungsten wire emits a copious stream of electrons which is focused upon the target by means of a simple focusing tube.   Only a small fraction of the energy of the electrons is converted into X-rays.   By far the major portion is converted into heat which is usually dissipated by means of a water-cooling system or by air-cooled radiator fins.   A simplified sketch which illustrates the essential features of an X-ray apparatus is shown in Fig. 1.   Later in this chapter, we shall describe a number of commercial tubes suitable for carrying out metallographic investigations.

The X-ray Emission Spectrum.   The target emits a continuous spectrum upon which a line spectrum characteristic of the

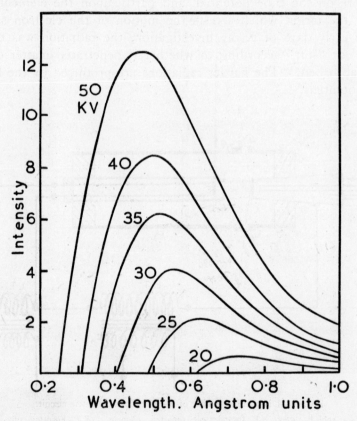

FIG. 2.—Continuous X-ray spectra at different constant tube potentials, emitted by tungsten anticathode (Ulrey).

element comprising the target is superimposed. In order to excite the characteristic radiations, a limiting voltage must be exceeded. For potentials below this limit, the X-ray spectrum is composed entirely of continuous or "white" radiation. The continuous spectrum of tungsten excited at different tube potentials below the initial value to excite the characteristic K radiations is illustrated in Fig. 2.

The spectra end abruptly at a definite short-wave limit, which decreases as the tube potential increases, and tail away slowly on the long-wave side. The minimum wavelength λ_m which can be excited is governed by the Quantum relation

$$Ve = \frac{hc}{\lambda_m}$$

where V = potential applied to the tube,
     e = charge on the electron,
     h = Planck's constant,
and c = velocity of light.

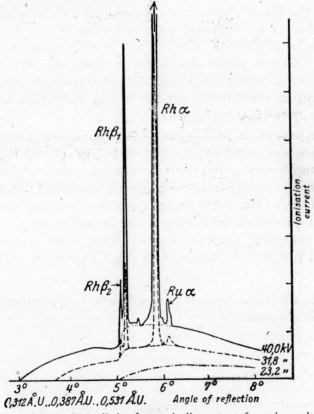

FIG. 3.—Analysis of X-radiation from a rhodium target, for various voltages.
(From *The Spectroscopy of X-rays*, SIEGBAHN; O.U.P., 1925.)

Putting V in volts instead of absolute units, we obtain for the minimum wavelength

$$\lambda_m = \frac{1 \cdot 234}{V} \cdot 10^{-4}.$$

Each element emits characteristic hard "K" radiations from the innermost or K electron shell of the atom, and soft "L" and "M" radiations from the L and M shells. Fig. 3, taken from the *Spectroscopy of X-rays*, by M. Siegbahn, illustrates the emission of characteristic K radiations by a rhodium target (containing a small amount of ruthenium impurity excited upon exceeding the critical voltage).

The Rh Kα line really consists of a close triplet α_3, α_1, and α_2 whose intensities are roughly in the ratio 4 : 100 : 50. The feeble α_3 component is rarely seen, so that for most practical purposes we may speak of the "α-doublet", meaning the resolved pair of lines α_1 and α_2. The intensity ratio of α_1 to α_2 seems to be 2 : 1 for all elements. The Kβ radiations also consist of a series of components grouped very closely together. For most of the X-ray investigations involving the use of characteristic radiation which we shall describe later in the book, considerable simplification of the X-ray photographs can be effected by "filtering out" the Kβ radiations by means of suitable screens which absorb Kβ preferentially with respect to the Kα line. Usually the L and M spectra are so soft that they are absorbed in the thin foil window of the X-ray tube and play no part in the diffraction phenomena.

The Absorption of X-rays. The passage of X-rays through matter is accompanied by the loss of energy of the X-ray beam. Most of the energy is transformed into secondary radiations which have a longer wavelength than the primary beam, and into the energy of photoelectrons which are ejected from the absorbing material. A very small fraction of the energy is lost by scattering.

After traversing a thickness d, an X-ray beam of wavelength λ and initial energy I_0 is reduced to a value I given by

$$I = I_0 e^{-\mu d}$$

where μ is the linear absorption coefficient. We can re-write this equation in the form

$$I = I_0 e^{-\frac{\mu}{\rho} \cdot \rho d}$$

where $\frac{\mu}{\rho}$ is termed the mass absorption coefficient and ρd is the mass per square centimetre of the absorbing material.

Writing the formula this way, we express the absorption coefficients in terms of mass traversed rather than thickness, since it is the mass of matter and not its distribution in space which determines the magnitude of the absorption.

Absorption is a function of the electron grouping in the atoms of the absorbing element. It increases rapidly with increasing atomic number and increasing wavelength of the radiation. Each element exhibits a number of sharp discontinuities where the absorption coefficient suddenly falls and begins to rise again as the wavelength

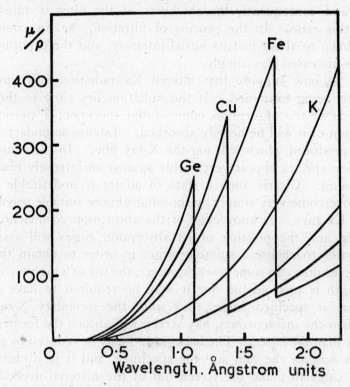

FIG. 4.—Mass absorption coefficients, $\frac{\mu}{\rho}$, of Ge, Cu, K and Fe. Note the sudden steps or "K" absorption edges of Ge, Cu and Fe.

increases. These so-called "absorption edges" occur when the radiation can excite the K, L or M spectra of the absorbing material. The effect is illustrated in Fig. 4, where the mass absorption coefficients for a number of elements are plotted as a function of the wavelength.

It must be stressed here that absorption plays a very important part in the X-ray examination of materials. The $K\beta$ radiations which add complications to the X-ray spectra in Debye-Scherrer and rotation photographs (see Chapter V) can be removed by using a filter. The filter consists of a thin foil of an absorbing element whose K absorption edge lies between the Kα and Kβ lines emitted by the anticathode. The Kβ rays lying on the short wavelength side of the absorption edge are heavily absorbed in the filter, while the longer Kα rays are transmitted relatively easily although somewhat diminished in intensity. When the intensity ratio of the transmitted Kα ray to Kβ is about 600 to 1, it is very unlikely that any spectra produced by the diffraction of Kβ will be visible on the photograph, and consequently the thickness of the filter is adjusted to obtain this ratio. In the process of filtration, the Kα component is cut down to about half its initial intensity, and the exposure time must be increased accordingly.

Let us now suppose that filtered Kα radiation falls upon the specimen being examined. If the radiation lies close to the short wave side of the absorption edge of the specimen, a considerable proportion of it will be heavily absorbed. Intense secondary X-rays will be produced which will fog the X-ray film. In such cases, the diffraction spectra appear very feebly against an intensely blackened background. Clearly such a state of affairs is undesirable and it can be overcome very simply by choosing a more suitable wavelength for the Kα rays. A knowledge of the absorption coefficient of the specimen and the position of its absorption edges will assist the investigator to choose a suitable target in order to obtain the best possible results. In some cases, however, the use of a highly absorbed wavelength is unavoidable, for it may be required to have certain reflexions at specified angles, but since the secondary X-rays are softer than the incident rays, any screen will absorb the former more strongly than the latter. The background may be reduced by placing a screen *between* the film and the specimen, and it is advantageous in such cases to make the screen out of the material needed for a β-filter and dispense with the filter in the incident beam. This is not always practicable, and thin films of celluloid or aluminium foil can be used instead, at the same time retaining the β-filter in the incident beam. Such a procedure will, however, materially increase the exposure time.

Specimens may also be self-screening, in that they absorb the β component very heavily. For example, in using Co Kα + β radiation on iron specimens, the Kβ component is heavily absorbed and only the Kα portion is reflected. In this case it is quite unnecessary to filter the incident beam with iron foil, and a considerable reduction in exposure time can be effected.

A list of targets, wavelengths and β filters devised by Dr. A. J.

Bradley [6] are given below in Table I. These will be found suitable for nearly all X-ray metallographic investigations.

The Choice of an X-ray Tube. Pitfalls likely to be encountered in the investigation of alloys were described above, when we explained some of the complications likely to occur when using unsuitable radiation. If the range of investigation is likely to cover a very wide field, in which alloys involving several different elements will occur, it is necessary for the experimenter to have at his disposal many different radiations, and this will govern in large measure the type of generating apparatus which he will be required to purchase.

Generally speaking, X-ray tubes fall into two main categories, namely sealed-off tubes, in which the vacuum is permanently maintained, and the continuously evacuated "demountable" types. The continuously evacuated tubes may either be of the "gas tube" variety, having a cold cathode, the electrons from which ionize the residual gases which are maintained at a constant pressure by means of a controlled leak, or the more powerful Coolidge type having a high vacuum produced by mercury vapour or oil diffusion pumps. Each type of tube has many features which recommend it, some being simplicity, ease of running, manœuvrability, initial cost and maintenance, and so on. There are now many such pieces of apparatus on the market by firms of repute both in this country and in the United States.

The user of a sealed-off tube is limited to one target which seriously restricts the range of enquiry. For example, a tube fitted with a copper target which emits characteristic Kα radiation heavily absorbed by iron would be quite useless for the study of the steels and those alloys of high iron content for which a Co target is more appropriate. In order to cover the range of investigation, it may be necessary to keep a whole battery of tubes with different targets. Although this may seem formidable, it must be pointed out that since each tube can be run in turn off the same high-tension equipment, and will be in use only part of the time, the cost when spread over a number of years compares very favourably with the more flexible demountable tubes.

Sealed-off tubes will run for a considerable period without any fluctuations in output, giving no trouble and requiring a minimum of attention. On the other hand, demountable tubes require frequent servicing if they are to run at maximum efficiency. The vacuum seals must be periodically attended to and the pumping equipment kept in first-class condition if the tube is to function at all satisfactorily. During the shut-down period, a small amount of

TABLE I

LIST OF TARGETS, WAVELENGTHS, AND β-FILTERS

Target				β-filter				
Element, Atomic Number	Line	Wavelength in X-units *	Peak kV.	Element, Absorption Edge		Mass Absn. Coeff. μ/ρ	Material Content gm./cm.^{2}	Thickness, mm.
Ag, 47	Kα_1	558·28	90	(Pd,	508·0)	13·1	0·096	0·079
	Kα_2	562·67		or				
	Kβ_1	496·01		Rh,	533·0			
Pd, 46	Kα_1	584·27	90	Rh,	533·0	14·6	0·091	0·073
	Kα_2	588·63		or				
	Kβ_1	519·47		(Ru,	558·4)			
Rh, 45	Kα_1	612·02	90	Ru,	558·4	15·4	0·077	0·064
	Kα_2	616·37						
	Kβ_1	544·49						
Mo, 42	Kα_1	707·831	80	Zr,	687·4	17·2	0·069	0·108
	Kα_2	712·105						
	Kβ_1	630·978						
Zr, 40	Kα_1	784·30	80	Sr,	768·4	18·1	0·053	0·210
	Kα_2	788·51						
	Kβ_1	700·28						
Au, 79	Lα_1	1,273·77	50	Ga,	1,190·2	37·0	0·028	0·047
	Lα_2	1,285·02						
Zn, 30	Kα_1	1,432·17	50	Cu,	1,377·4	42·0	0·019	0·021
	Kα_2	1,436·03						
	Kβ_1	1,292·55						
W, 74	Lα_1	1,473·36	50	Cu,	1,377·4	42·0	0·019	0·021
	Lα_2	1,484·38						
Cu, 29	Kα_1	1,537·395	50	Ni,	1,483·9	48·0	0·019	0·021
	Kα_2	1,541·232						
	Kβ_1	1,389·35						
Ni, 28	Kα_1	1,654·50	50	Co,	1,604·0	51·6	0·015	0·018
	Kα_2	1,658·35						
	Kβ_1	1,497·05						
Co, 27	Kα_1	1,785·29	45	Fe,	1,739·4	58·6	0·014	0·018
	Kα_2	1,789·19						
	Kβ_1	1,617·44						
Fe, 26	Kα_1	1,932·076	40	Mn,	1,891·6	61·9	0·012	0·016
	Kα_2	1,936·012						
	Kβ_1	1,753·013						
Mn, 25	Kα_1	2,097·51	40	Cr,	2,065·9	71·0	0·011	0·016
	Kα_2	2,101·49						
	Kβ_1	1,906·20						
Cr, 24	Kα_1	2,285·03	35	V,	2,263·0	77·3	0·009	0·016
	Kα_2	2,288·91						
	Kβ_1	2,080·6						

* See Note on facing page.

air and water vapour invariably leaks into the apparatus and so the vacuum during the first few hours of the running period is never quite as good as that in a sealed-off tube. This seems to assist the evaporation of tungsten vapour from the incandescent filament which condenses upon the target and windows. It is therefore necessary to dismantle the tube at frequent intervals in order to clean the surface of the target and replace the windows of the tube. There is also a marked tendency for the current output of the tube to rise during the early stages of running, and the operator must be at hand to adjust the current. The life of a sealed-off tube is limited by the life of the filament, which may be several hundred hours above the guaranteed life of 1,000 hours. In a demountable tube, a filament may last 150 to 200 hours and is very easily replaced. Considerable improvements to the output efficiency of sealed-off and demountable tubes can be effected by means of special circuits incorporating rectifying valves.

Sealed-off Tubes—Philips Industrial. Philips Industrial are well known for the quality of X-ray tubes and accessory equipment which they manufacture. In Fig. 5 is illustrated their latest high-power "Metalix" sealed-off X-ray diffraction tube for crystallographic work, which represents a marked advance on earlier types. The outer-casing of the tube is shock-proof and ray-proof, thus affording the operator the fullest protection. The electron stream from an incandescent tungsten spiral is focused on the water-cooled target as a sharp line, 12 mm. long by 1·2 mm. wide. The X-rays are taken off at an angle of approximately 10° to the surface of the target and pass with little absorption through four windows of Lindemann glass, making it possible to study four specimens simultaneously. The output of the tube depends on the target fitted. With copper radiation it is possible to run the tube continuously at 25 milliamps and 50 Kv. peak.

The tube has a diameter of 60 mm. so that a crystal analysis camera can be brought to within 35 mm. of the focal spot. It is possible to fix the tube on a movable bracket in order to incline it

---

* *Note.* (*a*) 1 Ångstrom Unit (Å) = 10^{-8} cm. The X-unit defined by Siegbahn on the basis of the atomic spacing in calcite is very nearly equal to 10^{-3}Å or 10^{-11} cm. It has been customary practice to use these Siegbahn wavelengths for computing atomic distances and dividing by 10^3 to express the results in "Siegbahn" Ångstroms. This practice has been criticized by H. Lipson and D. P. Riley [7]. To convert to "Absolute" Ångstrom smultiply "Siegbahn" Ångstroms by the factor 1·00203. All spacings and wavelengths in this book are on the Siegbahn scale.

(*b*) When the α_1—α_2 doublet is not resolved, the wavelength of the resultant α-line is taken as a weighted mean $\{2\lambda_{\alpha_1} + \lambda_{\alpha_2}\}/3$ on account of the intensity of the α_1 component being twice as great as α_2.

at any angle with respect to the specimen. This is of great value when massive specimens of metal cannot be manœuvred into position with regard to the X-ray equipment. In addition to the tube, high tension and low tension equipment is required, and can be obtained from Messrs. Philips Industrial.

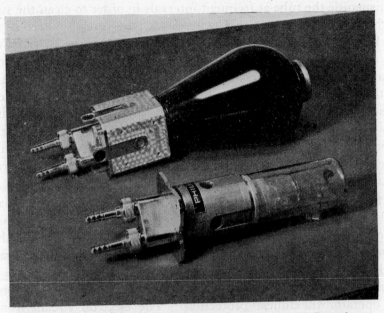

FIG. 5 (a).—Philips Industrial "Metalix" tube for X-ray crystallography.

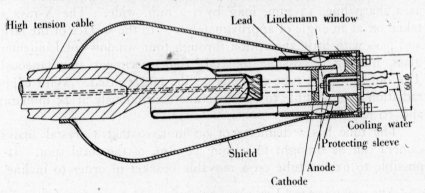

FIG. 5 (b).—Section of earthed anode X-ray tube.
(*Journal of Scientific Instruments*, 1934.)

A smaller and less powerful portable unit for crystal analysis is also manufactured by Philips Industrial. This outfit is illustrated in Fig. 6 and represents an ideal equipment for a metallurgical laboratory in which X-ray analysis is required to supplement the more usual methods of metallurgical investigation. Special cameras covering a wide field of enquiry have been designed for use with this tube, two of which are shown in position. A feature of par-

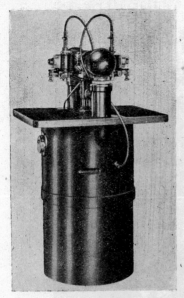

FIG. 6 (a).—Philips Industrial "Metalix" Crystal Analysis unit with two cameras in position.

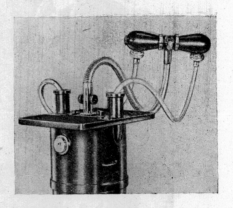

FIG. 6 (b).—Tube removed from stand, showing the flexible shockproof connexion cables.

ticular value is that the tube is detachable from the stand which houses the whole of the electrical equipment. By means of shockproof, flexible connexions, the tube may be brought into proximity with massive specimens.

Sealed-off Tubes—Victor X-ray Corporation Ltd. For industrial and research purposes, the Victor Corporation have developed a compact and versatile "XRD" X-ray diffraction unit. All the electrical equipment is contained within a square steel cabinet which stands the height of an ordinary office desk. The tube is mounted vertically and has four windows. Excellent rigid support is afforded to the X-ray cameras by means of four independently adjustable mountings, the bearing surfaces of which are accurately machined to give precision alignment of the cameras along their entire lengths. The XRD set is illustrated in Fig. 7, which shows four X-ray cameras in position. The range of cameras covers the majority of academic and industrial requirements. The entire unit is mounted on rubber wheeled castors for mobility and consequently may be used at any point at which electrical power and water connexions are available.

B

(*Courtesy Victor X-ray Corporation.*)

FIG. 7.—Victor XRD X-ray diffraction unit showing four cameras in position round central X-ray tube.

Demountable Tubes—Metrovick "Raymax".   The "Raymax" unit illustrated in Fig. 8 has been specially designed for the serious research worker.   The set illustrated in Fig. 8 comprises an X-ray tube, high voltage transformer and control equipment built as one compact unit occupying a floor space of approximately 6 ft. by 2 ft. 6 in.   The X-ray tube is continuously evacuated by a pumping plant situated immediately below it and connected by a length of pipe, thus leaving ample space below and around the tube to arrange cameras or any other desired apparatus.   A control panel 6 ft. high, mounted on the end of the main cubicle, carries all regulating handles, switches and instruments, and an illuminated mimic circuit diagram which lights up section by section as each part of the equipment comes into operation.

The X-ray tube is of the hot cathode (Coolidge) type, entirely

(a) Rear view showing X-ray head.

(b) Control panel mounted on the end of the X-ray equipment.

FIG. 8.—"Raymax" X-ray equipment for Crystallographic Analysis.

(*Metropolitan-Vickers Electrical Co., Ltd.*)

demountable and, with the exception of the porcelain insulator housed within the cabinet, of all-metal construction. The filament assembly and focusing shield are secured rigidly to the porcelain insulator, and the whole unit is fitted by means of an optically flat ground joint to the metal head, which carries the anticathode. It is therefore a comparatively simple matter to replace the filament. The water-cooled interchangeable target is attached to the head by means of a flat ground joint and is kept at earth potential. The metal head carries twin easily replaced aluminium or beryllium windows, and since the beam is taken from the target at an angle of 10°, two cameras may be used at the same time. All the ground joints are sealed with suitable Apiezon high vacuum waxes and greases. The tube is evacuated by means of a "Metrovac" 02 oil condensation pump backed by a high-speed rotary oil pump, and the degree of evacuation is observed by means of discharge tubes.

Two standard equipments are available, one which is fully automatic in operation and can be started up by the turning on of the water supply and closing one switch. The process of evacuating the tube is from then on automatic, and the mimic diagram on the control panel indicates the operation of the various parts of the equipment. The alternative equipment requires the operator to control the evacuating pumping plant sequence by hand. The tube is very powerful. With a copper target it can be run steadily at 25 milliamps and 50 Kv., but it may be overrun for short periods at 35 milliamps without serious consequences, as in the event of a breakdown usually caused by a punctured target, or more rarely, by a burned-out filament, replacement can be effected in a few minutes and at negligible cost. The massive steel construction of the equipment is particularly suited to mounting large heavy pieces of apparatus near the X-ray head.

Metropolitan-Vickers also manufacture Debye-Scherrer cameras of the Bradley type described in Chapter V, and a special universal camera suitable for various aspects of metallographical investigation.

Demountable Tubes—Hilger's "Dexrae" Unit. The Dexrae unit has been primarily designed for the applications of X-ray crystal analysis methods to industry. Illustrations of the equipment are given in Fig. 9a and b. A rotary oil-pump backs an oil diffusion pump connected to the X-ray tube via an elbow-shaped vacuum connexion which contains a Pirani vacuum gauge. The X-ray tube is of robust design and of all-metal construction except for the cathode mount. The X-ray beam passes vertically upwards through a

(Courtesy Adam Hilger Ltd., London.)

FIG. 9 (a).—The Hilger "Dexrae" Industrial Unit.

FIG. 9 (b).—Close-up of tube showing Debye-Scherrer camera mounted on its slide. Note stand for heavy specimens. Direction of beam is vertically upwards.

beryllium window, but the tube may be tilted so that the beam can be directed in any position from vertical to horizontal.

The tube is fully demountable. One of the useful features encountered is that four targets, Co, Cu, Cr and Ag, are incorporated in the one body so that a rotation of 90° moves a fresh target into position without the need of breaking the vacuum seal. A rotating disc containing suitable β-filters fits over the beryllium window. Special attention has been paid to camera design and a range of cameras covering all types of metallographical investigation has been constructed. Specimens up to 50 lb. in weight can be supported on the top plate of the trolley and rigidly clamped into position. Since the whole X-ray apparatus is mounted on rubber casters, the tube and camera equipment may be brought up to more massive specimens which can then be examined *in situ*.

A problem which often confronts the metallurgist is how to obtain X-ray photographs from the exact portion of the specimen on which a microscopical investigation has been carried out. Messrs. Hilger have given this problem their serious consideration. A metallurgical microscope with an inverted objective has been designed to fit into the slide normally occupied by the X-ray camera. It is therefore possible to carry out an optical examination of a polished and etched specimen as set up ready to receive the X-ray beam.

Future Trends in X-ray Tube Design. With the present arrangement of incandescent filament and water-cooled target, tube outputs greatly in excess of 30 milliamps at 50 Kv. do not seem very probable. There is, however, an urgent need for tubes of higher power, in order to cut down the exposure periods, which may range upwards from fifteen minutes to twenty-four hours and longer. Tubes with rotating targets capable of 1,000 milliamps at 50 Kv. have been experimented with and are just emerging from the laboratory stage. Such tubes would reduce the normal exposure periods down to a few seconds, and in industry, where the time factor is often of great importance, they would be a paying proposition.

CHAPTER III

THE SPACE LATTICE

The Crystal Form. Most chemical compounds and elements exist in crystalline forms characterized by their external geometrical shape. They usually crystallize out of solution or solidify from the melt, in the process of which the atoms or molecules arrange themselves in a regular fashion and thereby settle down into positions of lowest potential energy. It is usual that the slower the rate of crystallization, the more perfect are the resulting crystals. It is among the naturally occurring minerals that we find the most beautiful examples of crystals, which, having attained complete equilibrium as a result of the long period taken in cooling from the liquid state, have developed with perfectly plane faces which meet in sharply defined edges and corners.

In some parts of the earth, single crystals of native copper, silver and gold have been found having well-developed crystallographic faces, but these must be regarded rather as exceptions, for usually metals are aggregates of small crystals seldom bounded by the perfectly regular plane faces associated with minerals or crystals deposited from solution. Grain growth in a solidifying mass of metal proceeds from different centres or "nuclei" and the growing skeletal crystals, or dendrites, meet in irregular grain boundaries. Grain size has an enormous influence on the mechanical properties of alloys, and its control has been one of great concern to the industrialist. Control of grain size by the addition of grain refining elements to the molten metal and correctly adjusted heat treatment of the solidified mass is common metallurgical practice. Very beautiful columnar crystals several inches long can be seen in large billets and slabs which have been allowed to cool rather slowly after casting. Mainly for academic reasons, special techniques for growing large perfect crystals of metals have been developed, some involving slow cooling from the melt and others necessitating subjecting the crystal aggregate to a critical amount of strain followed by annealing at a suitable temperature. Large crystals of volatile metals such as magnesium can also be deposited directly from the vapour state.

One of the most important and most easily observed physical characteristics of a crystal is the property known as "cleavage". Many crystals, when struck with a hammer or pressed with the blade of a knife or a sharp point, break up by separating along certain well-defined planes.   Mica has an extremely well-defined cleavage which enables it to be split up into sheets of remarkable thinness.   A cube of galena cleaves very easily parallel to the original cube faces and is said to have a "cubic cleavage".   Diamond not only crystallizes in octahedra, but also splits or cleaves when struck along surfaces parallel to the eight faces of the octahedron.   The octahedron cleaved out of diamond will not necessarily have all its faces of the same size, but it may be reduced to the ideal geometric octahedron by flaking away slices parallel to the smaller faces until they are made equal. The cleavage planes have a smoothness and a brilliancy which cannot be exceeded by any artificial polish.   On the other hand, crystals of most pure metallic elements, however well formed, are soft and ductile. They have little resistance to shear, and slip in well-defined crystallographic directions producing the well-known slip bands or twinning bands upon the surface of the specimen.   The manner in which crystals grow and cleave and their physical properties such as hardness, refractive index, electrical conductivity and thermal conductivity which depend, vector-like, on the directions in which they are measured, are manifestations of the internal architecture which is on the atomic or molecular scale.

Crystal Symmetry.   Amorphous glass-like substances are isotropic, that is, their physical and mechanical properties are independent of the direction in which they are measured.   On the other hand, experiment shows that although a single crystal is anisotropic, there are nevertheless certain directions in which it is completely identical, both physically and geometrically.   It is this assemblage of equivalent directions which displays the symmetry of the crystal, and it is revealed most readily by the distribution on the crystal of the faces which bound it.   A crystal is said to possess a number of elements of symmetry, such that by the operation of one of these elements the crystal undergoes a self-coincidence transformation.   That is, the aspect of the crystal in its new orientation is quite indistinguishable from its appearance before carrying out the symmetry operation.   Experience of large numbers of crystals has shown that the number of elements of symmetry is remarkably small and consists of rotation axes, planes and centres of inversion and of a limited number of combinations of them.

An n-fold axis of symmetry operates in such a way that after rotation through $2\pi/n$, the crystal comes into a position of self-coincidence.   Only 2-, 3-, 4- and 6-fold axes of symmetry are possible. There are also axes of rotary inversion which operate in such a way that, after rotation through $2\pi/n$, the edges, corners and faces must be inverted through the origin in order to bring them into coincidence with the original aspect of the crystal.

As an illustration, let us consider a cubic crystal such as iron or copper (Fig. 10). The centre of the cube is a centre of symmetry or inversion, for it lies midway between pairs of corresponding points on the surfaces or edges. The cube can be reflected, as it were, across a symmetry plane which passes through the centre and which is parallel to a cube face. We can also have other planes of symmetry which pass through opposite pairs of edges. In addition to the planes of symmetry, there are axes of rotation. A four-fold symmetry axis passes through the centre of each face of the cube parallel to one of the edges. A rotation of 90° in either direction about one of these four-

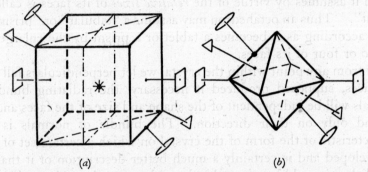

(a) (b)

FIG. 10.—(a) Symmetry elements of a cube 0, $\triangle$, $\square$, two-fold, three-fold, and four-fold axes of symmetry.

— $\cdot$ — $\cdot$ — Planes of symmetry.

✳ Centre of symmetry.

(b) Symmetry axes of the octahedron.

fold or tetrad axes turns the cube into a new position which is indistinguishable from the old. Similarly, the cube diagonals form a set of four three-fold axes, whereby the cube becomes self-coincident after a third of a rotation. In addition, we find axes of two-fold symmetry passing through the centres of opposite edges. The same symmetry elements are possessed by any crystal of the cubic class.

The symmetry properties of all crystals consist of a combination of one or more rotation axes, and planes and centres of symmetry which collectively form the "Point Group". A cubic crystal may not have its full complement of axes or planes, and will, in consequence, not display the highest form of cubic symmetry. Thus we find that among cubic crystals there exist as many as five point groups possessing progressively more and more elements of symmetry, until the full symmetry of the perfect cube is attained. Crystals are classified as belonging to one of seven systems according to the nature of their symmetry. These are the cubic, hexagonal, rhombohedral, tetragonal, orthorhombic, monoclinic and triclinic systems, and are described later. Each system possesses a definite number of point groups, and as a result of this, the seven systems give rise to a total of 32 point groups or crystal classes.

If we consider the case of diamond, we see that whatever the relative sizes of the faces, the angles between the faces are always those between the faces of a regular octahedron, namely 109° 28′, and the crystal can always be set so that its eight faces are parallel to those of a perfect octahedron. The eight faces corresponding to the octahedron are said to constitute a *form*. If the crystal is misshapen so that some faces have developed at the expense of the others, the form which it assumes by virtue of the *relative sizes* of its faces is called its "habit". Thus an octahedron may assume a "tabular" or "prismatic" habit according as it becomes a tablet or a prism by the enlargement of two or four of its faces.

If from any point within the crystal we let perpendiculars fall upon the faces, supposed produced if necessary, the radiating bundle of normals will be independent of the shape and size of the faces and will depend only on their direction. The bundle of normals is thus characteristic of the form of the crystal on which a certain set of faces is developed and is certainly a much better description of it than the actual shape would be, since this depends so much on the accidents of growth. We may describe a sphere about the origin of the normals and intersecting them in a set of points which will again be independent of the directions of the faces. The array of points on the sphere may be projected upon a great circle by means of the stereographic projection (see Chapter X) and so the form of the crystal, however complex, can be represented by the crystallographer in a relatively simple manner in two dimensions.

A crystal may have more than one form developed at the same time. For example, potassium alum, which crystallizes in octahedra, might have six faces corresponding to those of a cube as well as the octahedral faces, but for the same crystal the relative directions of the faces are fixed. A very definite rule can be laid down which governs the relative directions of the crystal faces known as the *Law of Rational Indices*. This lays down the geometrical foundations of crystallography and we shall see later how it follows as a natural consequence from the internal architecture of the crystals.

The Law of Rational Indices. First of all, it is necessary to choose a set of axes fixed in the crystal to which the directions of the faces can be referred. This is done by choosing three non-parallel faces of the crystal whose intersections give the crystal axes. Any three such faces will serve, but generally some set of axes suggests itself as most convenient from the symmetry of the crystal; for example, in a cubic crystal the three contiguous edges of the cube would be taken, giving a set of rectangular axes. A fourth face is then chosen which cuts all three axes, and is called a *standard plane*.

Let *ABC* (Fig. 11) be such a plane and let it make intercepts OA $(= a)$, OB $(= b)$, OC $(= c)$ on the axes Ox, Oy, Oz, respectively. The experimental law, the Law of Rational Indices, which is found to govern the *directions* of the other faces of the crystal, may now be stated as follows: "A face which is parallel to a plane whose intercepts on the three axes are Ha, Kb, Lc, where H, K and L are whole numbers, is a possible face of the crystal, and for the planes which commonly occur, H, K and L are small whole numbers."

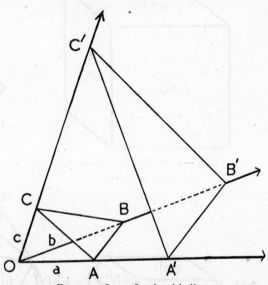

FIG. 11.—Law of rational indices.

For all planes parallel to a given direction, the *ratio* of the intercepts on the axes is the same, so that if $A'B'C'$ be a possible crystal face, we have from the rational intercept law enunciated

$$OA':OB':OC' = Ha:Kb:Lc = a/KL:b/LH:c/HK$$
$$= a/h:b/k:c/l \qquad . \qquad . \qquad . \qquad (1)$$

where h, k, l are again small whole numbers. The numbers h k l define the plane, to which the symbol in round brackets (hkl) may be given, and are called its Miller Indices after Miller who introduced them. The Miller indices are always whole numbers having no common factor, and are, for the commonly occurring faces of a crystal, *small* whole numbers.

The Miller indices have the property that a face which is parallel to an axis has a corresponding index zero. A distinction must be made between positive and negative intercepts on the axes, the latter being denoted by a bar placed over the index. For example, the indices (hkl), ($\bar{h}\bar{k}\bar{l}$) denote two parallel faces on opposite sides of the crystal.

The naming of faces is illustrated by the forms of a cubic crystal in Fig. 12.

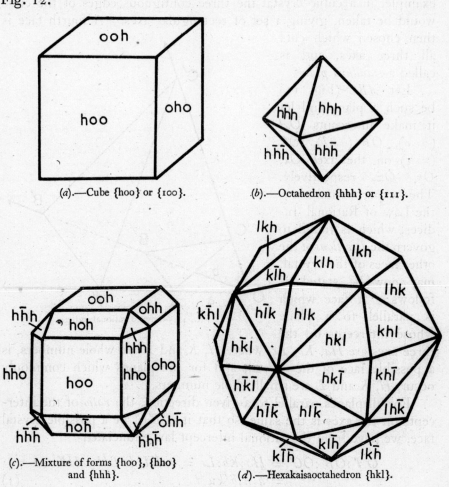

(a).—Cube {hoo} or {100}.

(b).—Octahedron {hhh} or {111}.

(c).—Mixture of forms {hoo}, {hho} and {hhh}.

(d).—Hexakaisaoctahedron {hkl}.

FIG. 12.—Some of the forms of a cubic crystal.

The complete set of crystal faces identical in type which constitute the crystal form is denoted by the indices in curly brackets {hkl}. This implies all planes of the type (hkl) with the appropriate permutations and changes of sign, e.g. (hkl), (khl), (klh), ($\bar{h}\bar{k}\bar{l}$), ($h\bar{k}l$), etc.

In order to understand why crystal faces grow as planes in certain specified directions, we shall first of all have to describe how the atoms or molecules in the crystals combine as a regular three-dimensional array to form the "space lattice".

The Two-Dimensional Lattice. Suppose we have a point which is repeated again and again at regular intervals a and b in the directions OA, OB (Fig. 13a). The points can be seen to lie upon a regular network or two-dimensional "lattice" composed of repeating parallelograms or *unit cells*, such as $OACB$. Any lattice point such as C is shared among four adjoining unit cells so that only one-quarter of it actually belongs to the cell $OACB$. But because each unit cell has four such points, it follows that, in all, one point belongs to each unit cell. There are thus just as many lattice points as there are unit cells, or to put it another way, there is a *one to one correspondence* of lattice points and unit cells.

The method of determining the unit cells is not unique, even though the array of points or lattice is fixed. The same array of points can be accommodated in the network of Fig. 13 (b) so that in each case the one to one correspondence is maintained. The precise

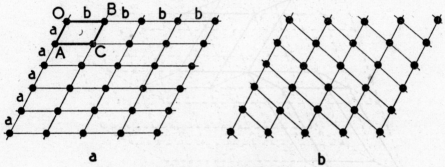

FIG. 13.—(a) Simple two-dimensional array.
(b) Alternative method of outlining unit cells.

shape of the unit cell is quite arbitrary. The choice of cell is conditioned by symmetry considerations and by convenience.

The same considerations apply when identical *groups of points* lie clustered round each corner of a unit cell. Each point in the group repeats itself in the same regular intervals a, b, so that every point on the original lattice is surrounded by an identical cluster of points. The one to one correspondence is still maintained, one *group* of points now belonging to each unit cell, which therefore contains a complete *unit* of pattern.

Let us suppose that any one of the groups in the extended pattern has n points in it. We may then regard the pattern in one of two ways. We may consider it as built up by the group as a unit, repeated by *pure translation* in the intervals a, b, or alternatively by the interleaving of n identical lattices which have corresponding axes parallel and whose origins form one of the characteristic groups of n points.

In crystals, the atoms or molecules form a three-dimensional unit of pattern and the array of points at which the pattern repeats is called a *space lattice*. The space can be divided into a vast number of parallel-sided unit cells, each of which contains a complete unit of pattern. By repeating the unit in three dimensions in a manner analogous to the two-dimensional lattice, the crystal is built up. There are many alternative ways of outlining the unit cell, some of which are shown in Fig. 14, each type of cell containing a complete unit of pattern and enclosing the same volume of space.

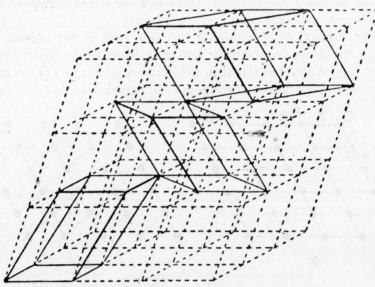

FIG. 14—A Space Lattice with alternative ways of outlining the unit cell.
(W. L. Bragg, *The Crystalline State*).

Because each cell has eight corners, with each corner common to eight cells, we again have the one to one correspondence which was shown to exist in the two-dimensional lattice.

In general, the simplest unit cell, in which the edges are made as short as possible, is chosen. Whenever this rule is not observed, it is because a more complicated unit cell may display the symmetry of the lattice to better advantage.

Fig. 15 illustrates a unit cell of the most general type. This is defined by the edges and angles:

$$OA = a \qquad\qquad BOC = \alpha$$
$$OB = b \qquad\qquad AOC = \beta$$
$$OC = c \qquad\qquad AOB = \gamma$$

a, b and *c* are termed the *axial lengths, primitive translations* or *lattice*

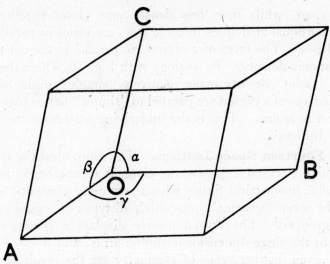

FIG. 15.—Unit cell having no symmetry (Triclinic or Anorthic).

parameters. The vectors OA, OB, OC, define the axes of the crystal. For any point having the co-ordinates (xyz) measured parallel to the axes, there will be a similar point at

$$(x + pa, y + qb, z + rc)$$

where p, q and r are whole numbers.

Lattice Planes and Crystal Faces. In a two-dimensional point array, as in Fig. 16, the most closely packed rows are obviously

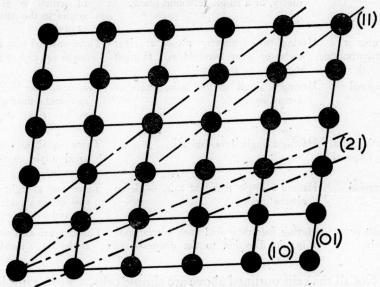

FIG. 16.—Formation of rows with "simple" indices.

farthest apart, while rows less dense come closer together. The three-dimensional analogues to these rows are series of parallel sheets or net planes. The faces of a crystal are parallel to the net planes of highest atomic density. By analogy with Fig. 16, where the rows of different "point" density make relatively "simple" angles with each other, the faces of a crystal are parallel to "simple" lattice planes which are richest in atoms. This is the underlying reason for the "Law of Rational Indices".

The Fourteen Space Lattices. The more ideal the conditions under which a crystal is grown, the closer it approaches in perfection to a regular geometrical figure whose symmetry elements belong to one of the seven "systems" into which all types of crystal symmetry can be grouped. The crystal merely displays a symmetry which belongs to the three-dimensional atomic array, and it can be shown that the seven distinct types of symmetry are the result of fourteen unique types of space lattice. These are illustrated in Fig. 17.

The seven systems with their corresponding space lattices are as follows:

Crystal Type	*Symmetry Elements*	*Space Lattice*
Triclinic or Anorthic	Possessing no symmetry at all or at most a symmetry centre. In the first case, opposite faces of the crystal will have different properties, in the second, the same properties.	Three unequal axes making unequal angles with each other (1).
Monoclinic	Possessing a single two-fold axis of symmetry, or a single reflexion plane.	Three unequal axes, one of which is at right angles to the other two (2 and 3).
Rhombic or Orthorhombic	Having two symmetry planes at right angles or three two-fold axes at right angles to one another.	Three unequal axes at right angles (4, 5, 6 and 7).
Hexagonal	Having a single six-fold axis, single or alternating.	Two equal axes inclined at 120° and a third unequal axis at right angles to them (8).
Rhombohedral or Trigonal	Having a single three-fold axis.	Three equal axes making equal angles with each other (9).
Tetragonal	Having a single four-fold axis, single or alternating.	Three axes at right angles, two of which are equal (10 and 11).
Regular or Cubic	Having four three-fold axes, corresponding in direction to the diagonals of a cube.	Three equal axes at right angles (12, 13 and 14).

Not all the cells outlined above are simple cells. For example, the cubic cells (13) and (14) are not true unit cells of the space lattice since

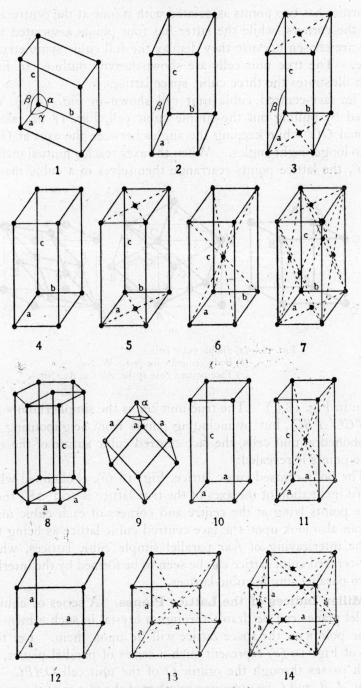

FIG. 17.—The fourteen space lattices.

(W. L. BRAGG, *The Crystalline State*.)

1. Triclinic. 2. Monoclinic. 3. Monoclinic, one face centred. 4. Orthorhombic. 5. Orthorhombic, one face centred. 6. Orthorhombic, body-centred. 7. Orthorhombic, all faces centred. 8. Hexagonal. 9. Rhombohedral. 10. Tetragonal. 11, Tetragonal, body-centred. 12. Cubic. 13. Cubic, body-centred. 14. Cubic, face-centred.

the former has two points associated with it (one at the centre and one from the corners) while the latter has four points associated with it. They are chosen because they display the full cubic symmetry of the lattice. The true unit cells are shown heavily outlined in Fig. 18, which illustrates the three cubic space lattices.

The face-centred cubic unit cell shown in Fig. 18 (*c*), can be derived by pulling out the simple cubic cell, Fig. 18 (*a*), along the diagonal *OO′* while keeping the angles between the axes at *O* equal, but no longer right angles. When the axes reach a mutual inclination of 60°, the lattice points rearrange themselves in a cubic manner as

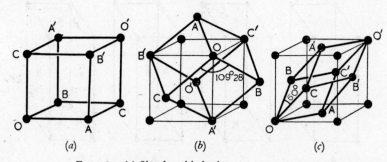

FIG. 18.—(*a*) Simple cubic lattice.
　　　　　(*b*) Body-centred cube (α-Fe, W, Na).
　　　　　(*c*) Face-centred cube (γ-Fe, Al, Cu, Au, Ni).

shown in Fig. 18 (*c*). The true unit cell is the simple rhombohedron *OAB′CO′A′BC′*, but by including points from neighbouring simple rhombohedral unit cells, the face-centred cubic nature of the array of lattice points is revealed.

The body-centred cubic lattice, Fig. 18 (*b*), is obtained when the mutual inclination of the axes of the true lattice is 109° 28′, the cubic lattice points lying at the centre and corners of each cubic unit cell. We can also look upon the face-centred cubic lattice as being formed by the interleaving of *four* parallel simple cubic lattices, while the body-centred cubic lattice can be seen to be formed by the interleaving of two parallel simple cubic lattices.

Miller Indices of the Lattice Planes. A series of equidistant parallel planes can be drawn through a crystal in such a manner that all the points on the space lattice will lie upon them. Let the fine lines of Fig. 19 (*a*) represent such a series of parallel planes, one of which passes through the origin *O* of the unit cell *OABC*. If the points *A*, *B*, and *C* lie upon one or other of the planes of this particular set, it follows that all the lattice points will lie upon this set since the lattice is built up by the repetition of the primitive translations *OA*,

OB, *OC*. The parallel planes must divide the axes *OA*, *OB*, *OC* into an integral number of parts; for example, *OA* is divided into *h* parts, each of length *a*/*h*, *OB* into *k* parts of length *b*/*k* and *OC* into *l* parts each of length *c*/*l*. Such a set of parallel planes is denoted by the Miller indices (*hkl*). The Miller indices of the family of parallel planes in Fig. 19 (*a*) are (321). When a family of planes is parallel to one of the axes, their intercepts upon this axis must be infinite in length and the corresponding Miller index is zero. Fig. 19 (*b*) illustrates a family of planes with the indices (210).

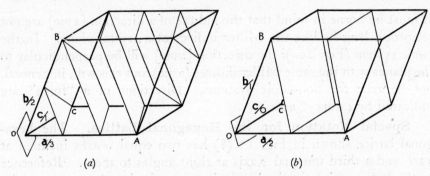

FIG. 19.—Miller indices of net planes. (*a*) Planes (321). (*b*) Planes (210).

It will be noticed that the Miller indices have no common factor. The planes (2*h* 2*k* 2*l*), for example, are parallel to the planes (*hkl*) but are half as far apart. Since all the lattice points can be accommodated upon the planes (*hkl*), it follows that every alternate plane in the series (2*h* 2*k* 2*l*) is void of lattice points. In other words, all possible lattice planes can be adequately described by a set of Miller indices which do not have a common factor, and the same must be true of the Miller indices of the crystal faces, since here only the relative orientations of the faces are important.

Crystal Zones and Zone Axes. By a crystal zone we mean that set of non-parallel crystal faces which, produced if necessary, intersect each other in a series of parallel straight lines. Thus, faces belonging to the same zone lie parallel to a line which is termed the zone axis and which defines a specific direction in the crystal. A line passing through one of the lattice points as origin and another neighbouring lattice point whose co-ordinates in terms of the primitive translations are *ua*, *vb*, *wc*, defines the direction of the zone axis [*uvw*]. The indices of the direction, which are integral, are enclosed in square brackets to distinguish them from the indices of a crystal face. If *u*, *v*, *w* are small whole numbers, the zone axis will pass through a row of closely packed lattice points and will lie, therefore, in one of a family of equidistant net planes of high atomic density, which, as we saw above, forms one of the crystal faces. Now just as two intersecting planes can determine a zone axis, two intersecting zone axes define a plane and therefore a possible crystal face. If the indices of the zone axes are $[u\ v\ w]$, $[u'v'w']$, then the Miller indices (hkl) of the face which they determine are given by the relations

$$h = vw' - wv'$$
$$k = wu' - uw'$$
$$l = uv' - vu'.$$

It must be borne in mind that the indices of a direction $[uvw]$ are not reciprocal lengths like the Miller indices of a crystal plane. In the cubic system (Fig. 20a), the direction $[uvw]$ will be perpendicular to the planes with the same Miller indices (uvw), but this will, in general, not be true for non-cubic systems. Directions of a "form" are indicated by carats $\langle uvw \rangle$.

Special Notation for the Hexagonal Lattice. The hexagonal lattice shown in Fig. 17 (8) has two equal a-axes inclined at 120° and a third unequal c-axis at right angles to them. Reference to the lattice points in the basal plane reveals that there are actually three alternative ways in which the choice of a-axes could have been made. To have chosen two of them arbitrarily would have failed to reveal the true hexagonal nature of the lattice and so in this special case reference is made to all three of them as well as to the c-axis.

If the intercepts made by a lattice plane on two of the equal axes are a/h, a/k, it is easy to show that the plane makes an intercept of $-\dfrac{a}{(h + k)}$ on the third (Fig. 20). The indices of planes of a hexagonal lattice are therefore referred as follows to four axes:

$$(h, k, \overline{h + k}, l), \text{ or } (h\ k\ i\ l)$$

where $i = -(h + k)$.

Lattice directions are also written as if they were referred to four axes, viz. $[11\overline{2}0]$ and $\langle u,\ v,\ \overline{u + v},\ r \rangle$ in order to indicate the hexagonal nature of the crystal. This introduces a complication in the indexing which is not present when the zone axes are referred to three co-ordinate axes. We have to derive the directional indices $[uvwr]$ from the co-ordinates of the lattice points, (p, q, r) as described below.

The length of the vector joining the origin to a point P (pqr) in the hexagonal lattice is given by the vector sum

$$S = pa_1 + qa_2 + rc \quad . \qquad . \qquad . \quad (1)$$

where a_1, a_2 and c are the primitive translations. The same vector S referred to the four hexagonal axes a_1, a_2, a_3, c may be written

$$S = ua_1 + va_2 + wa_3 + rc \qquad . \qquad . \qquad . \quad (2)$$

Equations (1) and (2) must be identical. Since the vectors a_1, a_2, a_3 are at $120°$ to each other, their sum

$$a_1 + a_2 + a_3 = 0 \qquad . \qquad . \qquad . \qquad . \quad (3)$$

We may therefore substitute $-(a_1 + a_2)$ for a_3 in equation (2) and by comparing coefficients with equation (1) we obtain

$$p = u - w; \quad q = v - w \qquad . \qquad . \qquad . \quad (4)$$

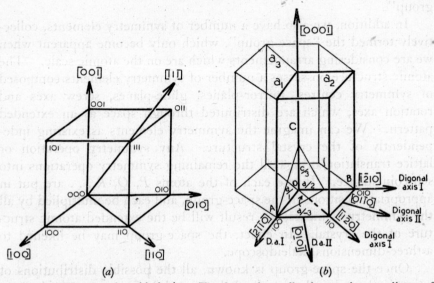

(a)

(b)

FIG. 20.—(a) Directions in cubic lattice. The figures in small print are the co-ordinates of the lattice points.
(b) Derivation of indices of lattice plane $(12\bar{3}3)$ and lattice directions [] referred to the four hexagonal axes $a_1\ a_2\ a_3\ c$.

If by analogy with the indexing of *planes* in the hexagonal system we write $u + v = -w$, we immediately obtain

$$u = \frac{2p - q}{3}; \quad v = -\frac{p - 2q}{3}; \quad w = -\frac{p + q}{3}. \qquad . \quad (5)$$

The zone indices $[uvwr]$ of the lattice direction through the origin and the point (pqr) are given by equations (5). For example, the co-ordinates of A (Fig. 20b) are (1, 0, 0). The indices $[uvwr]$ of the direction OA are therefore given by

$$u = \frac{2.1 - 0}{3} = \frac{2}{3}, \quad v = -\frac{1 - 0}{3} = -\frac{1}{3}, \quad w = -\frac{1 + 0}{3} = -\frac{1}{3}, \quad r = 0.$$

Eliminating the common factor, the required indices are $[2\bar{1}\bar{1}0]$.

The hexagonal axis c is the lattice direction [0001] which is also normal to the basal plane (0001).   The a-axes [$2\bar{1}\bar{1}0$], [$1\bar{2}10$], [$11\bar{2}0$] are axes of two-fold symmetry and are therefore referred to as the Digonal Axes I.   In hexagonal close-packed lattices they are also the directions in which the atoms pack with the greatest row density. The lattice direction [$10\bar{1}0$] is also an axis of two-fold symmetry and is consequently designated as the Digonal Axis II.   There are three such axes mutually inclined at 120° in the basal plane.

The Space Group.   The symmetry of the crystal as a whole is represented by a group of symmetry elements known as the "point-group".

In addition, we also have a number of symmetry elements, collectively termed the "space-group", which only become apparent when we are considering arrangements which are on the atomic scale.   The atomic structure possesses a number of symmetry elements composed of symmetry centres, mirror-planes, glide-planes, screw axes and rotation axes, which are distributed through space as an extended pattern.   We can imagine the symmetry elements as existing independently of the crystal structure.   Any symmetry operation or lattice translation brings all the remaining symmetry operations into self-coincidence.   If one each of the atoms P, Q, R . . . are put in appropriate positions in the space-group, and each be multiplied by all the symmetry elements, the result will be the extended atomic structure of the crystal.   In effect, the space-group may be likened to a three-dimensional kaleidoscope.

Once the space-group is known, all the possible distributions of points in the unit cell are easily deduced and the point group and space-lattice follow as a consequence of the space-group.   It is also possible to define the crystal by giving the space-group and the position of certain atoms.   If these are correctly chosen, the positions of all the other atoms can be determined immediately by the space-group operations.

The number of space-groups is limited to 230.   They have been classified by a number of different workers.   The most convenient compilation for the use of crystal structure analysis is that given in the *Internationale Tabellen zur Bestimmung von Kristallstrukturen.*

CHAPTER IV

THE DIFFRACTION OF X-RAYS BY THE CRYSTAL LATTICE

The Laue Equations. As far as the diffraction of X-rays is concerned, the action of the crystal lattice is exactly the same as that of a three-dimensional grating. Let us first of all discuss the simple case of a plane uniformly ruled optical grating, and then extend the result to the three-dimensional case.

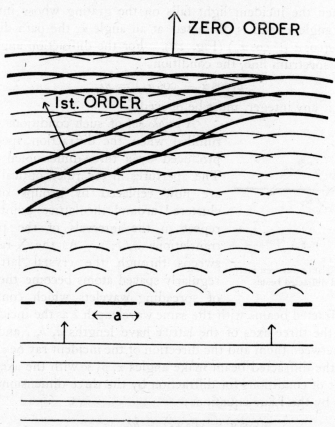

FIG. 21.—Diffraction by a plane grating.

Suppose the grating to be irradiated by monochromatic light of wavelength λ from a distant source, so that the almost plane wavefront falls normally upon its surface (Fig. 21). Each transparent aperture in the grating simultaneously becomes the source of a set of cylindrical wavelets which spread out with the velocity of light and which have the same wavelength λ as the incident radiation. The wavelets will combine at some distance from the grating to build up a series of plane wave fronts which travel away from the grating in the directions of their normals as a set of diffracted beams in the manner shown in the figure. The diffracted beams are said to be spectra of the zero, first, second . . . or nth order according to the phase changes which occur in their formation. For example, the wave front of the first-order spectrum is outlined by linking together wavelets such that the path difference for waves proceeding from successive apertures in the grating is one wavelength; it is 2λ for the second order and $n\lambda$ for the nth order. In the more general case, when the incident light falls on the grating whose interval is a, at an angle α_0 and is diffracted at an angle α, the path difference is then $a(\cos\alpha \pm \cos\alpha_0)$ (Fig. 22). For the diffraction angle to be that of a spectrum line, the condition

$$a(\cos\alpha \pm \cos\alpha_0) = n\lambda,$$

where n is any integer, must be obeyed.

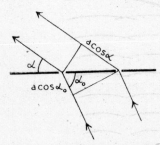

FIG. 22.—Relation between incident and diffracted beams.

A *triple* set of such conditions must be fulfilled when the diffraction spectra are produced by a three-dimensional grating. The apertures in the ruled optical grating are now replaced by groups of atoms clustered around the lattice points which repeat in the intervals of the primitive translations a, b, c. As the X-ray beam sweeps through the crystal lattice, the regularly spaced atoms become the centres of spreading wavelets which combine to form diffracted beams with the same wavelength λ as the incident ray.

Let the three axes of the lattice have lengths a, b, c and let the angles between them and the direction of the incident ray be $\alpha_0, \beta_0, \gamma_0$, and let the diffracted beam make angles α, β, γ with the axes. The triple set of conditions for diffraction by the three-dimensional lattice is given by the Laue equations:

$$a(\cos\alpha \pm \cos\alpha_0) = h\lambda \qquad . \qquad . \qquad . \qquad . \quad (1)$$
$$b(\cos\beta \pm \cos\beta_0) = k\lambda \qquad . \qquad . \qquad . \qquad . \quad (2)$$
$$c(\cos\gamma \pm \cos\gamma_0) = l\lambda \qquad . \qquad . \qquad . \qquad . \quad (3)$$

The triple set of integers hkl must be used to describe the diffractions produced by the crystal lattice, just as a single integer n is used for the simple line grating. Since this triple set of equations must be satisfied simultaneously, we can quite easily see that the occurrence of a diffraction spectrum from a three-dimensional lattice must be comparatively rare owing to the stringency of the conditions as compared with the simple equation for the linear grating. This is because the three Laue equations are not completely independent of each other. Since the direction of the incident beam is fixed, the angles α_0, β_0, and γ_0 are fixed. Let us suppose h and k to be integers, then these fix α and β, and since two angles are sufficient to fix the direction of a line, the angle γ must also be fixed. That is, the third equation is dependent on the first two, and if l is not an integer, destructive interference will occur among the diffracted waves so that in general no diffraction spectrum will be produced. Before a diffracted beam can arise, it is necessary to do one of two things, (*a*) alter the angle of incidence, or (*b*) alter the wavelength or use a continuous X-ray spectrum from which a value of λ can be selected which will satisfy the three Laue equations simultaneously.

The Bragg Law. When parallel light falls upon the surface of a mirror, it is easy to show by the well-known Huyghen's construction that the wavelets which combine to form the plane wave front of the reflected ray must be in phase with each other and have equal optical paths. W. L. Bragg [3] was able to show that the diffraction of X-rays by the three-dimensional array of lattice points governed by the triple set of Laue equations could be regarded very simply as a reflexion of the rays in the lattice planes.

Consider the unit cell outlined in Fig. 23, which has the primitive translations *a*, *b*, *c*. The three Laue equations tell us that waves scattered by *A*, *B* and *C* are *h*, *k*, *l*

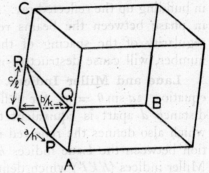

FIG. 23.—Equivalence of Laue and reflexion conditions,

wavelengths ahead, respectively, of the waves scattered by *O*. Let $OP = a/h$, $OQ = b/k$, $OR = c/l$. Then the waves scattered by *P*, *Q*, *R* are each one wavelength ahead of the waves scattered by *O* and consequently they are in phase with each other. By analogy with the reflexion of light by a mirror, this is equivalent to saying that the diffracted ray appears to be the *reflexion* of the incident ray in the plane *P*, *Q*, *R* because of the equality of optical paths. Also, since *h*, *k*, *l* are integers, it follows that the plane *PQR* must be parallel to a set of lattice planes which will contain all the lattice points.

Fig. 24 shows a section through a series of parallel planes with the indices *hkl* which are spaced regularly at a distance *d* apart. The path difference between the reflected beams derived from the same incident beam and reflected at successive planes at a glancing angle θ is easily seen to be $MO + ON = 2d \sin \theta$. For a reflexion to occur, this path difference must clearly be a whole number of wavelengths. Bragg's law states that if a diffracted beam is pro-

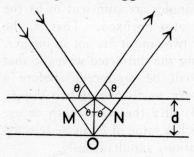

duced when a beam of X-rays passes through a crystal, it must be in such a direction that it may be considered as derived by a reflexion of the incident beam from one of the sets of lattice planes. Such a reflexion will only occur if the condition

$$2d \sin \theta = n\lambda \qquad . \qquad . \qquad (4)$$

FIG. 24.—Derivation of the Bragg Law.

is satisfied, where θ is the glancing angle of incidence of the X-ray beam on the planes in question and *d* is the spacing, *n* being an integer.

Many thousands of planes parallel to *PQR* will play their part in building up the reflected ray. If there is the smallest disagreement in phase between the beams reflected from successive planes, the regularity of the spacing of the planes, together with their huge number, will cause destructive interference.

Laue and Miller Indices. We have shown how the Bragg equation $2d \sin \theta = n\lambda$ for reflexion by the planes *hkl* spaced a distance *d* apart is equivalent to the triple set of Laue equations which also defines the reflected ray. There is an important distinction between the Laue indices *hkl* which define a reflexion and the Miller indices ($h'k'l'$) which define a set of lattice planes or a crystal face. We showed above in Chapter III that the Miller indices never have a common factor, yet they are sufficient to define a series of parallel lattice planes which contain all the lattice points, and also the crystal faces. On the other hand, the Laue indices *hkl* which define the number of wavelengths in the path difference between X-rays scattered at *O* and at the lattice points *A, B, C*, may have a common factor.

The Bragg law expresses the fact that when the *n*th order of reflexion occurs from the lattice planes with the Miller indices $h'k'l'$, there will be a path difference equal to *n* wavelengths for waves reflected at successive planes. Now since there are h' planes between *O* and

A, the waves scattered by A will be nh' wavelengths ahead of the waves scattered by O, and similarly B and C are nk' and nl' wavelengths ahead of O. We therefore have the following relations between the Laue indices hkl and the Miller indices $(h'k'l')$ of the reflecting planes

$$h = nh'$$
$$k = nk'$$
$$l = nl'$$

In other words, a reflexion which is described by the set of Laue indices hkl simply means that it is the nth order reflexion from lattice planes having the Miller indices $(h'k'l')$, n being the common factor of the Laue indices. Thus reflexions with Laue indices 231, 462, 693, are merely the 1st, 2nd and 3rd order reflexions from planes with the Millerian indices (231). As is customary in descriptive crystallography, the Miller indices (hkl) will be put in brackets and the indices of a reflexion will simply be given as hkl without brackets.

The Relation between the Interplanar Distance and the Lattice Parameters. Consider the set of parallel planes having the Miller indices $(h'k'l')$ belonging to the space lattice which has primitive translations or lattice parameters a, b, c (Fig. 25). The normal N drawn from the origin to the set of planes intersects the plane nearest the origin at a distance d which is the same as the perpendicular distance between

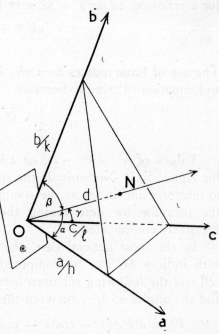

FIG. 25.—Relation between the interplanar spacing ON($=d$), the lattice parameters a, b, c, and the Miller indices (h, k, l).

adjacent planes in the set. If the direction cosines of the normal are $\cos\alpha$, $\cos\beta$ and $\cos\gamma$, then the interplanar distance is given by

$$d = \left(\frac{a}{h'}\right)\cos\alpha = \left(\frac{b}{k'}\right)\cos\beta = \left(\frac{c}{l'}\right)\cos\gamma \quad . \qquad . \qquad . \quad (5)$$

and therefore it follows that

$$d^2\left\{\left(\frac{h'}{a}\right)^2 + \left(\frac{k'}{b}\right)^2 + \left(\frac{l'}{c}\right)^2\right\} = \cos^2\alpha + \cos^2\beta + \cos^2\gamma.$$

By taking into account the relations between the direction cosines and the angles between the axes, we obtain formulæ for the interplanar spacings in any crystal system. For example, in the cubic system, where the lattice parameters a, b, c form an orthogonal set, and are equal in length, equation (5) becomes

$$d^2\left\{\left(\frac{h'}{a}\right)^2 + \left(\frac{k'}{a}\right)^2 + \left(\frac{l'}{a}\right)^2\right\} = \cos^2\alpha + \cos^2\beta + \cos^2\gamma = 1 . \quad (6)$$

and hence

$$a = d\sqrt{(h')^2 + (k')^2 + (l')^2} \quad . \qquad . \qquad . \quad (7)$$

We can now express the Bragg angle as a function of the Miller indices and the axes of the lattice. For a cubic crystal, the condition for a reflexion $2d \sin\theta = n\lambda$ may be written

$$a = \frac{\lambda}{2} \cdot \frac{\sqrt{(nh')^2 + (nk')^2 + (nl')^2}}{\sin\theta} \quad . \qquad . \quad (8)$$

The use of Laue indices $h = nh'$, $k = nk'$, $l = nl'$ is to be preferred, and equation (8) simply becomes

$$a = \frac{\lambda}{2} \cdot \frac{\sqrt{h^2 + k^2 + l^2}}{\sin\theta}$$

Values of $h^2 + k^2 + l^2$, or Σh^2, for cubic crystals are given in the Appendix. Not only do the spectra become increasingly difficult to interpret and index as the symmetry of the crystal is lowered, but the formulæ for determining the lattice parameters become progressively complicated.

In the most general case, the interplanar distance d for planes with indices hkl can be computed from the volume V of the unit cell and the following relations between the lattice parameters a, b, c, and the angles α, β, γ, between the edges of the unit cell:

$$V^2 = a^2b^2c^2(1 - \cos^2\alpha - \cos^2\beta - \cos^2\gamma + 2\cos\alpha\cos\beta\cos\gamma).$$
$$S_{11} = b^2c^2\sin^2\alpha \qquad S_{12} = abc^2(\cos\alpha\cos\beta - \cos\gamma)$$
$$S_{22} = a^2c^2\sin^2\beta \qquad S_{23} = a^2bc(\cos\beta\cos\gamma - \cos\alpha)$$
$$S_{33} = a^2b^2\sin^2\gamma \qquad S_{13} = ab^2c(\cos\gamma\cos\alpha - \cos\beta)$$

Using these relations and the Bragg equation $2d \sin\theta = n\lambda$, we obtain the formulæ given in Table II for the various lattices.

TABLE II

TABLE OF INTERPLANAR SPACINGS

Cubic

$$\frac{1}{d^2} = \frac{h^2 + k^2 + l^2}{a^2}$$

$$\sin^2\theta = \left(\frac{\lambda}{2}\right)^2 \frac{h^2 + k^2 + l^2}{a^2}$$

Hexagonal

$$\frac{1}{d^2} = \frac{4}{3} \cdot \frac{h^2 + hk + k^2}{a^2} + \frac{l^2}{c^2}$$

$$\sin^2\theta = \left(\frac{\lambda}{2}\right)^2 \left\{ \frac{4}{3} \cdot \frac{h^2 + hk + k^2}{a^2} + \frac{l^2}{c^2} \right\}$$

Tetragonal

$$\frac{1}{d^2} = \frac{h^2 + k^2}{a^2} + \frac{l^2}{c^2}$$

$$\sin^2\theta = \left(\frac{\lambda}{2}\right)^2 \left\{ \frac{h^2 + k^2}{a^2} + \frac{l^2}{c^2} \right\}$$

Orthorhombic

$$\frac{1}{d^2} = \left(\frac{h}{a}\right)^2 + \left(\frac{k}{b}\right)^2 + \left(\frac{l}{c}\right)^2$$

$$\sin^2\theta = \left(\frac{\lambda}{2}\right)^2 \left\{ \frac{h^2}{a^2} + \frac{k^2}{b^2} + \frac{l^2}{c^2} \right\}$$

Rhombohedral

$$\frac{1}{d^2} = \frac{(h^2 + k^2 + l^2)\sin^2\alpha + 2(hk + kl + lh)(\cos^2\alpha - \cos\alpha)}{a^2(1 - 3\cos^2\alpha + 2\cos^3\alpha)}$$

$$\sin^2\theta = \left(\frac{\lambda}{2}\right)^2 \frac{(h^2 + k^2 + l^2)\sin^2\alpha + 2(hk + kl + hl)(\cos^2\alpha - \cos\alpha)}{a^2(1 - 3\cos^2\alpha + 2\cos^3\alpha)}$$

By changing the axes and re-indexing the planes, it is often convenient to refer rhombohedral crystals to hexagonal axes, but the new unit cell will not be the simplest unit of structure.

Monoclinic

$$\frac{1}{d^2} = \frac{h^2}{a^2\sin^2\beta} + \frac{k^2}{b^2} + \frac{l^2}{c^2\sin^2\beta} - \frac{2hl\cos\beta}{ac\sin^2\beta}$$

$$\sin^2\theta = \left(\frac{\lambda}{2}\right)^2 \left\{ \frac{h^2}{a^2\sin^2\beta} + \frac{k^2}{b^2} + \frac{l^2}{c^2\sin^2\beta} - \frac{2hl\cos\beta}{ac\sin^2\beta} \right\}$$

Triclinic

$$\frac{1}{d^2} = \frac{1}{V^2} \{ s_{11}h^2 + s_{22}k^2 + s_{33}l^2 + 2s_{12}hk + 2s_{23}kl + 2s_{13}hl \}$$

$$\sin^2\theta = \left(\frac{\lambda}{2}\right)^2 \frac{1}{V^2} \{ s_{11}h^2 + s_{22}k^2 + s_{33}l^2 + 2s_{12}hk + 2s_{23}kl + 2s_{13}hl \}.$$

CHAPTER V

EXPERIMENTAL METHODS OF OBTAINING
DIFFRACTION PATTERNS

SINCE the discovery of the diffraction of X-rays by the crystal lattice by Laue, Friedrich and Knipping, numerous methods of obtaining and recording the diffracted beams have been devised. Each method has been evolved in order to simplify the recording or the interpretation of the diffraction pattern, to emphasize some special feature, or to overcome difficulties experienced in obtaining diffraction patterns from the abundant variety of specimens which have to be investigated. It is our object to describe only a limited number of these methods, confining ourselves to those which have been outstandingly useful in metallographic studies. Many of these methods were originally devised for the purpose of determining the atomic arrangements in the crystals, but in metallurgy, where the arrangement is often known in advance, they are used for problems connected with the structures rather than for structure determination.

The Laue Method. In the Laue method, the experimental arrangement is extremely simple. A heterogenous beam of X-rays is limited to a fine pencil about 0·5 mm. in diameter by means of pinholes in lead screens and falls upon a thin slice of stationary crystal. The unabsorbed transmitted beam impinges normally upon a photographic plate or film, wrapped in black paper, yielding an intense centre-spot which is surrounded by a pattern of spots produced by the various diffracted beams. Such a "Laue" pattern obtained by G. L. Clark [9] from a single crystal of iron is illustrated in Fig. 26. A fundamental property of the Laue photograph is the symmetry of the pattern which reveals the symmetry of the crystal. Another feature is that the spots lie at the points of intersection of a series of ellipses

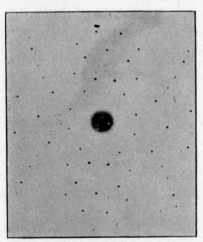

FIG. 26.—Laue photograph of iron crystal. X-ray beam normal to cube face. Pattern reveals the four-fold symmetry of the lattice.

(G. L. CLARK.)

having one end of their major axis at the centre spot (Fig. 27). Since the transmitted beam is usually very strong, the photograph would be seriously fogged by the scattered X-rays and photo-electrons produced when the beam strikes the film. This difficulty is over-come by placing a small disc of lead over the plate at the position of the centre spot, which strongly absorbs the main transmitted beam without causing serious scatter. If film is used, it is customary to punch a small hole through the centre of the film, thus allowing the direct beam to pass through the film without striking it.

We saw in Chapter III that in order to obtain a reflexion by waves of wavelength λ, the Bragg condition $n\lambda = 2d \sin \theta$ must always

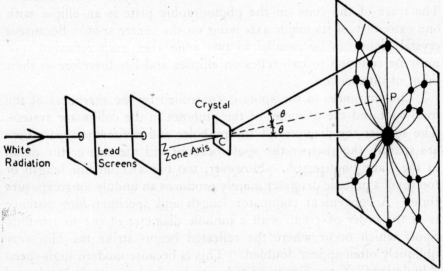

FIG. 27.—Production of Laue photograph. A series of spots on a given ellipse is formed by a set of planes lying parallel to a common zone axis, such as ZCP.

be satisfied. Now since in the Laue method the direction of the X-ray beam is fixed and the crystal is stationary, the angles made by the incident beam with every possible set of reflecting planes are fixed in advance. The only variables are n and λ. If λ were fixed, reflexions would be purely a matter of chance and their occurrence would be extremely rare, because n must be an integer before a reflexion can be produced. The essence of the Laue method lies in the use of heterogeneous or "white" radiation, usually from a tungsten or platinum target, which emits a *continuous* spectrum over a wide range of λ's. The wavelength is consequently continuously variable, and it is therefore possible to find discrete values of λ which satisfy the Bragg condition whatever. the orientation of the lattice planes. In other words, with white radiation, the crystal planes behave just like a simple mirror reflecting X-rays whatever their angle of incidence.

In a crystal, we find families of lattice planes which are parallel to a given direction. Such a set of planes is said to belong to the same zone, and the common direction is said to constitute the zone axis. All the Laue spots lying upon a given ellipse are produced by reflexions from planes parallel to a common zone axis.

Consider the planes parallel to the zone axis ZCP which lies at an angle θ to the incident beam (Fig. 27). The reflected rays must also lie at an angle θ to each plane, and therefore at an angle θ to the zone axis, thus lying on the surface of a cone of semi-vertical angle θ. The trace of the cone on the photographic plate is an ellipse with one extremity of its major axis lying on the centre spot. Because a crystal plane can be parallel to two zone axes, each reflexion spot must be common to two reflexion ellipses and lies therefore at their point of intersection.

The sharpness of the spots is controlled by the sharpness of the focal spot and the diameter of the pinholes in the collimator system. The smaller the diameter of the pinholes and the farther apart they are spaced, the sharper the spots become and the clearer the detail in the Laue photograph. However, too big a collimator length or too small a pinhole diameter merely produces an unduly long exposure time. A convenient collimator length and specimen-film distance is of the order of 5 cm. with a pinhole diameter of 0·5 to 1·0 mm. Spots which occur where the reflected beams strike the film very obliquely often appear doubled. This is because modern high-speed "dupletized" X-ray film is coated with an emulsion on each side and each reflected beam produces a spot in the emulsion of each side of the film, which to the eye appear out of alignment. Because the minimum value of the wavelength is controlled by the voltage applied to the tube (page 9), there will be a well-defined minimum value of θ at which reflexions occur, whatever the nature of the specimen. For this reason, the pattern of spots in the Laue photograph is cut off sharply at a definite distance from the centre spot.

As far as the determination of the atomic arrangement within the crystal is concerned, the Laue photograph is difficult to use because each spot is made up of several overlapping orders of different wavelength, each of which has a different photographic effect on the film. That is, the intensities of the spots do not depend on the structure alone, but on the distribution of energy in the continuous X-ray spectrum and the spectral sensitivity of the X-ray film. Nevertheless, the Laue photograph has been used with great success for the elucidation of crystal structures, although simpler and more powerful methods of structure analysis in which monochromatic radiation is employed have been developed.   This does not mean that as far as metallographic investigation is concerned, the Laue photograph is of little importance.   On the contrary, the Laue method in a modified form offers a very useful means of studying the distortion of metal crystals, of investigating rolling and drawing textures and studying grain size and crystal fragmentation.   These topics will be dealt with in later chapters.   All that need be mentioned here is that it is not always necessary to make detailed measurements and lengthy calculations in order to interpret the photographs.   Very often, all that is required is a series of photographs corresponding to known states of the metal.   Simple comparison of photographs from specimens under investigation with those from carefully prepared standards will often yield extremely valuable information.

Surface Reflexion Methods.   In our discussion of the Laue method, we saw that the angle of incidence θ was kept fixed, and, in order to satisfy the reflexion condition, the wavelength λ had to be varied, and so polychromatic radiation was employed.   All the other

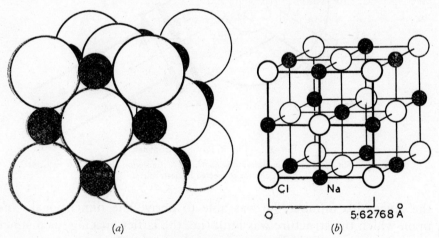

(a)   (b)

FIG. 28.—The Atomic Structure of Rock-salt.

(a) Packing model showing relative sizes of Na (black) and Cl (white) ions.
(b) Open model representing ion centres.

methods of X-ray analysis make use of a constant value of λ and vary θ until the reflexion condition is fulfilled.   The original method, using monochromatic radiation, was founded directly upon the idea of the "reflexion" of X-rays by a set of crystal planes.   In 1913, W. L. Bragg [3] made use of the ionization chamber, which his father had just invented, to detect and measure quantitatively the intensities and directions of the rays reflected by the lattice planes parallel to the faces of a natural sodium chloride (rock-salt) crystal (Fig. 28). These measurements enabled him to calculate with certainty the atomic arrangement of the Na and Cl ions in the rock-salt structure which had been postulated many years previously on theoretical grounds by Barlow. In addition, by using the atomic weights of sodium and chlorine, the density of the sodium chloride crystal and

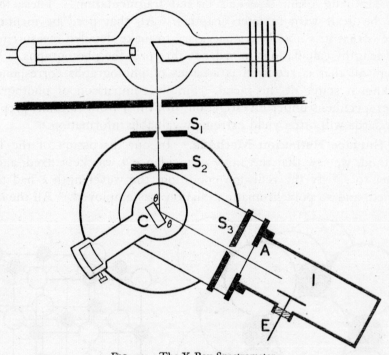

FIG. 29.—The X-Ray Spectrometer.

S_1, S_2, S_3 = Slits. A = Aluminium foil window. I = Ionization chamber. C = Crystal.
E = Collector connected to electrometer.

the Avogadro number, he was able to derive the dimensional *scale* upon which the structure was built (i.e. the lattice spacing) as distinct from the geometrical arrangement of the atoms.

With the establishment of the atomic pattern from the X-ray data and the determination of the lattice spacing, it was then possible to deduce the wavelength of the radiation emitted by the tube. The experimental arrangement is shown diagrammatically in Fig. 29.

The crystal is mounted in the centre of a spectrometer table, while an ionization chamber filled with methyl bromide, which is a heavy gas easily ionized by X-rays, takes the place of the telescope.

The ionization chamber is slowly rotated at the same time and at twice the speed of the crystal until a reflexion "flashes" out at the Bragg angle when the condition $2d \sin \theta = n\lambda$ is satisfied. The degree of ionization produced by the reflected X-ray beam is recorded by a sensitive electrometer connected with the electrode of the ionization chamber, and thus a very accurate measure of the absolute intensity of the X-ray energy in the reflected beam is obtained. The positions of the spectra are read on the angular scale of the spectrometer table.

The spectra can only be detected one at a time, which makes work with the ionization chamber extremely slow. For the solution of difficult structures, which necessitate absolute and not relative measurements of intensity, the method is unrivalled. Fortunately, the structures of the commercially important metals and alloys are

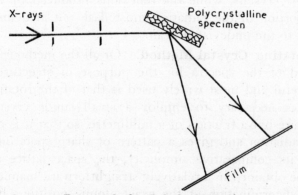

FIG. 30.—Surface Reflexion Method.

The specimen is usually oscillated through a few degrees or given a translatory motion in its own plane.

comparatively simple, and speedier methods of investigation can be employed which, nevertheless, retain certain features of the ionization chamber method. An extremely important modification, often used in the study of grain orientation, occurs where the ionization chamber is replaced by a photographic film which records several of the reflected beams simultaneously (Fig. 30).

If the specimen consists of a plate of polycrystalline metal having a number of crystals irradiated by the X-ray beam, some of these can be rotated into a reflecting position by rocking the specimen through a limited range of angles while maintaining the film in a fixed position. This procedure finds a number of variants. In one, both specimen and film are kept fixed with respect to each other, while in another variation, the specimen is kept fixed while the film is moved. A third variation, where the film and specimen are oscillated together, is also employed. Which method is adopted depends, of course, entirely upon the nature of the problem to be solved and the type of specimen available for examination.

It is very important to realize that when we talk about monochromatic radiation, we usually mean the filtered Kα doublet which is superimposed upon a relatively weak background of white radiation. If the specimen is held stationary, we obtain a *weak* Laue pattern from each crystal in the polycrystalline specimen. The X-ray photograph will thus consist of a strong pattern of spots produced by the intense monochromatic component, together with a relatively feeble background of Laue spots corresponding to several superimposed Laue photographs. Oscillation of the specimen through comparatively small angles is sufficient to destroy the "Laue background", since the positions of the Laue spots change continuously with the setting of the crystals, while the reflexions produced by the monochromatic portion of the radiation must flash out at definite angles with respect to the undeviated beam.

The Rotating Crystal Method. Of all the methods of obtaining a record of the spectra for the purpose of structure analysis, the most useful and most widely used is that of the rotation photograph. It is necessary to employ a small single crystal, whose dimensions are but a fraction of a millimetre, so that it is completely bathed in radiation and gives a pattern of sharp spots on the film. Because of its comparative simplicity, the space lattice and space group can be obtained in a relatively straightforward manner, leading finally to a determination of the exact atomic positions by the use of the relative intensities of the large number of diffraction spots on the photograph.

Suppose monochromatic X-rays, confined to a very narrow pencil, fall upon a single crystal which is so small that the incident radiation is not completely absorbed. By setting the crystal in slow rotation about a fixed axis, a large number of lattice planes will move in turn into reflecting positions and the diffracted beams will flash out momentarily as the crystal passes through the appropriate Bragg angles, producing a pattern of spots known as a rotation photograph upon a plate set to receive the reflexions. The plate is set a few centimetres from the crystal with its plane perpendicular to the incident beam. An alternative method is to receive the pattern of spots upon a cylindrical film whose axis is the axis of rotation of the crystal.

In the rotating crystal method, the crystal is set up so that an important zone axis is parallel to the axis of rotation. The incident beam is perpendicular to this axis. Let *A* and *B* (Fig. 31) represent the distance between successive lattice points along the zone axis about which the crystal is rotated.   The Laue condition for diffraction to take place is that the path difference for rays scattered by A and B should be an integral number of wavelengths.

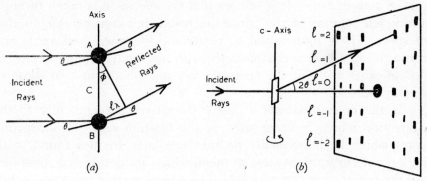

FIG. 31.—The formation of "layer-lines" in a rotation photograph.

If, for example, the crystal should be mounted with the c-axis parallel to the axis of rotation, then a spectrum will be formed in a direction making an angle ϕ with the c-axis, such that

$$c \cos \phi = l\lambda,$$

c being the lattice spacing parallel to the c-axis and l a whole number. The diffracted beams must lie, therefore, on the surfaces of a family of cones; these cones will have the crystal as vertex and the rotation axis as a common axis.   Their semi-vertical angles ϕ are obtained by putting $l = 0, 1, 2, \ldots -1, -2$ in the relation $c \cos \phi = l\lambda$. This family of cones will intersect the photographic plate in a series of hyperbolas, and therefore the spots in the rotation photograph must be on this series of hyperbolas or *layer-lines*, as they are called. These layer-lines are denoted by the value of the integer l to which they correspond.   Planes parallel to the c-axis reflect the X-rays horizontally, and thus the spots which correspond to the hko reflexions form a horizontal row on the plate, running through the central spot. Since $l = 0$, this is termed the zero layer-line.   These reflexions with $l = 1$, i.e. $hk1$, are thrown upwards, making an angle ϕ_1 with the vertical given by

$$c \cos \phi_1 = \lambda$$

and these constitute the first layer-line.   It is quite clear from the above that the vertical spacing of the layer-lines depends only upon the identity period between the lattice points which lie on the zone axis about which the crystal is rotated.   This period can be directly calculated from the vertical interval between the layer-lines on the photograph and the distance of the plate from the specimen which yield the angle ϕ.

If rotation photographs are taken about all three axes separately, the spacings a, b and c, and hence the dimensions of the unit cell, can be determined.   It is seldom that the specimen is taken through a complete rotation of $360°$ since this results in a considerable number of spots.   It is more usual to rotate the specimen backwards and forwards by a cam mechanism through an angular range of $20°$ or $30°$ in order to limit the spots on any one photograph to those of certain indices.

If the crystal has its a and b directions perpendicular to the c-direction which is being used as the rotation axis, the diffraction spots which lie horizontally on the layer-lines are also found to lie on a set of curves transverse to them, which are designated row-lines. All the points on a common layer-line have the same value of l, while all the points on a common row-line have the same values of h and k. For example, 040, 041, 042, 043, 044, etc., all lie on the same row-line, while the spots 013, 023, 033, 043, etc., all lie on the third layer-line distant from the zero order layer-line passing through the centre spot.

When a metal, which usually consists of a randomly oriented mass of polycrystals, is subjected to a drawing process and turned into wire, the crystals are rotated so that important zone axes take up preferential orientations in the direction of drawing.   Rotation photographs taken with the drawing or "fibre" direction as the axis of rotation are strikingly similar to the pattern of a single crystal rotated about the same axis (cf. Chapter X).   From such a fibre diagram the extent of the preferred orientation of the crystals at various depths in the wire can be deduced by the simple expedient of dissolving away the outer layers of the wire.   Similarly, the fibre texture of rolled metal sheet can also be determined by means of rotation photographs.   All these fibre patterns are seldom perfect since the crystals have their zone axes oriented with a definite *scatter* about some mean position.   The fibre pattern is a cross between the single crystal rotation photograph and the "Powder Photograph", to be discussed in the next section.

The Powder Method.   The powder method discovered by Debye and Scherrer, and independently by Hull, satisfies the need of a technique for studying crystals which are normally too small to be examined by the ionization chamber or by the rotating single crystal method, for many crystalline solids only exist in a fine state of sub-division or as a conglomerate mass of minute polycrystals.

A powder photograph * is obtained by allowing a narrow beam of monochromatic X-rays to fall upon a small specimen of the powder under investigation. Since the orientations of the crystal fragments are perfectly random, a certain number of them will be in such a direction that the Bragg condition for reflexion is satisfied. The crystal fragments giving rise to these reflexions must each be set at a grazing angle θ to the incident beam, although each may have any orientation about the incident beam as axis. The result is that the diffracted beams with the same indices hkl all lie upon the surface of a cone which has a semi-vertical angle 2θ. Each diffraction hkl is recorded upon a flat plate, or upon a cylindrical film. When a flat plate or film is used, each diffraction hkl is recorded as a circular diffraction halo surrounding a central spot (Fig. 32). Only a limited

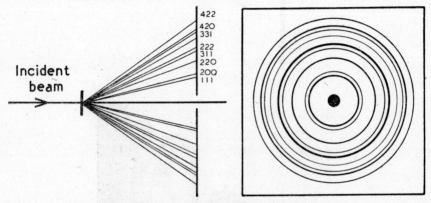

FIG. 32.—Debye-Scherrer Rings on a flat film from a powder specimen with a face-centred cubic lattice.

number of diffraction haloes restricted to the lower orders can be accommodated upon a flat plate, and when the highest orders are required to be recorded, namely when θ approaches an angle of 90°, the flat film is interposed between the X-ray target and the specimen, with the collimator tube passing through the centre of the film. The pattern so obtained is known as a back-reflexion photograph. Its greatest use lies in the precision determination of lattice spacings. A typical back-reflexion camera, manufactured by the Victor Corporation, is illustrated in Fig. 33.

Transmission and back-reflexion photographs suffer from the

* The term powder photograph is here used to cover diffraction patterns obtained from actual powders or from polycrystalline solid aggregates. The essential feature is that the large number of small crystals in the irradiated portion give rise to well-defined diffraction haloes.

defect that only a portion of the available pattern can be recorded upon each film. When it is required to make a record of the whole spectrum, the film is curved into a narrow cylinder concentric with

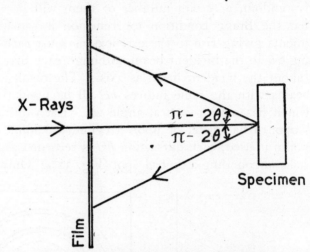

FIG. 33 (*a*).—Principle of Back-Reflexion Method.

FIG. 33 (*b*).—A typical Back-Reflexion X-Ray Camera.
(*Victor X-Ray Corporation.*)
The X-ray tube is on the right of the picture.

the specimen. This enables the high and low orders to be registered simultaneously on the one film, which, when unrolled, presents a complete pattern of lines in a convenient strip-like form strongly

reminiscent of an optical line spectrum. The experimental arrangement is illustrated in Fig. 34.

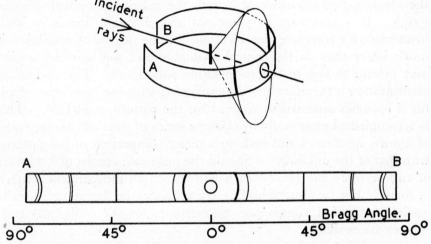

FIG. 34.—Formation of a Debye-Scherrer powder photograph on a cylindrical film.

Fig. 35 illustrates a typical 19-cm.-diameter Debye-Scherrer
camera of the Bradley type, manufactured by Unicam. Photographs
taken with this type of apparatus with radiation emitted by a Metropolitan-Vickers Raymax tube are illustrated in Fig. 36.

The Debye-Scherrer pattern is created in a manner fundamentally
different from its analogue produced by an optical spectrograph. In
the latter case, each individual atom in a source heated to incandes-
cence, emits a series of discrete wavelengths each of which corresponds
to an energy jump by the electrons in the outer shells of the excited
atoms. The prism or grating of the spectrograph sorts these wavelengths out and records them as a pattern of lines in ascending order
of wavelength. Thus each line in the optical spectrum corresponds
to only one particular wavelength emitted by the source. Although
such a spectrum may consist of several hundred lines, each element
emits an entirely different set of wavelengths, and so it is possible
to ascertain the presence of any one of the constituent atoms in the
source with absolute certainty merely by identifying one or two
characteristic lines.

In producing the Debye-Scherrer photograph, only one wavelength is used. Each line in the pattern is produced by the co-
operative effort of all the different atoms in the crystal lattice, and
not by any single atom acting individually. Since no two substances
are alike, no two Debye-Scherrer patterns are the same in all details,

c*

and therefore each Debye-Scherrer pattern is characteristic of an individual compound. Thus the powder method presents a means whereby a compound may be identified with the same assurance as the identification of an element with the aid of the optical spectrograph. It is necessary to point out that a single line is in itself insufficient for complete identification, for the degree of resolution is much lower than in the optical analogue, and the line in question may belong to one of several possible substances. The process of identification is therefore more complicated with the powder method, for it becomes essential to account for the pattern as a whole. This is accomplished most easily by taking a series of standard photographs of known substances and making a direct comparison of the patterns with that of the unknown. Should the unknown consist of a mixture of two or more substances, each will record an independent pattern of lines. The two intermingling patterns may be disentangled quite easily if standard comparison photographs of the individual substances are available.

A card index of the most important lines for several hundred substances has been prepared by the American Society for Testing Materials with the co-operation of the Cavendish Laboratory, and a list of crystallographic data for 1,000 substances has been compiled by J. D. Hanawalt [10] of the Dow Chemical Corporation. These should be of immense assistance in the identification of unknown substances by means of the powder method, particularly in those laboratories where the number of standard patterns in the files is inadequate for direct comparisons to be made.

The powder method is of considerable value in the study of complicated alloy thermal equilibrium diagrams where the recognition of new phases by microscopic methods is difficult. Any changes within the crystal lattice are readily followed by X-ray methods, and this enables points of detail to be incorporated in an equilibrium diagram which pass unrecognized by the microscope.

Transmission and back-reflexion Debye-Scherrer patterns are employed for the study of grain size, lattice distortion and crystal orientation. Each method possesses certain advantages, but the one to be adopted will be immediately apparent to the investigator from the nature of the problem. For example, a massive block of metal which must be examined in the "as received" condition would clearly be investigated by the back-reflexion or surface reflexion method.

Finally, and perhaps most important of all, the powder method may be used for the elucidation of the atomic arrangements in crystals. Its range is restricted principally to crystals with a high degree of symmetry such as cubic, hexagonal and tetragonal. Crystals with low symmetry yield such complicated patterns that their internal structures can only be investigated by the more powerful single crystal methods.

The Preparation of Cylindrical Powder Specimens for Debye–Scherrer Work. Specimens of ductile alloys are most conveniently obtained by filing the ingots of metal gently with a scrupulously clean sharp jeweller's file or by drilling with a high-speed steel drill. Care must be taken to generate as little heat as possible during this operation. Brittle alloys are readily powdered in a small hardened steel rock crusher and then finely ground under ether or toluene in an agate mortar. Any impurity picked up in the preparatory stages gives rise to its own interference pattern in the powder photograph and may lead to confusion in its interpretation unless removed or prevented.

The powder, having been sieved, is heat-treated to remove the lattice distortion introduced by the cold-work during its preparation and to bring it into thermal equilibrium corresponding to a prescribed temperature. It is then mixed with Canada balsam into a thick paste and coated on a hair or fine glass fibre clamped in a special holder, forming a smooth cylinder some 0·25–0·5 mm. thick, and about 1 cm. long. The hair is kept taut with a small lead weight suspended well below the beam incident on the specimen. This ensures that when the camera is level, the specimen is automatically parallel to the camera's axis, which would not necessarily be the case if a rigid specimen were used.

The greatest precautions must be observed in the preparation of the specimen, for, because of the minute amount of material irradiated by the X-ray beam, any faults in technique at this stage will inevitably seriously diminish the amount of information to be obtained from the X-ray photograph and may even lead to serious errors in its interpretation. Care must be taken to ensure that the powder is truly representative of the bulk of the material from which it is obtained. All the powder should go through the finest sieve employed. This is to avoid differential sieving whereby a brittle constituent in a two-phase alloy passes through the meshes of the sieve, leaving the main bulk of the more ductile phase behind.

The sharpest and most informative powder photographs are obtained when the powder has been passed through a sieve of about 350 meshes per linear inch, and when the specimen is steadily rotated without any wobble about its axis for the whole of the exposure period. Stopping the rotation for as little as a minute results in spotty lines.

Rotation ensures that as many crystal fragments as possible are given a chance to reflect, which would not be the case if the specimen were kept stationary. By taking these precautions, the sharpness and smoothness of the lines enables accurate measurements of their positions by means of a travelling microscope to be made, and in addition a high accuracy in the photoelectric determination of the line intensities can be obtained. If, however, the specimen is coarsely crystalline and stationary, then instead of smooth, continuous spectrum lines, the haloes are broken up into a series of dots or streaks which are useless for precision work. For ordinary identification work, however, sieving through 100 mesh or finer gauze is quite sufficient provided that the specimen is rotated continuously throughout the exposure period.

When very light elements or light alloys are being examined, the broad diffraction haloes from the amorphous Canada balsam adhesive have an intensity comparable with the lines of the main alloy pattern and can be an objectionable feature on the photograph. Other methods of specimen making must then be resorted to. The author has found it convenient to damp the finely sieved powder with a dilute solution of seccotine in water. The resulting paste is forced into a thick-walled glass capillary tube of some 0·3 mm. internal diameter lubricated with a trace of Cenco pump oil. The specimen is then pushed out of the tube with a length of piano wire and gently dried for a few minutes on a watch glass in an oven at 50–100° C. The tiny cylindrical specimen is extremely fragile and must be handled very carefully when fixing it with plasticine or soft wax to the rotation holder of the X-ray camera. Very thin-walled tubes of Lindemann glass made by fusing together lithium carbonate and boric oxide are sometimes used to hold the powder. The tubes are difficult to make and fill and the X-rays scattered by them tend to increase the density of the background of the powder photograph. They are best employed when the specimen is readily attacked by air. For high temperature work, where oxidation of the specimen must be prevented, thin-walled silica tubes have proved very satisfactory.

The Identification of the Spectra on the Powder Photograph. The lines on the powder photograph are identified by finding by trial a unit cell such that the reflexions in the planes hkl will give the same values of $\sin^2 \theta$ as is found by measurement of the film.

Since in the case of a cubic crystal

$$a^2 = \left(\frac{\lambda}{2}\right)^2 \frac{h^2 + k^2 + l^2}{\sin^2 \theta},$$

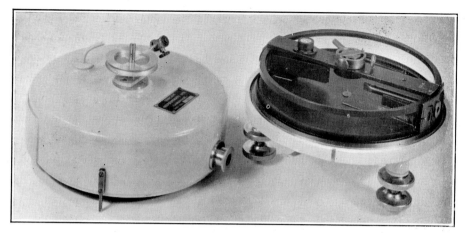

(Courtesy of "Electrical Times.")

FIG. 35.—Cylindrical type camera of 19-cm. diameter, for recording X-ray powdered crystal photographs. (Unicam Ltd.)

(Courtesy Dr. A. J. Bradley, F.R.S., Cavendish Laboratory, Cambridge.)

FIG. 36.—Powder photographs taken in 19-cm. diameter Debye-Scherrer camera.

(a) Aluminium, Cobalt Kα radiation.   Face-centred cubic pattern.
(b) Iron, Cobalt Kα radiation.   Body-centred cubic pattern.
(c) Zinc, Copper Kα radiation.   Hexagonal close-packed pattern.

(Reproduced ⅔ full size.)

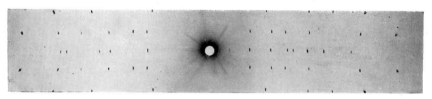

(*a*) Rotation photograph. Diameter of camera, 10 cm. Radiation, Cobalt Kα. Oscillation, 30°.

(*b*) Debye-Scherrer photograph. Diameter of camera, 19 cm. Radiation, Cobalt Kα. Note the intensity calibration steps on the edge of the film as described in Chapter VI.

FIG. 37.—Comparison of single crystal and powder patterns of $Fe_8Ni_3Al_{29}$.

we merely have to find values of the integer $h^2 + k^2 + l^2$, or Σh^2 such that the ratios

$$\frac{h^2 + k^2 + l^2}{\sin^2 \theta} = \text{a constant.}$$

Actually, with most cubic crystals, a little experience enables the experimenter to index the lines at sight.

As the symmetry of the crystals becomes progressively less, the powder photographs become increasingly more complex. Hexagonal, rhombohedral and tetragonal crystals involve a cell edge and an axial ratio. It is possible to identify the lines in their photographs by means of Hull charts, as described in the Appendix. With crystals of still lower symmetry, the number of lines becomes very large. It is possible to identify the lines if anything is known about the unit cell from other sources.

Should it be necessary to account for all the lines in the pattern in order to establish with certainty whether the alloy is single phase or not, after comparison methods have failed, a series of single crystal rotation photographs should, if possible, be taken, from which the dimensions of the unit cell may be computed. From these dimensions, all possible $\sin^2 \theta$ values can be obtained for comparison with those found by measuring the powder diagram. A single crystal rotation photograph of $Fe_8Ni_3Al_{29}$ taken with Co Kα radiation in a 10-cm. diameter camera is shown in Fig. 37 with a powder photograph of the same alloy taken in a 19-cm. Debye-Scherrer camera. The task of indexing the reflexion spots in the single crystal photograph is much simpler than in the corresponding powder diagram.

Typical Cylindrical Debye–Scherrer Cameras. The earliest crystallographic X-ray tubes had very small outputs and exposure times were often extremely long, often running into hundreds of hours in the more extreme cases. In order to keep exposure times down to an absolute minimum, the cameras tended to be rather small, seldom exceeding 5 or 6 cm. in diameter, but in recent years, as the performance of X-ray tubes has improved, and the problems to be elucidated by the powder method have necessitated the study of increasingly more complex photographs, cameras of larger diameter and higher resolving power have been developed which keep the exposure period down to a reasonable time. The use of 9- and 19-cm. diameter Debye-Scherrer cameras is now standard in a number of X-ray laboratories in this country, while for exceedingly complex patterns a 35-cm. diameter camera has been put into use.

For examining specimens which yield simple powder patterns it is unnecessary to use a camera of larger diameter than 9 cm. This in turn entails a great saving in the exposure period. In a sense, the approach is analogous to the technique employed with a microscope where it is undesirable to use a higher magnification than is absolutely necessary.

The Bradley 19–cm. Diameter Camera. Fig. 38, taken from a paper by A. J. Bradley,[12] shows the details of a typical Debye-Scherrer camera in plan and section. A circular base A, mounted on

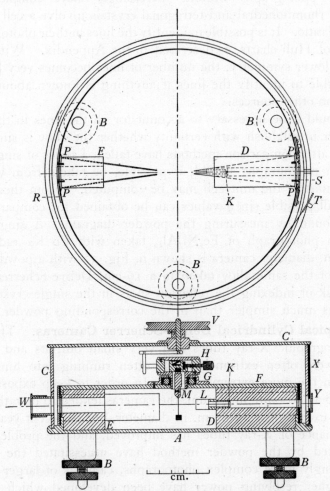

FIG. 38.—Plan and vertical section of 19-cm. camera.

(A. J. BRADLEY, *Journal of Scientific Instruments*, 18, 1941.)

three levelling screws, B, carries a light-tight cover, C. To the base, A, are rigidly attached two blocks, one, D, carrying the collimator system and the other, E, acting as a trap to catch the undiffracted beam.

These blocks are channelled at the sides to allow as large a part as possible of the diffraction pattern to be recorded. Mounted on top of the blocks D and E is a circular flanged plate, F, accurately coaxial with A and forming, with a flange of the same diameter as A, a cylinder on the surface of which the film is mounted. Four large holes are symmetrically cut in F in order to allow easy access to the interior of the camera. F also carries in its centre the bearing G, for the rotating specimen holder, H, and a small circular spirit level. The specimen holder may be easily removed from the bearing.

The Collimator System. To take full advantage of the output of the X-ray tube without affecting the sharpness of the lines, three conditions must be fulfilled. First, the specimen must not be too broad; secondly, the camera must be so adjusted that the rays are taken from the target at a grazing angle; and thirdly, the height of the specimen illuminated must not be too small, which would result in unduly long exposures, or too great, which would result in line broadening. When the second condition is fulfilled, the rays may be considered as diverging from a point or vertical line source. In fulfilment of the third condition, the beam is limited by a slit, K, of which the height is 4 mm.; the width is not so important, but it has been found inconvenient to work with a slit narrower than 0·8 mm.

The construction of the slit is shown in Fig. 39 (a). It is made separate from the rest of the camera since its dimensions are rather critical and it may need to be adjusted. This applies particularly to the side pieces, L, which serve to prevent any radiation diffracted by the slit from reaching the film. These side pieces should be as close as possible to each other without actually fouling the incident beam.

The Rotation Head. The construction of the rotation head or specimen holder is shown in section, H, in Fig. 38 and in plan in Fig. 39 (b). The specimen is held in a small clamp, M, which is screwed into the bottom of a square block. In two perpendicular channels in the top of this block work two discs rigidly fastened by two screws, N. The rotation of either of these screws will thus move the block in a direction parallel to the screw axis, and so motion of the specimen in the two perpendicular directions is readily obtained. A spring in a recess in the top of the block, butting against the cover of the rotation head, prevents tilting during movement.

The clamp, M, may be replaced by a drilled screwed rod for holding rigid specimens. Powder specimens are usually mounted as shown in Fig. 38, on a hair held taut with a small lead weight. The powder to be examined is made into a thick paste with Canada balsam, and is coated on to the hair. This has the advantage over

rigid specimens that, if the camera is level, the specimen is automatically parallel to the axis of the camera.

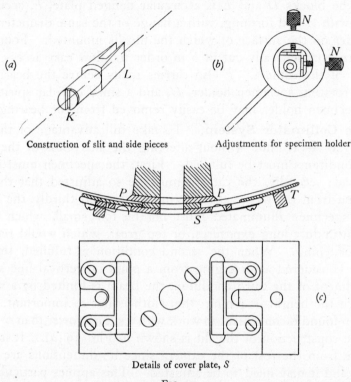

(a) Construction of slit and side pieces   (b) Adjustments for specimen holder

(c) Details of cover plate, S

FIG. 39.

The bearing of the rotation head is fitted with a ball race which
allows for smooth rotation without any tendency to wobble, and that
portion of the rotation head which fits into the bearing is slotted to
give a tight spring fit.

The Film Holder. The 19-cm. diameter camera takes two
films of the same length, the exposed part being that which lies
between the two flanges of A and F. The ends of the exposed parts
are defined by knife-edges, P, which lie accurately on the cylinder
formed by the flanges. One end of each film, together with a sheet
of black paper, fits between the knife-edge plate and a cover plate, R,
to which are attached two strips of spring steel. These strips, when
drawn round the camera as shown in the lower half of the plan,
Fig. 38, hold the film firmly against the flanges. In the top half
of the plan the operation is shown completed. The two strips are
attached to a metal piece, T, which fits between the knife-edge plate
and the cover plate, S, and is held firmly by the friction of phosphor-

bronze springs which pass through slots cut in *S*. This construction is shown in Fig. 39 (*c*). To facilitate withdrawal of the piece, *T*, it has a short pin attached to it, this pin protruding through an open slit in *S*.

The Light–Tight Cover. The cover, *C*, fits into a groove in the base, *A*, and its orientation with respect to the camera is fixed by a small notch in the edge which fits over a pin projecting into the groove. The cover carries a pulley, *V*, for rotating the specimen holder, and a black paper window, *W*, through which the X-rays emerge. The front of the cover has an additional protection, *X*, of lead, 1 mm. thick, on which is mounted a small pocket, *Y*, for holding filters.

The Bradley Type 19–cm. High–Temperature Camera. Quite a number of high-temperature cameras have been described in the literature which for various reasons have not been entirely satisfactory in operation. One of the most promising cameras recently

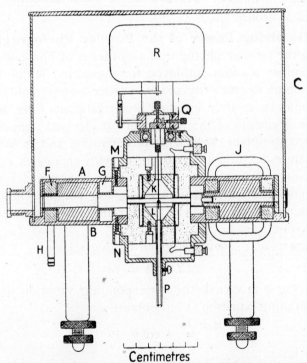

Fig. 40.—The 19-cm. diameter High-Temperature Camera.
(A. J. C. Wilson, *Proceedings of the Physical Society*, **53**, 235, 1941.)

built has been constructed on the lines of the 19-cm. diameter camera as originally designed by Bradley, after several years of experiment. Some details of the camera are shown in Fig. 40.

The specimen consisting of metal filings is sealed inside a thin-walled silica tube which protects it from oxidation, and is rotated by the synchronous motor, R, between two miniature furnaces, K and L, which consist of oxidation-resistant steel. The windings are of platinum insulated from the steel formers by mica. Each furnace element is held by screws in refractory blocks held to the camera by the circular brass clamps, M, N. The specimen is surrounded by a small ring-type PtRh-Pt thermocouple, P.

In order to keep the body of the camera and the films cool, water, cooling channels, F, G, of about 1 cm. section are provided. At the higher furnace temperatures it is necessary to interpose an opaque screen between the furnace and the film in order to prevent fogging by the light emitted.

Apart from the extra skill required in operating the high-temperature camera, it is used in exactly the same manner as the standard 19 cm. model. Further details are to be found in a paper by A. J. C. Wilson.[13]

The Resolving Power of the Powder Photograph. Apart from using the powder photograph as a means of phase or compound identification, it is often employed for measuring lattice parameters with a very high degree of accuracy in order to determine the position of phase boundaries after specified heat treatments have been carried out. Measurements of the parameters at elevated temperatures can also be used to obtain coefficients of expansion and to follow fundamental changes in atomic arrangement with change in composition. High accuracy in parameter measurement is obtained from the use of those reflexions which have a Bragg angle approaching 90°, that is, by making use of rays which are reflected back nearly into the incident X-ray beam.

The interplanar spacing is given by the relation

$$2d \sin \theta = n\lambda \qquad . \qquad . \qquad . \qquad . \qquad (1)$$

If the spacing d is varied, the corresponding variation in θ is given by differentiating equation (1) to obtain

$$\frac{\varDelta d}{d} = -\cot \theta . \varDelta\theta \qquad . \qquad . \qquad . \qquad (2)$$

It is evident that when θ approaches 90°, $\cot \theta$ is very nearly zero and any errors in measuring θ produce much smaller proportionate errors in the calculated value of d. Regarding equation (2) in another way, we can see that small variations in d produce considerable variations in θ, so that the resolving power in the highest orders is very great. By making use of lines which occur at high angles of reflexion, it is possible to calculate lattice parameters with an accuracy of 1 part in 50,000, although an even higher degree of precision has been claimed by more recent workers.

Since the film is bent into a circle round the central specimen, the pattern of lines recorded on the film is symmetrical about the diameter defined by the incident X-ray beam.   The angle of reflexion θ can easily be deduced from the angle between two equivalent lines lying one on each side of the incident beam which subtend an angle

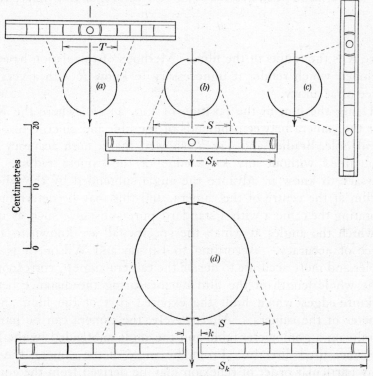

FIG. 41.—The usual film-arrangement in Debye-Scherrer cameras and the types of film resulting from each.   The dotted lines join corresponding points on the film rolled and flat.

(a) Van Arkel arrangement.
(b) Bradley arrangement.
(c) Ievinš and Straumanis' asymmetric arrangement.
(d) Arrangement of two symmetrical films in Bradley 19-cm. diameter camera.

(H. LIPSON and A. J. C. WILSON, *Journal of Scientific Instruments*, **18**, 144, 1941.)

of 4θ at the centre of the camera.   Film shrinkage is a factor which would normally lead to considerable errors in the determination of the θ's.   Partly to overcome this source of inaccuracy, different types of Debye-Scherrer camera have been devised which differ in the manner in which the film is mounted.[14]   These are illustrated in Fig. 41, together with the types of photographs obtained when the films are unrolled.

The method of Van Arkel (Fig. 41a), is probably the best arrangement for a camera of less than 10 cm. diameter. The incident beam enters through a hole in the film and leaves the camera via the gap between the ends. The arrangement is such that when the film is unrolled, the high order lines lie symmetrically disposed about the hole, and error due to film shrinkage is therefore considerably reduced because of the very short film distance between the equivalent lines. If T is the linear distance between two corresponding lines, then

$$\theta = \frac{\pi}{2} - \frac{T}{4R}$$

where R is the radius of the film. Methods of calculation have been developed which render it unnecessary to know R with a very high degree of accuracy.

Using the film in the position of Fig. 41 (b), where the X-rays enter the camera between the ends of the film and emerge through a central hole, Bradley and Jay [15] showed that a high accuracy could be obtained without any knowledge of the camera radius. It is necessary to know in advance the angle subtended by the whole of the film at the centre of the camera, and this may be determined by calibrating the camera with a standard pure substance such as quartz for which the angles at which the spectra fall are known to a high degree of accuracy. According to Lipson and Wilson, it is much simpler and more accurate to derive the camera angle θ_k corresponding to the whole length of the film by measuring the distance between the knife-edges which limit the exposed part of the film, and the diameter of the camera. Alternatively, the camera can be mounted centrally on a goniometer table and the angle subtended by the knife-edges measured directly. From the angle of the camera, the angle of any particular order of reflexion may be derived from the equation

$$\frac{\theta}{\theta_k} = \frac{S}{S_k}$$

which holds if the film shrinkage is uniform along the film.

In Fig. 41 (c) is illustrated the asymmetric method of Ievinš and Straumanis. With this arrangement, it is unnecessary to know the camera dimensions, and knife-edges as fiducial marks are not required. Zero angle is the mean of the positions of the low order lines and 90° is the mean of the positions of the high order lines. By interpolation between these two angles, the θ's of all the other lines may be obtained.

With larger cameras, the film is cut into shorter sections for convenience in manipulation. The 19-cm. diameter camera used by Bradley (Fig. 41d) uses two strips of film and two sets of knife-edges which sharply define the limits of the exposed parts. The linear distance k between the low angle knife-edges is taken as a constant of the camera, for although its effective length will vary as the film shrinkage varies, the error in spacing due to this effect can be shown to be of the order of five parts per million and is consequently negligible. Given the value of k, the 19-cm. camera is used exactly as the smaller Bradley camera.

Debye-Scherrer cameras are often employed with notches cut at intervals along the periphery of the flanges, and by this means a series of fiducial marks is printed along the edge of the film during the exposure period, from which the θ's of neighbouring lines can be deduced. This arrangement can be very useful with non-cubic crystals and has much to recommend it.

Measurement of the Film. In aiming at the highest accuracy in lattice parameters which can be obtained with the cameras described above, a comparator with a traverse of 300 mm. and reading to 0·01 mm. is required in order to measure the films with a sufficient degree of precision. The reading microscope must have a magnification not greater than 2 or 3 diameters, for above this the grain of

FIG. 42.—Direct-reading measuring microscope.
(J. E. SEARS and A. TURNER, *Journal of Scientific Instruments*, **18**, 17, 1941.)

the film makes itself evident and the spectra appear indistinct, the weakest lines being lost to view in the general background. The illumination must be such that the film remains cool during the whole period of measurement in order to avoid undesirable shrinkage effects. An instrument designed by Sears and Turner which has proved very satisfactory for the purpose of measuring Debye-Scherrer films is shown in Fig. 42.

The Elimination of Systematic Errors from the Lattice Parameter Determination. When the X-ray beam diverges from the target upon the cylindrical specimen of radius r, a finite amount of the radiation is absorbed in the specimen before reaching one of the reflecting crystals in the specimen, and a further amount of absorption takes place before the reflected beam emerges from the specimen after reflexion. The effect of the absorption is to make the distribution of X-ray intensity in the reflected beam skew in the direction of higher θ. (See Fig. 43.) Moreover, a further error in θ is introduced by the eccentricity of the specimen holder.

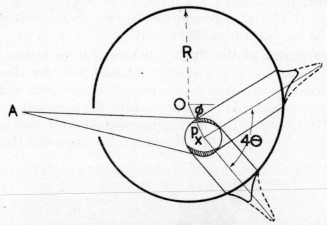

FIG. 43.—Errors in line position produced by eccentricity of the specimen and absorption of X-rays.

Shaded regions show the effective portions of the specimen.

Bradley and Jay [15] have shown that the errors introduced into θ by absorption and eccentricity together produce the proportionate error in spacing given very closely by the expression

$$\frac{\Delta d}{d} = \left(\frac{p.\cos\phi}{R} - \frac{r}{2\theta R} - \frac{r}{2\theta AX} \right) \cos^2\theta \quad . \quad . \quad (1)$$

where $p\cos\phi$ is the displacement of the axis of rotation in the direction of the X-ray beam, r is the radius of the specimen, R is the radius of the film and AX is the distance from the target of the X-ray tube to the specimen. Thus the relative error in d is very nearly *a linear function of* $\cos^2\theta$, and is zero when $\cos^2\theta = 0$, or $\theta = 90°$. In the case of a cubic crystal, where

$$a = \frac{\lambda}{2} \frac{\sqrt{h^2 + k^2 + l^2}}{\sin\theta}$$

the true value of a is obtained by plotting the apparent value of a

calculated from each reflexion against the corresponding $\cos^2 \theta$ values and extrapolating to $\cos^2 \theta = 0$ (or more conveniently to $\sin^2 \theta = 1$) as in Fig. 44.

Finally, a small correction has to be applied to the extrapolated value of a to take into account the index of refraction of the crystal fragments for X-rays which causes a very slight deviation from the

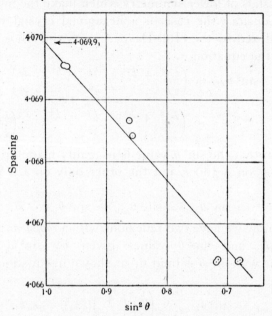

FIG. 44.—Extrapolation curve for the lattice spacing of aluminium at 200° C.   It is plotted against $\sin^2 \theta$, as tables of this are more readily available than tables of $\cos^2 \theta$.

Bragg Law.   The correction is applied by increasing the lattice parameter by a fraction $(1 - n)$ of itself, n being the refractive index for the wavelength used.   It may be calculated from the formula

$$1 - n = \frac{Ne^2\lambda^2\rho}{2\pi mc^2}\frac{\Sigma A}{\Sigma W}$$

where N is Avogadro's number, e the electronic charge, m the electronic mass, ρ the density, c the velocity of light, ΣA the sum of the atomic numbers of the atoms in the unit cell and ΣW the sum of their atomic weights.   Putting λ into Ångstrom units, and ρ in grams/cc. and substituting numerical values, this becomes

$$1 - n = 2 \cdot 71 . 10^{-6}\lambda^2\rho\Sigma A/\Sigma W.$$

For cubic crystals, this expression reduces to

$$(1 - n)a = 4 \cdot 47 . 10^{-6}\left(\frac{\lambda}{a}\right)^2\Sigma A$$

where a is the side of the unit cell.

The final value for the lattice parameter is then

$$a_{corrected} = a + (1 - n)a,$$

the correction added having a magnitude of about 1 part in 50,000.

Application to Non-cubic Crystals. The extrapolation method is easy to apply in the case of cubic crystals, but complications arise with crystals of lower symmetry which make the method difficult to apply. Consider the case of a hexagonal crystal whose spectra have been indexed by the Hull-Davey Charts and whose $\sin^2 \theta$ values are given by the equation

$$\sin^2 \theta_{hkl} = \left(\frac{\lambda}{2}\right)^2 \left\{ \frac{4}{3} \cdot \frac{h^2 + hk + k^2}{a^2} + \frac{l^2}{c^2} \right\}$$

$$= \left(\frac{\lambda}{2}\right)^2 \left\{ \frac{4}{3} \cdot \frac{h^2 + hk + k^2}{a^2} \right\} + \left(\frac{\lambda}{2}\right)^2 \left\{ \frac{l^2}{c^2} \right\} . \quad (2)$$

It will be seen that the $\sin^2 \theta$ value is in reality made up of two parts, one depending on h and k and the other only on l. We can write therefore

$$\sin^2 \theta_{hkl} = \sin^2 \theta_{hk0} + \sin^2 \theta_{00l} \quad . \quad . \quad . \quad (3)$$

Suppose now we have two reflexions with a *common l index*, namely $(h_1 k_1 l)$, $(h_2 k_2 l)$, and $\sin^2 \theta$ values given by $\sin^2 \theta_{h_1 k_1 l}$, $\sin^2 \theta_{h_2 k_2 l}$. Because of the way $\sin^2 \theta$ is built up as shown in equations (2) and (3), we may write

$$\sin^2 \theta_{h_1 k_1 l} - \sin^2 \theta_{h_2 k_2 l} = \left(\frac{\lambda}{2}\right)^2 \left(\frac{4}{3a^2}\right) \{(h_1^2 + h_1 k_1 + k_1^2) \\ - (h_2^2 + h_2 k_2 + k_2^2)\}.$$

In other words, we can eliminate the common portion to the two equations to obtain an expression which contains the a parameter only. If h_2 and k_2 each equal zero, the expression reduces very simply to

$$\sin^2 \theta_{h_1 k_1 l} - \sin^2 \theta_{00l} = \sin^2 \theta_{h_1 k_1 0}$$

$$= \left(\frac{\lambda}{2}\right)^2 \left(\frac{4}{3a^2}\right) \{h_1^2 + h_1 k_1 + k_1^2\} . \quad . \quad (4)$$

The higher the values of h_1 and k_1 and the lower the values of l, the greater is the accuracy in determining a, for then $\theta_{h_1 k_1 l}$ lies at a high angle and the factor $(h_1^2 + h_1 k_1 + k_1^2)$ is large, while $\sin^2 \theta_{00l}$ is numerically small and the error in it does not greatly affect the final value of a. Alternatively, the higher the value of l and the lower the value of h_1, k_1 and h_2, k_2 (using reflexions where

$$(h_1^2 + h_1 k_1 + k_1^2) = (h_2^2 + h_2 k_2 + k_2^2)$$

to eliminate a), the greater is the accuracy in obtaining c. The values of a and c obtained by solving a whole series of simultaneous equations are extrapolated to $\cos^2 \theta = 0$. The extrapolation yields values of a and c which give fairly accurate $\sin^2 \theta_{hk0}$ and $\sin^2 \theta_{00l}$ values, which are used to repeat the solutions of type (4) in order to obtain still more accurate extrapolation curves. The procedure is rather clumsy, and may be avoided by using a method of least squares as described by Cohen [16] which is applicable to crystals of any class.

As an example, the equation of a tetragonal crystal may be written in the form

$$\frac{\lambda^2}{4a^2}(h^2 + k^2) + \frac{\lambda^2}{4c^2}l^2 = \sin^2 \theta \quad . \qquad . \qquad . \quad (5)$$

For a small error, $\Delta\theta$ in measurement, the error in $\sin^2 \theta$ is $\sin 2\theta . \Delta\theta$, and the error due to absorption and other factors is approximately proportional to $\sin 2\theta$ (equation 1), so that the error is $\sin^2 2\theta$. We can therefore apply a correcting term to equation (5), to obtain

$$\frac{\lambda^2}{4a^2}(h^2 + k^2) + \frac{\lambda^2}{4c^2}l^2 + G \sin^2 2\theta = \sin^2 \theta \quad . \qquad . \quad (6)$$

where G is a constant. By the method of least squares, the best values of the coefficients of $h^2 + k^2$ and of l^2 may be found and a and c deduced from them.

The Method of Mixtures. A means of dispensing with extrapolation methods or the necessity of knowing the radius or the angle of the camera is to be found in the method of mixtures. A small percentage of a powdered material of known lattice parameters is mixed with the substance under investigation and the X-ray powder patterns of the two are simultaneously registered on the same film. The angles of the lines belonging to the material investigated can then be interpolated from the known positions of the lines due to the calibrating substance.

The method is not without its difficulties, for there may be overlapping of lines in just that part of the film in which the investigator is interested. Even with comparatively simple spectra, it is advisable to avoid the complications introduced by extra patterns on the photograph.

The Seemann–Bohlin Focusing Method. The Debye-Scherrer method, as outlined above, makes use of a narrow specimen of limited height, which is irradiated by the X-ray beam. Even with all the improvements made in X-ray tubes and cameras, exposure times for metals can range from as little as ten minutes up to several hours, according to the nature of the specimen. By making use of a "focusing" method, the Seemann–Bohlin camera exposes a large area of specimen in such a way that the reflected rays with the same indices *hkl* pass through a sharp focus. The principles underlying the method are shown in Fig. 45 (*a*) and (*b*).

The incident beam passes through a fine slit at P diverging upon the polycrystalline specimen occupying the arc AB of the camera periphery $PABQP$. All rays of indices *hkl* reflected by crystals lying on the arc AB will pass through Q since angles PAQ, PBQ, subtended by the common chord PQ are equal and their supplements equal to 2θ. It is thus possible to extend the specimen over a wide arc and by this means increase the total intensity of the reflected beams. By virtue of the focusing action it is also possible to increase the radius of the camera without causing a proportionate increase in the exposure period.

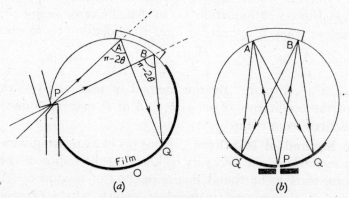

FIG. 45.—(*a*) The Seemann-Bohlin focusing method.
(*b*) The Back Reflexion focusing method.

The camera has a serious drawback not encountered in the Debye-Scherrer camera. It is not capable of recording all reflexions with θ's ranging between 0° and 90° upon the same film. As many as three cameras are required to cover the whole range. Focusing cameras of the back-reflexion type as shown schematically in Fig. 45 (*b*), recording the highest orders only, are used principally for precision lattice parameter determinations.

High-temperature cameras based on the focusing principle have been constructed. The chief difficulty encountered in this type of apparatus is getting the specimen uniform in temperature not only over the total area irradiated but also to a reasonable depth. The temperature is measured by means of thermocouples embedded in the specimen just below the reflecting surface. For further information on this topic, the reader is referred to the work of E. A. Owen and his collaborators.

Structure Integrating Camera.   C. S. Barrett [17] describes a camera for the study of preferred orientations in wrought metals or alloys having a relatively large grain size.   The apparatus is illustrated in Fig. 46.

A large specimen, 2 in. by 6 in., is mounted in a specimen holder between the slit system and the film cassette.   The specimen holder is moved horizontally along a track.   At the end of the traverse, the

FIG. 46.—Structure Integrating Camera.
(C. S. BARRETT, *Symposium on Radiography*.)

direction of motion is automatically reversed and at the same time the specimen is raised a distance equal to the width of the X-ray beam.   This scanning action enables the whole of the specimen to contribute to the pattern and therefore a good average of the distribution of orientations is obtained.   The specimen holder can also be set at various angles with respect to the X-ray beam so that "pole figures" of the resulting patterns can be obtained as described in Chapter X.

Combined Unit for Examination of Stresses.   When specimens are very massive, it is often more convenient to manipulate the X-ray tube and camera into a position of correct alignment rather than attempt to manoeuvre the specimens themselves.   This is particularly the case with large welded structures where the heating and cooling effects promote severe internal stresses and X-ray diffraction methods provide the only non-destructive means of their measurement.   For such work, it is essential to take back-reflexion photographs from three directions with respect to the surface, and from the variations in lattice parameter and the elastic moduli we can then compute the magnitudes of the principal stresses in the specimen by the methods described on page 244.

A typical unit, shown in Fig. 47, is of a Philips "Metalix" sealed-off crystallographic tube to which is attached a back-reflexion camera. The tube and camera swivel together as a single unit, in such a manner that any selected point on the specimen can be photographed from

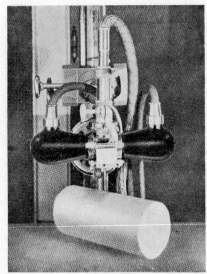

(*Courtesy Philips Industrial.*)

FIG. 47.—Back-reflexion camera combined with Philips Metalix X-ray tube on universal joint, as used in the measurement of internal stresses in large specimens.

three different predetermined positions in turn, without any change in the film-specimen distance. Since the specimen is stationary, it is necessary to rotate or oscillate the film in its own plane to smooth out the limited number of back-reflexion spots into uniform haloes in order to make accurate spacing measurements possible. This is done by means of a small electric motor suitably geared to the film holder. A sectored disc is provided to enable all three pictures to be recorded on the same film.

Crystal Monochromatizers. It was explained in Chapter II that a considerable simplification can be effected in the X-ray diffraction patterns by eliminating the β-component in the radiation by means of a suitable filter. The transmitted radiation is still not strictly monochromatic, for an appreciable amount of continuous radiation still passes through the filter together with the readily transmitted α-component.   The presence of this white radiation is, for the majority of cases, in no way detrimental, for it merely adds to the general background upon which the diffraction pattern is super-imposed.   If for any special reason it is desirable to reduce the back-ground level to an absolute minimum, the X-ray beam may first of all be reflected from a crystal set at the correct angle to *reflect* the α-component into the slit system of the camera as illustrated in Fig. 48. By this means, all the continuous radiation and the β-component are suppressed.

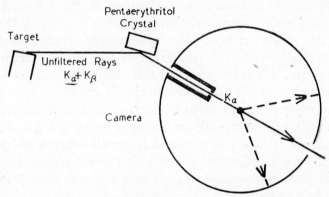

FIG. 48.—Method of taking X-ray photographs with strictly monochromatic Kα radiation obtained by reflexion of K (α + β) incident radiation from pentaerythritol crystal.

Rock-salt and pentaerythritol are eminently suitable as crystal monochromatizers.   Each gives a very strong reflexion at a low angle θ which does not produce serious polarization of the reflected X-ray beam.   As the air which fills the camera also scatters the X-ray beam to some extent, thereby increasing the background level, further improvements can be effected by evacuating the camera or filling it with hydrogen.   This procedure is most beneficial when a soft, easily scattered radiation, such as chromium Kα, is employed.   Finally, the incoherent radiation produced when part of the incident beam is scattered with change of wavelength by the specimen may be absorbed by placing a thin sheet of paper, celluloid or aluminium foil immedi-ately in front of the X-ray film.

CHAPTER VI

THE INFLUENCE OF THE ATOMIC PATTERN ON THE INTENSITIES OF THE X-RAY REFLEXIONS

INSPECTION of the X-ray photographs in the previous section immediately reveals that the reflexions have different intensities. A large number of factors influence the intensities of the reflected beams. These depend upon the experimental methods employed, the angles at which the reflexions occur, the arrangement of the atoms in the lattice and finally upon the perfection of the crystals irradiated by the X-ray beam. It is the object of this chapter to account for these differences and to apply the results to simple examples such as occur among the more common metallic elements and their alloys.

Upon striking the crystal, the incident beam penetrates through many hundreds of layers of atoms and a small fraction of its energy is scattered by the individual atoms which now become the starting centres of trains of secondary waves which have the same wavelength as the incident beam.

In order that the scattered waves may reinforce each other to form a reflected beam, they must be in phase with each other. This condition has been expressed by the Bragg equation $2d \sin \theta = n\lambda$. There is also a small amount of scattering which involves a change in wavelength and gives rise to the *incoherent* part of the scattered radiation, that is, radiation which is void of any phase relationship. This portion of the scattered energy, the "Compton Scattering", gives rise to the general background upon which the X-ray spectra are superimposed. We shall neglect this in our discussion.

Corresponding to several possible values of n, each set of lattice planes will in general produce several diffracted beams. The Bragg Law expresses the fact that the path difference between the two trains of waves scattered at a glancing angle θ by two consecutive lattice planes (hkl) is a whole number n of wavelengths. Since a path difference λ corresponds to a phase difference of 2π, the phase difference between these two trains is $2\pi n$ radians.

We have already seen how the atoms clustered round the lattice points may be considered as belonging to parallel sets of simple lattices which interleave to form a composite lattice. Since the planes (hkl) corresponding to any one of these simple lattices are parallel to and have precisely the same spacing d as the planes (hkl) of every other of the simple lattices, it follows that the composite lattice will also diffract the incident X-ray beam in the same direction as one of its simple components.

The waves reflected at the angle θ by the set of planes (*hkl*) from one of the simple lattices will all be in phase, but the reflexions from the parallel sets of planes from the different lattices will not, in general, be in phase with each of the other sets. The intensities of the reflexions will be considerably influenced by the relative positions of the interpenetrating lattices, for it is clear that when the reflected trains of waves from all the lattices are in phase with each other, an intense reflexion will occur, but when they are out of phase, the effect of the beams on each other is subtractive and only a weak reflexion or no reflexion at all will be the result. Thus, the intensities of the spectra are governed by the distribution of the atoms within the crystal. The art of structure analysis is to work back from the observed positions and intensities of the X-ray reflexions and to deduce the type of space lattice, the shape and size of the unit cell and finally to deduce the arrangement of the atoms within the unit cell.

Scattering by a Single Atom. Before we can understand how the X-rays in the reflected beams are affected by the distribution of the atoms, we must first of all see how the incident beam is scattered by each individual atom. The scattering of the radiation is done almost entirely by the electrons associated with the atoms * grouped round the lattice points. The theory for a single free electron was first of all worked out on the basis of classical electromagnetic theory by J. J. Thomson, and was subsequently applied by several workers to the scattering by the bound electrons in the atom.

When an electromagnetic wave of amplitude A passes over a free electron of charge e and mass m, the electron is set vibrating and becomes the centre of a scattered wave whose amplitude a distance r from the centre is

$$\frac{A}{r} \frac{e^2}{mc^2}$$

where c is the velocity of light. Here the electric vector of the incident wave is perpendicular to the plane containing the incident and scattered rays. When, however, the beam is polarized so that the electric vector lies in the plane of the incident and scattered rays, the amplitude takes the form

$$\frac{A}{r} \frac{e^2}{mc^2} \cos 2\theta$$

* See Chapter VII for a description of the electronic structure of the atoms.

where 2θ is the angle between the direction of the incident wave and the direction in which the scattered amplitude is measured.

If Z is the atomic number of an atom, we expect its scattering power to be Z times the scattering power of a free electron. This, however, is not so, because of the destructive interference of the waves scattered from different parts of the atom. This destructive interference grows less as the angle θ gets smaller, until the ratio of atomic scattering power to the scattering power of a single unbound electron ultimately approaches the value of the atomic number.

We can treat the problem of scattering by an atom in very much the same way as the diffraction of light by a slit. Let the distribution

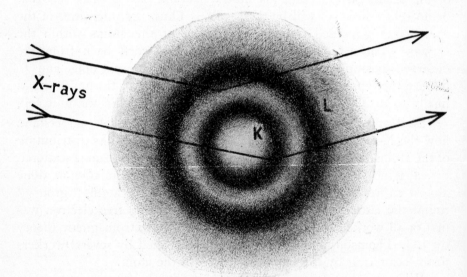

FIG. 49.—Interference of X-rays scattered by different regions of atom. Electron density $U(r)$ represented by shading with maxima at K and L shells.

of the electrons within the atom have a density $U(r)$, which is such that within the spherical shell between the radii r, $r + dr$ there are $U(r)dr$ electrons (Fig. 49). It can be shown that the atomic scattering power f, which is the ratio of the amount scattered by the atom to that which would be scattered by an electron in the same place is

$$f = \int_0^\infty \frac{U(r) \sin\left(\dfrac{4\pi r \sin\theta}{\lambda}\right)}{\dfrac{4\pi r \sin\theta}{\lambda}} \cdot dr$$

Thus we can see that f is dependent on the value of $\dfrac{\sin\theta}{\lambda}$, or for a given radiation, the direction in which the X-rays are scattered. A typical *f*-curve, namely the one for iron, is shown in Fig. 50.

It has been shown in a number of experimental investigations that the atomic scattering factor depends on the wavelength of the radiation. The atomic scattering factor is *depressed* by the use of

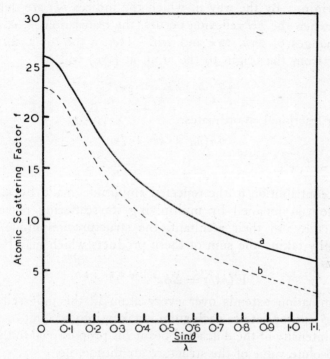

FIG. 50.—Atomic scattering factor *f* of iron.
(*a*) Scattering power of Fe with Mo or Cr Kα radiation, each far from absorption edge.
(*b*) Scattering of Fe with Co Kα radiation.

radiation whose frequency lies close to the critical K absorption frequency of the scattering element. This fact was expected on theoretical grounds, and is analogous in principle to anomalous dispersion in the optical region. Tables of f as a function of $\dfrac{\sin \theta}{\lambda}$ are given in the Appendix.

The Structure Factor. We shall now discuss the coherent scattering by the atoms grouped round the lattice points. Each atom will scatter some radiation and will contribute its share of radiant energy to the amplitude of the reflected wave having the indices *hkl*. We can form a general expression for the resultant, termed the *structure amplitude*, which we shall denote by $F'(hkl)$. Let each atom have a scattering power denoted by ϕ which is equal to f times the

D

amplitude of a wave scattered by a single electron. We measure the co-ordinates (xyz) of a typical atom from a suitable origin in the lattice parallel to the primitive translations whose lengths are a, b, c. The different waves scattered by each atom are combined by finding the *phase difference* between each of them and a standard wave scattered at the origin. By the way in which the indices hkl are defined, we see that when the hkl reflexion occurs, the translations a, b, c involve phase changes of $2\pi h$, $2\pi k$ and $2\pi l$. Hence the total *phase change* in going from the origin to the atom at (xyz) will be

$$2\pi h\frac{x}{a} + 2\pi k\frac{y}{b} + 2\pi l\frac{z}{c}$$

or, using fractional co-ordinates,

$$2\pi(hu + kv + lw)$$

where $u = \dfrac{x}{a}$, etc.

The contribution to the reflected amplitude made by each individual atom is obtained by multiplying its scattering power by its phase factor, and their resultant, the structure amplitude, is then obtained by taking the sum of these products which may be written concisely

$$F'(hkl) = \Sigma\phi\, e^{2\pi i(hu + kv + lw)} \qquad . \qquad . \qquad . \quad (1)$$

This summation extends over every atom in the unit cell and the value of ϕ appropriate to each atom is taken into account.

The intensity of the diffracted beam I is proportional to the square of the absolute value of the structure amplitude, i.e.

$$I \propto |F'(hkl)|^2$$
$$\propto \{\Sigma\phi\,\cos 2\pi(hu+kv+lw)\}^2 + \{\Sigma\phi\,\sin 2\pi(hu+kv+lw)\}^2 \qquad . \quad (2)$$

A considerable simplification occurs in this expression if the crystal lattice possesses a centre of symmetry which is chosen as the origin of co-ordinates. Since there will be as many atoms on the positive side of the origin as on the negative side, the sum of the sine terms will be zero and equation (2) takes the simplified form

$$I \propto \{\Sigma\phi\,\cos 2\pi(hu + kv + lw)\}^2.$$

Now the incident beam may be polarized, and corresponding to the two extreme states of polarization we may have

$$\phi_1 = f.\frac{e^2}{mc^2}$$

and

$$\phi_2 = f.\frac{e^2}{mc^2}.\cos 2\theta.$$

If, as is generally the case, the incident radiation is unpolarized, the average value of the electric vector must be used, and we therefore put

$$\phi^2 = \left(\frac{e^2}{mc^2}\right)^2 f^2 \frac{1 + \cos^2 2\theta}{2}$$

for each kind of atom into equation (2). The factor $\frac{1}{2}(1 + \cos^2 2\theta)$ is known as the "polarization factor".

The *structure factor* $F(hkl)$ is given by

$$F(hkl) = \Sigma f e^{2\pi i (hu + kv + lw)} \qquad . \qquad . \qquad . \quad (3)$$

u, v, w being the fractional co-ordinates of the centre of the atom whose scattering factor is f, the summation being taken over all the atoms in the unit cell. The fractional co-ordinates u, v and w are known as the *atomic parameters* of the atoms in the unit cell. The space group determines only the symmetrical arrangements of the atoms, but the parameters fix their positions exactly.

The Intensity of the Reflected Beam. Let us consider the case of a very small crystal irradiated by a beam of X-rays which suffers a negligible amount of absorption within the specimen. In order to ensure that a reflexion occurs, we shall rotate the crystal with a uniform angular velocity ω about an axis parallel to a set of reflecting planes. It can be shown that when the reflexion flashes out, the total amount of energy, E, in the reflected beam is proportional to v, the volume of the crystal.

Let $P(\theta)$ be the reflecting power of the small crystal of volume v in the direction θ, and I_0 the intensity of X-rays per unit time falling on the crystal, then the total energy reflected in the time t must be

$$E = \int P(\theta) I_0 dt$$

$$= \int P(\theta) I_0 \frac{d\theta}{\omega}$$

since $\omega = \dfrac{d\theta}{dt}$, so that the *integrated reflexion*

$$\int P(\theta) d\theta = \frac{E\omega}{I_0} = Qv . \qquad . \qquad . \qquad . \quad (4)$$

where,

$$Q = \frac{N^2 \lambda^3}{\sin 2\theta} |F(hkl)|^2 \left(\frac{e^2}{mc^2}\right)^2 \frac{1 + \cos^2 2\theta}{2}$$

N = the number of unit cells per cm³.
θ = the Bragg angle,
and $F(hkl)$ = the structure factor.

Equation (4) gives the total energy reflected by the crystal as it rotates through a range of angles which includes a spectrum.   This angular range is very small and is dependent on the state of perfection of the crystal.   When the crystal is set at an angle which differs by a small amount from the Bragg angle, the phase difference of 2π between the waves reflected from adjacent planes is changed by a small amount.   This small change in phase is cumulative over the large number of lattice planes involved in the reflexion so that mutual interference occurs which results in a very rapid decrease in the reflected intensity.

The Temperature Factor.   The atoms in the lattice are in a continual state of thermal vibration.   This heat motion has the effect of making the reflecting planes more diffuse and this results in making the spectra weaker than they might otherwise have been, particularly in the higher orders.   A method of allowing for this has been devised by Debye and by Waller.   To obtain the value of f of the atomic scattering factor at room temperature, we multiply f_0, the value of the atomic scattering factor at absolute zero by a factor $e^{-\frac{B \sin^2 \theta}{\lambda^2}}$. B is related to $\overline{u^2}$, the mean square displacement of an atom in a direction perpendicular to the reflecting planes by the equation

$$B = 8\pi^2 \overline{u^2}$$

The Debye-Waller relation which has been worked out for the case of a simple cubic lattice, but which holds with a good degree of approximation for close-packed lattices with atoms of one kind only is

$$B \frac{\sin^2 \theta}{\lambda^2} = \frac{8\pi^2 \overline{u^2} \sin^2 \theta}{\lambda^2}$$

$$= \frac{6h^2}{mk\Theta}\left(\frac{1}{4} + \frac{\phi(x)}{x}\right).\frac{\sin^2 \theta}{\lambda^2}$$

where h = Planck's constant,
   k = Boltzmann's constant,
   Θ = the characteristic temperature of the substance,
   $x = \Theta/T$, T being the absolute temperature,

$$\frac{\phi(x)}{x} = \frac{1}{x^2}\int_0^x \frac{\xi.d\xi}{e^\xi - 1},$$

and m is the mass of the vibrating atom.

Strictly speaking, we should use a different value of B for each atom in the cell, since there is no justification for assuming that all the atoms have the same amplitude of vibration.   It is very difficult to do this and we must be content with an approximate value of B which is used for the lattice as a whole, an assumption which in many cases does not involve serious errors.

We can therefore re-write the structure factor

$$F(hkl) = \Sigma f_0 e^{-\frac{B \sin^2 \theta}{\lambda^2}} e^{2\pi i(hu + kv + l\omega)}$$
$$= e^{-\frac{B \sin^2 \theta}{\lambda^2}} \Sigma f_0 e^{2\pi i(hu + kv + lw)}$$

G. W. Brindley [18] has shown in the case of zinc that the scattering factor is not a smooth function of $\sin \theta / \lambda$. Owing to an asymmetry in the Debye factor, reflecting planes making small angles with the basal plane of the structure yield relatively low scattering factors, while planes making angles approximating to 90° with the basal plane give relatively high scattering factors. These results are consistent with the view that the amplitude of the thermal vibrations are greater along the c-axis than in the basal plane. It has been stated that raising the temperature broadens the X-ray reflexions. This is not so ; perfectly sharp, though weakened, lines persist right up to the melting point of the material.

The Intensity of Reflexion from a Powder Specimen. We may consider the arrangement of the crystalline particles in the specimen to be perfectly random. Not all of the crystals are in a position to reflect, and the specimen is usually rotated in order to bring as many of them as possible into a reflecting position.

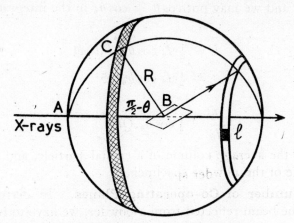

FIG. 51.—Derivation of the Probability Factor.

BC is the normal to the reflecting plane.
l is the section of Debye-Scherrer ring which is microphotometered.

Let the specimen B lie at the centre of a Debye-Scherrer camera of radius R, and let AB be the direction of the incident beam, which has the intensity I_0 (Fig. 51). Let the rays reflected from the planes hkl form a cone of semi-vertical angle 2θ, which intersects the film in a Debye-Scherrer halo.

With the specimen as centre, describe a sphere of radius R. The normals to the reflecting planes intersect this sphere in the *circle of reflexion* which is the base of a hollow cone of semi-vertical angle $ABC = \dfrac{\pi}{2} - \theta$. The divergency of the X-rays travelling from the finite source through the slit system spreads the circle of reflexion into a belt of angular width $d\theta$. Now since the distribution of the particles is a random one, the probability that a normal lies within the range $\dfrac{\pi}{2} - \theta$ and $\left(\dfrac{\pi}{2} - \theta\right) + d\theta$ is equal to the ratio of the area of the shaded belt of the sphere to the entire surface area of the sphere as shown in Fig. 51, that is, to

$$\tfrac{1}{2} \cos \theta . d\theta.$$

If there are ν crystal particles in the powder specimen, having an average reflecting power $\bar{P}(\theta)$, the total energy E reflected into the Debye-Scherrer halo will be

$$E = \int I_0 \bar{P}(\theta) . \tfrac{1}{2}\nu \cos \theta . d\theta$$

where the integration is carried out over all values of θ. Only a very small range of angle in the neighbourhood of θ_0, the Bragg angle, is effective, and we may put $\cos \theta = \cos \theta_0$ in the integration, so that we obtain

$$E = \tfrac{1}{2}\nu I_0 \cos \theta_0 \int \bar{P}(\theta) d\theta$$
$$= \tfrac{1}{2}\nu I_0 \cos \theta_0 Q \bar{v}$$

or,

$$\frac{E}{I_0} = \tfrac{1}{2} \cos \theta_0 . QV \qquad . \qquad . \qquad . \qquad . \quad (5)$$

where $\bar{v} =$ the average volume of a crystal particle, and $\nu\bar{v} = V$ the total volume of the powder specimen.

The Number of Co-operating Planes. In deriving the intensity of the beam reflected from a powder, we have to bear in mind that there may be a number of planes with the same spacing which will contribute to the same spectrum line. If there are p such planes, then the corresponding value of E/I_0 must be increased by the *planar factor* or multiplicity factor, p. Hence

$$\frac{E}{I_0} = \tfrac{1}{2}p \cos \theta_0 . QV \qquad . \qquad . \qquad . \qquad . \quad (6)$$

The value of p is equal to the number of faces in a form if the crystal has a centre of symmetry and twice this number if there is no symmetry centre. A table of planar factors for use with powder photographs is given in the appendix.

In practice we only measure the energy passing through a short length l of a halo. The amount of energy passing through l is proportional to the ratio $l/$(circumference of halo), which is clearly equal to $l/2\pi R \sin 2\theta_0$. Equation (6) must therefore be modified to

$$\frac{E}{I_0} = \tfrac{1}{2}p \cos \theta_0 . QV . \frac{l}{2\pi R \sin 2\theta_0} . \qquad . \qquad . \qquad (7)$$

The Effect of Absorption. In deriving equation (7), no allowance was made for the absorption of X-rays within the specimen, which cuts down the intensity of the energy in the reflected beam, reducing the intensities of the lower orders by a greater amount than those reflexions which occur at the higher angles. To some extent, then, the effect of absorption on the reflected intensity is to act in the opposite direction to the temperature factor. If we let the absorption factor be represented by A, we may include it in equation (7), and thus obtain

$$\frac{E}{I_0} = \tfrac{1}{2}pA \cos \theta_0 . QV . \frac{l}{2\pi R \sin 2\theta_0} \qquad . \qquad . \qquad (8)$$

which on substituting for Q becomes

$$\frac{E}{I_0} = pAe^{-\frac{2B \sin^2 \theta}{\lambda^2}} |F(hkl)|^2 N^2 \lambda^3 \left(\frac{e^2}{mc^2}\right)^2 \frac{1 + \cos^2 2\theta}{\sin^2 2\theta} . \cos \theta . \frac{Vl}{16\pi R}$$

$$= pAe^{-\frac{2B \sin^2 \theta}{\lambda^2}} |F(hkl)|^2 N^2 \lambda^3 \left(\frac{e^2}{mc^2}\right)^2 \frac{1 + \cos^2 2\theta}{2 \cos \theta \sin^2 \theta} \frac{Vl}{16\pi R}$$

or, the energy measured in the length l of the halo may be written

$$E = \text{const.} \, p.Ae^{-\frac{2B \sin^2 \theta}{\lambda^2}} . \frac{1 + \cos^2 2\theta}{\cos \theta \sin^2 \theta} . |F(hkl)|^2 . \qquad . \qquad (9)$$

Calculation of the Absorption Factor for a Cylindrical Specimen.* In the absence of absorption, the intensity of the reflected beam was shown to be proportional to V, the total volume of the crystal powder, and, for a cylindrical specimen, this volume would be $\pi r^2 h$, where h is the height of the specimen and r its radius. In the presence of absorption, the contribution of a minute fragment of crystal of volume dv to the reflected beam is reduced by the fraction $e^{-\mu a}$, where μ is the average linear absorption coefficient of the specimen, and a is the total length of path traversed by the ray through the specimen before and after reflexion from the fragment (Fig. 52).

* For recent developments by the author, see Appendix.

The total intensity of the reflexion is obtained by integrating the value of $e^{-\mu a}dv$ throughout the volume of the specimen and using this expression instead of the factor V in the intensity formula.   For a cylindrical specimen, its volume $\pi r^2 h$ is replaced in the intensity formula by $h \iint e^{-\mu a}d\sigma$ where $d\sigma$ is a small element of the cross-section of the specimen.   The integration is carried out over the whole cross-section.

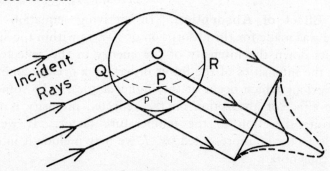

FIG. 52.—The effect of absorption on a cylindrical Debye-Scherrer specimen.

The total path of the ray reflected by a small element of volume dv at P is $p + q = a$. QPR is the locus of all points having a constant value of a.   Note how absorption alters the shape of the reflected line besides cutting down the value of the integrated intensity.

The intensity of reflexion is, therefore, cut down by the absorption factor in the ratio

$$A = \frac{1}{\pi r^2} \iint e^{-\mu a}d\sigma.$$

A is termed the absorption factor.   We may re-write it in the form

$$A = \iint e^{-\mu r x}ds$$

where $x = a/r$
and $ds = d\sigma/\pi r^2$.

The evaluation of this integral is extremely difficult.   Bradley [19] has accomplished this, using a series solution which gives results accurate to about 1 per cent., and has drawn up a set of tables giving A for different values of μr for special angles.   The values of A for intermediate angles are obtained by interpolation.

To obtain the value of μr, we first of all cut a section out of the cylindrical specimen with a razor blade and measure its length h and radius r with a travelling microscope.   We then place the specimen on a microscope cover slip and dry it gently with filter paper after dissolving away the Canada Balsam with toluene.   The mass m of the metal in the specimen is then obtained by weighing on an assay balance. Looking up the value of the mass absorption coefficient $\frac{\mu}{\rho}$ of the metal in tables, we have

$$\mu r = \rho r . \frac{\mu}{\rho}$$

$$= \frac{m}{\pi r^2 h} . r . \frac{\mu}{\rho}$$

$$= \frac{m}{\pi r h} . \frac{\mu}{\rho}$$

from which the appropriate value of A can be obtained from tables.

Should the specimen consist of more than one element, the value of μr is obtained from the relation

$$\mu r = \frac{m}{\pi r h} \left(\frac{\mu_1}{\rho_1} x_1 + \frac{\mu_2}{\rho_2} x_2 + \frac{\mu_3}{\rho_3} x_3 + \ldots \right),$$

where x_1, x_2, x_3 ... are the weight fractions of the constituents with mass absorption coefficients $\frac{\mu_1}{\rho_1}$, $\frac{\mu_2}{\rho_2}$, $\frac{\mu_3}{\rho_3}$, etc. Values of A for various values of μr are given in the appendix.

The Mosaic Crystal. The ideally perfect crystal would not only have perfectly developed faces, but would possess an atomic lattice completely free from defects and distortion. It is probably true to say that a crystal with an ideally perfect lattice does not exist, although diamond probably approximates to it very closely. By far the majority of crystals have internal defects whereby the lattice loses its perfection of alignment every few thousand atoms or so, and thereby takes on the character of an irregular mosaic. As the irradiated crystal rotates in the X-ray beam, the pseudo-blocks move, in turn, into a reflecting position, thus causing the Bragg reflexion to occur over several minutes of arc, and make the reflected intensity proportional to $|F(hkl)|^2$, a result we tacitly assumed in the derivation of the integrated reflexion. For perfect crystals, the angular range over which the Bragg reflexion can occur is much smaller than that obtained from a mosaic, and, in addition, the integrated intensity becomes proportional to $|F(hkl)|$.

If the mosaic blocks are large, the planes nearest the surface reflect so much of the X-ray energy that the deeper planes within the same block are shielded from the incident radiation and are thereby prevented from making their contribution to the reflected beam. This phenomenon is known as *primary* extinction. *Secondary* extinction occurs when the lower blocks of a crystal mosaic are partially screened from the incident radiation by the upper blocks which reflect it. With Debye-Scherrer photographs, it can be overcome to a large extent by finely powdering the specimen. Extinction has the effect of cutting down the intensities of the strongest reflexions while scarcely affecting the weaker lines. Methods of allowing for it have been devised, but they are not completely satisfactory. Fortunately, extinction is not very troublesome with alloy powder specimens and we may neglect this in our consideration of the line intensities.

The Number of Atoms per Unit Cell. In general, each unit cell contains a atoms of atomic weight A, b atoms of atomic weight B, c atoms of atomic weight C, etc. Thus the total number of atoms is $(a + b + c \ldots)$ and the total mass associated with each unit cell is

$$(aA + bB + cC + \ldots) \times 1 \cdot 65029 \times 10^{-24} \text{ grams}$$

where $1 \cdot 65029 \times 10^{-24}$ is the mass of the hydrogen atom. If the molecular weight of the crystal is M, and the number of molecules per unit cell is n, we have

$$nM = (aA + bB + cC + \ldots).$$

The density of the unit cell must also be the same as the density ρ of the single crystal, and we therefore have

$$\rho = \frac{nM \times 1 \cdot 65029 \times 10^{-24}}{V}$$

where V is the volume of the unit cell in cm³. Remembering that $1 \mathring{A} = 10^{-8}$ cm., we can write for the number of molecules per unit cell:

$$n = \frac{\rho V}{1 \cdot 65029 M}$$

where V is in $\mathring{A}^3$ (on Siegbahn Scale).

If we are considering a pure element of atomic weight M containing n atoms per unit cell, the total volume of space occupied by a single atom is $\dfrac{V}{n}$ or $1 \cdot 65029 \dfrac{M}{\rho} \mathring{A}^3$. It is also customary to define the atomic volume as atomic weight/density of crystal, which yields the atomic volume in cm³/gram-atom.

Examples of Structure–Factor Calculations.

(1) *Simple Body-Centred Cube.* (Fig. 53*b*.) This unit of structure has one atom at the centre of the cube and one atom at a cube corner ($\frac{1}{8}$ of 8 corner atoms) making a total of two atoms in the

unit cell. The equivalent point co-ordinates are: 000, $\frac{1}{2}\frac{1}{2}\frac{1}{2}$. The structure factor is therefore

$$F = \Sigma f e^{2\pi i(hu + kv + lw)}$$
$$= f e^{2\pi i(h.0 + k.0 + l.0)} + f e^{2\pi i(h.\frac{1}{2} + k.\frac{1}{2} + l.\frac{1}{2})}$$
$$= f(1 + e^{\pi i(h + k + l)})$$
$$F = f(1 + 1) = 2f \text{ when } h + k + l \text{ is even}$$
$$F = f(1 - 1) = 0 \text{ when } h + k + l \text{ is odd.}$$

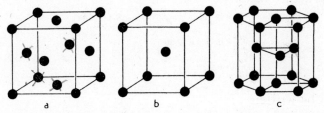

FIG. 53.—(a) Face-centred cube. (b) Body-centred cube. (c) Hexagonal close-packing.

Therefore, only those reflexions can occur for which $h + k + l$ is even, from which it follows that $h^2 + k^2 + l^2$ is even; i.e. $2.4.6.8.10.12$. The lines thus follow at regularly spaced intervals on the powder pattern. Alternatively, we could have written

$$F = f(1 + e^{\pi i(h + k + l)})$$
$$= f\{1 + \cos \pi(h + k + l) + i \sin (h + k + l)\}$$

and since $h + k + l$ are whole numbers, the sine term vanishes and we are left with

$$F = f\{1 + \cos \pi(h + k + l)\}$$
$$= f\{1 \pm 1\}$$

according to whether $h + k + l$ is even or odd.

(2) *Face-Centred Cubic Unit Cell.* (Fig. 53a.) Taking one of the corner atoms of the cube as origin, the equivalent point co-ordinates of the four atoms belonging to the unit cell are: 000, $\frac{1}{2}\frac{1}{2}0$, $\frac{1}{2}0\frac{1}{2}$, $0\frac{1}{2}\frac{1}{2}$. The structure factor is therefore

$$F = f\{e^{2\pi i(h.0 + k.0 + l.0)} + e^{\pi i(h + k + 0)} + e^{\pi i(h + 0 + l)} + e^{\pi i(0 + k + l)}\}$$
$$= f\{e^{\pi.0} + e^{\pi i(h + k)} + e^{\pi i(h + l)} + e^{\pi i(k + l)}\}$$
$$= f\{\cos 0 + \cos \pi(h + k) + \cos \pi(h + l) + \cos \pi(k + l)\}$$
$$= 4f \cos \pi(h + k + l) \cos \pi\left(\frac{k + l}{2}\right) \cos \pi\left(\frac{h + l}{2}\right) \cos \pi\left(\frac{h + k}{2}\right)$$

Therefore $F = 4f$, if $h + k$, $h + l$ and $k + l$ are even, that is, if h, k and l are all odd or all even,

and $F = 0$, if $h, k, l,$ are mixed.

Thus it follows that with the face-centred cube, only those lines appear in which $(h^2 + k^2 + l^2)$ has the values 3, 4, ... 8, .. 11, 12, ... 16, .. 19, 20, ... 24 .. etc. The lines belonging to a face-centred cube follow each other in a characteristic sequence on the Debye-Scherrer photograph, namely, two lines close together, then one, then two, and so on, which makes the identification of the lattice very easy.

(3) *Hexagonal Close-Packed Unit Cell* (Fig. 53c.). The equivalent point co-ordinates of the two atoms in the unit cell are: ooo; $\frac{1}{3}\frac{2}{3}\frac{1}{2}$.

The structure factor is

$$F = f\{e^{2\pi i(h.0 + k.0 + l.0)} + e^{2\pi i(h.\frac{1}{3} + k.\frac{2}{3} + l.\frac{1}{2})}\}$$

$$= f\{1 + e^{\frac{\pi i}{3}(2h + 4k + 3l)}\}$$

$$= f\{1 + e^{\pi i l}.e^{\frac{\pi i}{3}(2h + 4k)}\}$$

which can be written

$$F = f\{1 + \cos \pi l \cos \frac{\pi}{3}(2h + 4k)\}$$

the sine terms again vanish.

Inspection shows that

$F = 0$ when l is odd and when $h + 2k = 3n$

$F = \sqrt{3}f$ when l is odd and when $h + k = 3n + 1$ or $3n + 2$.

$F = 2f$ when l is even, $h + 2k = 3n$.

$F = f$ when l is even, $h + 2k = 3n + 1$ or $3n + 2$.

Calculation of Interatomic Distances. The distance between any two atoms may be calculated using the ordinary rules of three-dimensional co-ordinate geometry. In crystals whose axes are mutually perpendicular, the distance between two atoms with co-ordinates (x_1, y_1, z_1) (x_2, y_2, z_2) is given by the relation

$$S = \sqrt{(x_1 - x_2)^2 + (y_1 - y_2)^2 + (z_1 - z_2)^2}.$$

Densitometry—The Measurement of the Intensities of the Lines on Powder Photographs. We now come to one of the most important operations in the interpretation of the X-ray patterns, namely, the measurement of the relative intensities of the spectrum lines. For the derivation of simple atomic arrangements, visual observation in classifying spectra as strong, medium, weak, very weak, etc., is often all that is required to enable the investigator to establish the crystal structure beyond all reasonable doubt. Nevertheless, for the more difficult structures which yield complicated patterns with only partially resolved spectrum lines and for problems which demand an accurate knowledge of small intensity changes it is essential to use some form of precision densitometer or micro-photometer.

Of the many commercial microphotometers available, it cannot be said that any one of them is completely satisfactory from the X-ray worker's point of view. Automatic recording instruments are for the most part completely useless in so far as the record is produced on too small a scale to be of any value in serious work, and they do not offer any great saving in time. Manually operated non-recording instruments involving the reading of the deflexions of a galvanometer coupled to a photoelectric cell or sensitive thermoelement are also available. In using these instruments, as with the automatic recording apparatus, we have to convert the logarithms of the galvanometer deflexions into film density values before the readings are of any use, and this offsets any apparent saving in time.

The only really satisfactory type of instrument is one in which the film density is compared *directly* with the density of a neutral grey wedge by a null method. The principles of such an instrument were described by Dobson [20], but as there was no satisfactory machine capable of taking a 30-cm. length of film such as one obtains in using the 19-cm. Debye-Scherrer camera, the author had to construct one for himself, details of which are given below.

The principles upon which the microphotometer operates are illustrated by the sketch in Fig. 54. A lamp L which has a straight single coil filament sends beams of light through a graduated neutral wedge W and the film F which then fall upon a narrow slit C placed in front of a gas-filled photoelectric cell. In the photocell circuit is a sensitive Lindemann electrometer whose needle is observed by a low-power microscope. A reciprocating shutter S intercepts the light from the wedge, so that only the light which has passed through the film is able to enter the photocell. On depressing a small lever, the shutter is moved into a new position which cuts off the light from the film and allows the light from the wedge to enter the photocell. This is accompanied by an instantaneous movement of the electro-meter needle into a new position. The neutral wedge is then moved into a new position by means of an accurate metric screw geared to a revolution counter, until moving the reciprocating shutter produces no movement of the needle. In this balance position, the density of the film is equal to that of the neutral wedge, and the value of it is read directly upon the revolution counter, without any need of logarithmic conversion. The film is moved along in steps of 0·1 mm. by means of a metric screw of 1 mm. pitch which is also geared to a revolution counter, and wedge readings are taken at every position.

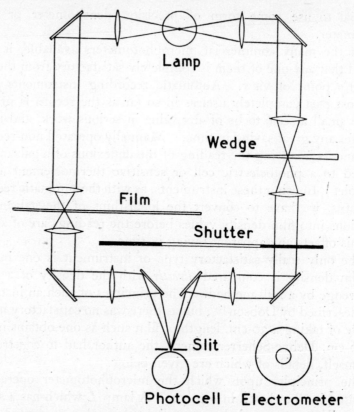

FIG. 54 (a).—Schematic layout of Dobson type microphotometer.

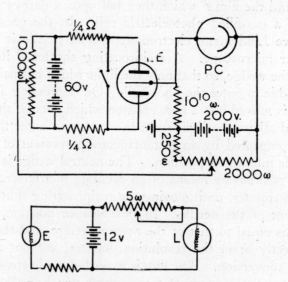

FIG. 54 (b).—Electrical circuit of microphotometer.

PC. Photoelectric cell.   LE. Lindemann Electrometer.   L. Lamp.   E. Electrometer illuminator.

With a little experience, the operational speed with this type of instrument is quite rapid and approaches that of an automatic recorder if an assistant is available to take down the readings, which are then plotted to a large scale on a roll of graph paper.

In Fig. 55 (*a*) and (*b*) are shown two views of the completed instrument, with a film in position. In Fig. 55 (*b*), the cover has

(*a*)

(*b*)

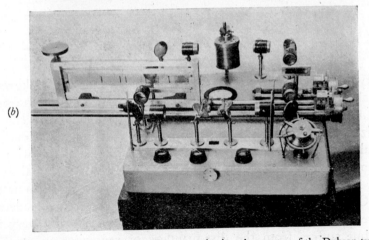

FIG. 55.—Two views of manually-operated microphotometer of the Dobson type.

been removed, revealing the electrometer and the adjustable slit. The photoelectric cell and 10^{10}-ohm liquid resistance to which it is connected and also the high tension and filament rheostats are all mounted under the cast aluminium base. The accumulators, which supply the high tension to the cell and electrometer and low-tension current for the lamp, are plugged into the sockets on the side of the instrument or plugged directly into a charging panel. In this way, all switches, save for the one for shorting the electrometer plates, are completely eliminated.

A high degree of accuracy can be attained, for, being a null instrument, the readings do not drift with the running down of the batteries or with the fatiguing of the photocell. Moreover, the apparatus can be used in a well-lit room, which is not the case with direct deflexion instruments. Since the time in doing the photometry is usually only a small fraction of the time involved in carrying out the various structural computations, it is well worth spending a little extra time in aiming at the high accuracy which only a null deflexion instrument can give.

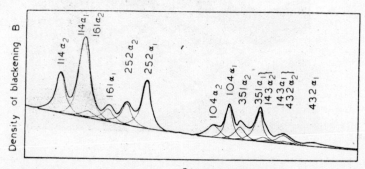

FIG. 56.—Typical photometer record resolved into component lines. NiAl$_3$. CrKα radiation. 19-cm. Debye-Scherrer camera. ($\frac{1}{4}$ full size.)

A typical record is shown in Fig. 56, upon which the background level has been drawn. The intensity of an X-ray line is measured by the *area* beneath the line contour and the background level. To minimize the effects of coarse grain size in the film emulsion, it is essential to adjust the slit height to about 3 mm. and the width to 0·1 mm. Kodak films, "Industrex D" and "Kodirex", and Ilford "Ilfex" film can be strongly recommended for all work of this nature. The "Crystallex" film, manufactured by Kodak, is a considerable improvement on these, since it gives high contrast with very fine grain, but suffers from the disadvantage of requiring an exposure time at least three times as great. In special cases, when the very highest accuracy is required and the time factor is of no consequence, this film is undoubtedly the one to use.

In general, the blackening of the film does not bear a strictly linear relationship to the intensity of the X-rays producing it. In order to correct for this effect, we must calibrate the film. After the X-ray photograph has been taken, the film is placed in a thin black paper envelope inside a brass container.   Four slits are cut in the container, so that four calibration strips near the edges of the film can be taken.   The container is then placed in a vertical position, close behind a rotating sectored wheel (Fig. 57) which is about 5 ft. from the X-ray tube.   This ensures a uniform beam over the exposed region.

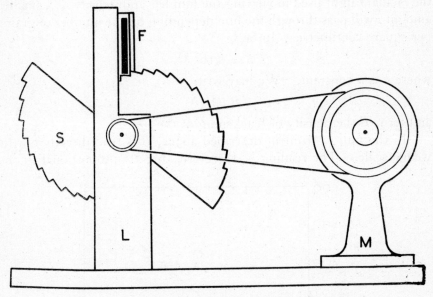

FIG. 57.—Sectored wheel assembly for calibrating X-ray film.

$F =$ Brass film holder with slot covered with black paper (top showing only). $S =$ Sectored wheel with 10° steps. $L =$ Lead shield. $M =$ Electric motor.

The sectored wheel consists of two symmetrical blades each with 18 steps subtending an angle of 10° at the centre.   It is rotated at a high speed for 30 seconds during which the X-ray tube is maintained at a steady output.   Eighteen exposed steps are obtained on $4\frac{1}{2}$ cm. of film, which have the relative exposure times 1, 2, 3, ... 18 (cf. Fig. 37, pattern of $Fe_8Ni_3Al_{29}$).

We shall now relate the exposure times on the calibration strip with the density of blackening measured by means of the microphotometer.   When the film is exposed to radiation, a certain number of grains per square centimeter are activated and these are reduced to silver on developing.   Their number, N, will be related to the intensity, I, of the radiation and the time of exposure, t.   The law relating N, I and t is given by Schwartzschild as:

$$N = It^p,$$

p being a parameter dependent on the wavelength of the radiation.

For very short light waves, such as X-rays, the value of p is unity and therefore the number of activated grains is strictly proportional to the intensity of the X-ray beam and to the time of exposure.

When the film has been processed, it is viewed or photometered by transmitted light. The developed grains absorb some of this light, making the more heavily exposed regions appear blacker. If the incident light used in viewing the film has an intensity i_0, a smaller amount i will pass through the film depending on the number of grains per square centimetre. In fact,

$$i = i_0 10^{-kN}$$

where k is a constant. We may write

$$B = kN$$

and term B the density of blackening of the film.

In the null instrument described above, B is read directly on the wedge scale. The reading is, therefore, directly proportional to the

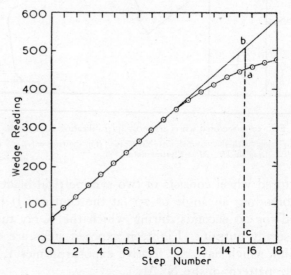

Fig. 58.—Calibration curve.

intensity of the X-rays and to the time of exposure since the Schwartzschild constant is unity. On the other hand, in direct deflexion instruments where the photoelectric cell is connected straight on to the galvanometer or amplifier, the deflexion δ is proportional to i, and in consequence, B is proportional to $- \log_{10}\delta$.

Since p is unity, we may now treat the calibration steps as if they were the result of exposures to beams of relative intensities $1, 2, 3, \ldots 18$. Now, because there are only a limited number of silver grains in the film emulsion, an increase in the exposure beyond the initial stages does not necessarily produce a proportional increase in the blackening. This is shown in the typical calibration curve in Fig. 58. Any density reading such as ac which occurs on the curved part of the line must be corrected by adding to it the amount ab. In this manner, all the higher wedge readings can be corrected, and the areas under the corrected peaks of the X-ray reflexions are then proportional to the integrated intensities of the diffracted beams. It is a decided advantage to try, as far as possible, to keep the intensity of the Debye-Scherrer pattern such that only the linear portion of the calibration curve need be used. In any event, the majority of the weak and medium lines will occur on the linear portion of the calibration curve and will not need correction. The strong lines will only have corrections added to their peak readings which form only a small fraction of the total areas.

NOTE ON A RECENT DEVELOPMENT.

Side-bands.—An optical grating with periodic errors in its rulings gives rise to extra spectra known as optical "ghosts". It has now been shown that a crystal produces similar ghosts in its X-ray diffraction spectra when the lattice-parameters vary in a periodic manner. Daniel and Lipson (*Proc. Roy. Soc.* (A), in the press) have found these ghosts in the form of diffuse side-bands lying one on either side of the main diffraction lines from Cu_4FeNi_3. This has been attributed to the incipient separation of the alloy into copper-rich and copper-poor constituents. A simple method of demonstrating the effect is given by Sir Lawrence Bragg and H. Lipson in the *J. Sci. Instr.*, **20**, 110, 1943.

CHAPTER VII

THE CRYSTAL STRUCTURES OF THE METALS

The Periodic Classification of the Elements According to Mendeleeff and Bohr. As we examine the known elements, it becomes increasingly clear that there are many which have strongly marked metallic properties, and many which are characteristically non-metallic in appearance and in behaviour. The departure from the metallic to the non-metallic character is one of gradual transition. A full understanding of metals and their alloys demands, as an important pre-requisite, a knowledge of the Periodic Classification of the elements. Perhaps the most useful system of classification is the one based on the relations between the physical and chemical properties of the elements taken as a whole, and their atomic weights. The elements, if arranged according to their atomic weights, exhibit a very evident periodicity of properties. This feature led the Russian chemist D. Mendeleeff to arrange the elements in a Periodic Table, in a manner which corresponded to their valencies and their distinctive chemical and physical properties. A modern version of the Table which includes the rare gases and several elements discovered after the time of Mendeleeff is given below in Table III.

The elements are arranged in nine vertical groups, ranging from Group O, which contains the inert gases, to Group VIII, which contains the transition elements, iron, cobalt and nickel, etc. These vertical groups arise from the way in which the continuous series of elements, written in order of ascending atomic weight, is broken up into Periods which are written one beneath the other. The lengths of the Periods are chosen in such a manner that each of the Groups contains a series of elements which have close similarities in their properties.

Writing down the elements helium, lithium, beryllium, ... fluorine in ascending order of atomic weight, we proceed from an element which is totally inert to one which is strongly electropositive and metallic. As we proceed further, this electropositive character is gradually lost until finally we arrive at fluorine, which is strongly electronegative. The element immediately following fluorine is neon, which is totally inert, and the properties of the first Period of eight elements are repeated once more in the series of eight elements which ranges from neon to chlorine.

Before the next full cycle of properties can be completed, we must write down a Long Series composed of eighteen elements ranging from argon to bromine. This is followed by a second Long Series of eighteen elements ranging from krypton to iodine, to be followed in its turn by yet another series of thirty-two elements which includes the rare-earth metals. Each Long Series is broken up in the middle by a set of three closely related transition elements which are put into Group VIII. These transition elements separate the intensely electronegative non-metallic elements of Group VII from the strongly electropositive metals of Group I, within each long period. Thus the elements in each Long Series are divided into two sets lying one below the other, and it follows from this that all the elements which fall in the same Group do not show the same degree of resemblance. In Group I, for example, we have the univalent family of alkali metals, lithium, sodium, potassium, rubidium and cæsium, and the univalent copper family, copper, silver and gold. The members of the first family, or subgroup A, are strikingly similar to each other in physical and chemical properties, but they have little in common with the members of the copper family, the B subgroup, from which they are differentiated in the table by being displaced a little to the left.

The Bohr Classification of the Elements. Most of the elements exhibit more than one valence, with the consequence that they each can show many different classes of chemical relationship. One of the chief defects of the Mendeleeff classification is that it tends to lay too much emphasis on only one of the possible valencies of each element. In order to bring their valencies and chemical properties into harmony with those of adjacent elements in the table, some elements do not appear in quite their true positions of ascending atomic weight. Thanks to the brilliant researches of Rutherford and Soddy on radioactivity and the classical work of Moseley which led to the conception of Atomic Numbers, a new electronic picture of the atom has been built up which explains away many of the difficulties of the Mendeleeff classification and furnishes a rational basis for the understanding of valence and the formation of the different types of chemical compounds.

On the basis of the more recent theories, the atom may be pictured as consisting of a central nucleus round which revolve a number of planetary electrons. The nucleus is extremely minute with dimensions of the order of 10^{-13} cm. It consists of a number of neutral particles, or neutrons, and protons, each of which has the mass of the hydrogen atom, their total mass yielding the atomic weight of the element. Each proton carries a charge $+e$ and a nucleus with

Series	Period	ZERO GROUP	GROUP I — R₂O	GROUP II — RO	GROUP III — R₂O₃	GROUP IV RH₄ RO₂
0						
1			Hydrogen H = 1·0078 No. 1			
2	1	Helium He = 4·002 No. 2	Lithium Li = 6·940 No. 3	Beryllium Be = 9·02 No. 4	Boron B = 10·82 No. 5	Carbo C = 12·01 No.
3	2	Neon Ne = 20·183 No. 10	Sodium Na = 22·997 No. 11	Magnesium Mg = 24·32 No. 12	Aluminium Al = 26·97 No. 13	Silico Si = 28·0 No. 1
4	3	Argon A = 39·944 No. 18	Potassium K = 39·10 No. 19	Calcium Ca = 40·08 No. 20	Scandium Sc = 45·10 No. 21	Titanium Ti = 47·90 No. 22
5			Copper Cu = 63·57 No. 29	Zinc Zn = 65·38 No. 30	Gallium Ga = 69·72 No. 31	Germaniu Ge = 72·6 No. 3
6	4	Krypton Kr = 82·9 No. 36	Rubidium Rb = 85·44 No. 37	Strontium Sr = 87·63 No. 38	Yttrium Y = 88·92 No. 39	Zirconium Zr = 91·22 No. 40
7			Silver Ag = 107·880 No. 47	Cadmium Cd = 112·41 No. 48	Indium In = 114·8 No. 49	Ti Sn = 118·7 No. 5
8	5	Xenon Xe = 130·2 No. 54	Caesium Cs = 132·81 No. 55	Barium Ba = 137·36 No. 56	Lanthanum La = 138·90 No. 57	Cerium Ce = 140·13 No. 58
9						
10	6					Hafnium Hf = 178·6 No. 72
11			Gold Au = 197·2 No. 79	Mercury Hg = 200·61 No. 80	Thallium Tl = 204·39 No. 81	Lea Pb = 207·2 No. 8
12	7	Radon Rn = 222 No. 86	No. 87	Radium Ra = 225·97 No. 88	No. 89	Thorium Th = 232·12 No. 90

Elements not classified in the table above :

Praseodymium Pr = 140·92 No. 59	Neodymium Nd = 144·27 No. 60	Illinium Il = 146(?) No. 61	Samarium Sm = 150·43 No. 62	Europium Eu = 152·0 No. 63
	Gadolinium Gd = 157·3 No. 64	Terbium Tb = 159·2 No. 65	Dysprosium Dy = 162·46 No. 66	

GROUP V RH_3 R_2O_5	GROUP VI RH_2 RO_3	GROUP VII RH R_2O_7	GROUP VIII		
Nitrogen $N = 14.008$ No. 7	Oxygen $O = 16.000$ No. 8	Fluorine $F = 19.00$ No. 9			
Phosphorus $P = 31.02$ No. 15	Sulphur $S = 32.06$ No. 16	Chlorine $Cl = 35.457$ No. 17			
Vanadium $V = 50.95$ No. 23	Chromium $Cr = 52.01$ No. 24	Manganese $Mn = 54.93$ No. 25	Iron $Fe = 55.84$ No. 26	Cobalt $Co = 58.94$ No. 27	Nickel $Ni = 58.69$ No. 28
Arsenic $As = 74.93$ No. 33	Selenium $Se = 79.2$ No. 34	Bromine $Br = 79.916$ No. 35			
Columbium $Cb = 93.3$ No. 41	Molybdenum $Mo = 96.0$ No. 42	Masurium $Ma = ?$ No. 43	Ruthenium $Ru = 101.7$ No. 44	Rhodium $Rh = 102.91$ No. 45	Palladium $Pd = 106.7$ No. 46
Antimony $Sb = 121.76$ No. 51	Tellurium $Te = 127.5$ No. 52	Iodine $I = 126.932$ No. 53			
Tantalum $Ta = 181.4$ No. 73	Tungsten $W = 184.0$ No. 74	Rhenium $Re = 186.31$ No. 75	Osmium $Os = 190.8$ No. 76	Iridium $Ir = 193.1$ No. 77	Platinum $Pt = 195.23$ No. 78
Bismuth $Bi = 209.00$ No. 83	No. 84				
No. 91	Uranium $U = 238.14$ No. 92	No. 93			

Holmium $Ho = 163.5$ No. 67	Erbium $Er = 167.64$ No. 68	Thulium $Tm = 169.4$ No. 69	Ytterbium $Yb = 173.5$ No. 70	Lutecium $Lu = 175.0$ No. 71

Z protons carries a net positive charge of $+Ze$. Because the atom in its normal state is electrically neutral, Z negative electrons spin planet-like in orbits or "shells" round the positively charged nucleus. Although the charge on the nucleus, or *Atomic Number Z* characterizes the position of the element in the Periodic Table, the nucleus itself is unimportant for the study of alloys, while on the other hand, the arrangements of the electrons in the various orbits play a vital part in the atomic structures of the elements and their alloys.

The mass of the electron is only $\frac{1}{1813}$ of the mass of the neutron, so that the contribution of the electrons to the atomic weight of the element may be considered to be negligible. From a detailed study of the atomic arrangements in several hundred compounds, it has been possible to assign a definite value to the effective radius of each atom. This turns out to be of the order of 10^{-8} cm. When we consider the great difference in magnitude between the atomic radius and the size of the nucleus, it at once becomes apparent that by far the greater portion of the atom must consist of comparatively empty space. It is, therefore, relatively easy for atoms to move past each other in the diffusion processes which take place in the solid state.

In Table IV is shown the Periodic Table as arranged by Bohr on the basis of the atomic numbers of the elements. Here the elements are arranged in such a way that each period is terminated by an inert gas. If we count the numbers of elements in each period, we find that they form a series

$$2, 8, 8, 18, 18, 32 \ldots$$

and the atomic numbers of the inert elements form the series

$$2, 2 + 8, 2 + 8 + 8, 2 + 8 + 8 + 18 \ldots$$

This strongly suggests that, as the atomic numbers of the elements increase, the electrons build up a succession of shells, each of which is fully completed when an inert element is reached. The reason for the chemical stability of the inert elements would appear to be found in the difficulty of removing electrons from closed shells, a fact which is borne out by the high electric potential which is required to ionize these elements.

We can now see why some atoms tend to form positively and some negatively charged ions. Each atom tends to lose or gain electrons so as to be left with a completed outer shell, which, like those of the inert elements, is very stable. For example, fluorine, which has an atomic number equal to 9, has two electrons in the innermost K shell, and seven electrons in the outermost L shell. The

TABLE IV

THE PERIODIC TABLE OF THE ELEMENTS (Bohr)

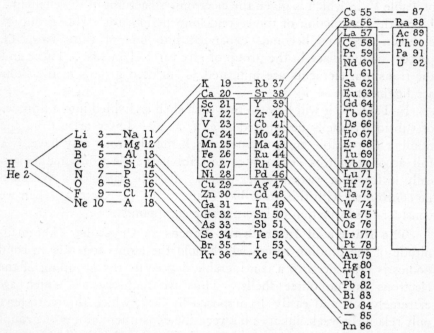

atom requires a single electron to complete the octet in its outermost group and is therefore univalent. When in the process of chemical combination it succeeds in completing the L shell, the atom as a whole carries an excess negative charge $-e$, and therefore behaves as a singly charged univalent negative ion. On the other hand, the alkali metals, lithium, sodium, potassium, rubidium and cæsium each have a solitary electron outside an inert gas shell, which requires very little energy to remove. This electron is removed in chemical processes, thus resulting in a univalent positively charged ion. Magnesium, with atomic number 12 has two electrons in the K shell, 8 electrons in the L shell and two more in the outermost M shell. Thus magnesium can easily lose either one or two electrons from the M shell and can be either monovalent or divalent when entering into chemical combination.

Beyond argon, which has the atomic number 18 (2K, 8L, 8M electrons), the stable groups of eight electrons expand into groups of eighteen. This process takes place in the *transition elements* of the Long Periods. Scandium, the element following calcium which has two electrons in the outermost N shell, adds the extra electron to the *inner* M shell, instead of adding it to the N shell, a process which is carried several stages further in the next six transition elements which terminate at nickel.   This process can best be followed by a study of Table V, in which is given the electronic structures of the elements. Upon the completion of the second long period, the stable group of eighteen electrons becomes expanded into one of thirty-two, the process taking place in the group of rare earth elements.   These and the transition elements are indicated as enclosed groups in the Bohr arrangement.

In Table V, it will be seen that each shell is divided into a number of subsidiary shells designated s, p, d, f . . .   These arise from the number of possible energy states which the electrons may have.   A full account of this necessitates describing the electrons mathematically in terms of waves, rather than as discrete particles.   We shall be confronted with this wave-like character of the electrons when we consider the formation of intermetallic compounds.

The Nature of Interatomic Forces in Crystals.   The magnitude of the binding forces which hold the atoms together in solid bodies is influenced to a considerable degree by the grouping of the electrons in the outer shells.   Thus we find crystals which are extremely soft and easily decomposed by heat, which therefore have only relatively weak linkages between the constituent atoms or groups of atoms, while the interatomic forces of hard and stable compounds must evidently be much greater in magnitude.   A survey of the atomic arrangements in several hundred substances has led to a somewhat arbitrary, but nevertheless extremely useful, division of interatomic linkages into a few discrete types, any one or all of which may be operative in a given compound.

The *heteropolar*, or *ionic bond*, is the kind of structural linkage which occurs in a crystal like sodium chloride.   The sodium atom has one valence electron in its outermost shell which is easily removed, leaving a positively charged ion with a stable, neon-like, L shell.   On the other hand, chlorine requires a single electron to form an argon-like octet in its outermost shell in order to become a stable negatively charged ion.   When sodium and chlorine enter into chemical combination, the sodium atoms yield up their loosely bound electrons to the atoms of chlorine.   The atoms then arrange themselves spacially to produce a system of least potential energy.   This condition is achieved when every negatively charged chlorine ion is surrounded by six positively charged sodium ions, and vice versa, so that on the whole the resulting structure consists of equal numbers of positively and negatively charged ions, and is consequently electrically neutral. The ionic bond may be looked upon very simply as the type of

TABLE V. ELECTRON CONFIGURATIONS OF THE ELEMENTS, NORMAL STATES

	K	L		M			N				O			P			
	1s	2s	2p	3s	3p	3d	4s	4p	4d	4f	5s	5p	5d	6s	6p	6d	7s
H	1																
He	2																
Li	2	1															
Be	2	2															
B	2	2	1														
C	2	2	2														
N	2	2	3														
O	2	2	4														
F	2	2	5														
Ne	2	2	6														
Na	2	2	6	1													
Mg	2	2	6	2													
Al	2	2	6	2	1												
Si	2	2	6	2	2												
P	2	2	6	2	3												
S	2	2	6	2	4												
Cl	2	2	6	2	5												
A	2	2	6	2	6												
K	2	2	6	2	6		1										
Ca	2	2	6	2	6		2										
Sc	2	2	6	2	6	1	2										
Ti	2	2	6	2	6	2	2										
V	2	2	6	2	6	3	2										
Cr	2	2	6	2	6	5	1										
Mn	2	2	6	2	6	5	2										
Fe	2	2	6	2	6	6	2										
Co	2	2	6	2	6	7	2										
Ni	2	2	6	2	6	8	2										
Cu	2	2	6	2	6	10	1										
Zn	2	2	6	2	6	10	2										
Ga	2	2	6	2	6	10	2	1									
Ge	2	2	6	2	6	10	2	2									
As	2	2	6	2	6	10	2	3									
Se	2	2	6	2	6	10	2	4									
Br	2	2	6	2	6	10	2	5									
Kr	2	2	6	2	6	10	2	6									
Rb	2	2	6	2	6	10	2	6			1						
Sr	2	2	6	2	6	10	2	6			2						
Y	2	2	6	2	6	10	2	6	1		2						
Zr	2	2	6	2	6	10	2	6	2		2						
Cb	2	2	6	2	6	10	2	6	4		1						
Mo	2	2	6	2	6	10	2	6	5		1						
Ma	2	2	6	2	6	10	2	6	6		1						
Ru	2	2	6	2	6	10	2	6	7		1						
Rh	2	2	6	2	6	10	2	6	8		1						
Pd	2	2	6	2	6	10	2	6	10								

TABLE V. Electron Configurations of the Elements, Normal States
(Continued)

	K	L		M			N				O			P			
	1s	2s	2p	3s	3p	3d	4s	4p	4d	4f	5s	5p	5d	6s	6p	6d	7s
Ag	2	2	6	2	6	10	2	6	10		1						
Cd	2	2	6	2	6	10	2	6	10		2						
In	2	2	6	2	6	10	2	6	10		2	1					
Sn	2	2	6	2	6	10	2	6	10		2	2					
Sb	2	2	6	2	6	10	2	6	10		2	3					
Te	2	2	6	2	6	10	2	6	10		2	4					
I	2	2	6	2	6	10	2	6	10		2	5					
Xe	2	2	6	2	6	10	2	6	10		2	6					
Cs	2	2	6	2	6	10	2	6	10		2	6		1			
Ba	2	2	6	2	6	10	2	6	10		2	6		2			
La	2	2	6	2	6	10	2	6	10		2	6	1	2			
Ce	2	2	6	2	6	10	2	6	10	1	2	6	1	2			
Pr	2	2	6	2	6	10	2	6	10	2	2	6	1	2			
Nd	2	2	6	2	6	10	2	6	10	3	2	6	1	2			
Il	2	2	6	2	6	10	2	6	10	4	2	6	1	2			
Sa	2	2	6	2	6	10	2	6	10	5	2	6	1	2			
Er	2	2	6	2	6	10	2	6	10	6	2	6	1	2			
Gd	2	2	6	2	6	10	2	6	10	7	2	6	1	2			
Tb	2	2	6	2	6	10	2	6	10	8	2	6	1	2			
Ds	2	2	6	2	6	10	2	6	10	9	2	6	1	2			
Ho	2	2	6	2	6	10	2	6	10	10	2	6	1	2			
Er	2	2	6	2	6	10	2	6	10	11	2	6	1	2			
Tu	2	2	6	2	6	10	2	6	10	12	2	6	1	2			
Yb	2	2	6	2	6	10	2	6	10	13	2	6	1	2			
Lu	2	2	6	2	6	10	2	6	10	14	2	6	1	2			
Hf	2	2	6	2	6	10	2	6	10	14	2	6	2	2			
Ta	2	2	6	2	6	10	2	6	10	14	2	6	3	2			
W	2	2	6	2	6	10	2	6	10	14	2	6	4	2			
Re	2	2	6	2	6	10	2	6	10	14	2	6	5	2			
Os	2	2	6	2	6	10	2	6	10	14	2	6	6	2			
Ir	2	2	6	2	6	10	2	6	10	14	2	6	7	2			
Pt	2	2	6	2	6	10	2	6	10	14	2	6	9	1			
Au	2	2	6	2	6	10	2	6	10	14	2	6	10	1			
Hg	2	2	6	2	6	10	2	6	10	14	2	6	10	2			
Tl	2	2	6	2	6	10	2	6	10	14	2	6	10	2	1		
Pb	2	2	6	2	6	10	2	6	10	14	2	6	10	2	2		
Bi	2	2	6	2	6	10	2	6	10	14	2	6	10	2	3		
Po	2	2	6	2	6	10	2	6	10	14	2	6	10	2	4		
—	2	2	6	2	6	10	2	6	10	14	2	6	10	2	5		
Rn	2	2	6	2	6	10	2	6	10	14	2	6	10	2	6		
—	2	2	6	2	6	10	2	6	10	14	2	6	10	2	6		1
Ra	2	2	6	2	6	10	2	6	10	14	2	6	10	2	6		2
Ac	2	2	6	2	6	10	2	6	10	14	2	6	10	2	6	1	2
Th	2	2	6	2	6	10	2	6	10	14	2	6	10	2	6	2	2
Pa	2	2	6	2	6	10	2	6	10	14	2	6	10	2	6	3	2
U	2	2	6	2	6	10	2	6	10	14	2	6	10	2	6	4	2

linkage which results from the electrostatic attractive forces between positively and negatively charged ions. There is no formation of discrete molecules in ionic structures even though characteristic atomic groupings such as SiO_4 groups may exist in the solid state.

When atoms which form purely electronegative ions are held together, the mechanism which produces the forces of attraction is rather different from that which obtains in the bond between electropositive and electronegative ions. The *homopolar bond* or covalent linkage which holds electronegative ions together is caused by the *sharing* of electrons, such that each shared electron spends part of its time in the outermost shell of one atom and part of its time in the outermost shell of its neighbour. Such an electron does a double duty by helping to fill up the shells of the atoms among which it is shared. The principal elements which form homopolar bonds are C and Si, N and P, O, S, Se, Te, H, F, Cl, Br and I. In crystals such as diamond and carborundum, SiC, the homopolar forces holding the atoms together are very strong, and the crystal, taken as a whole, may be considered as one gigantic molecule. Such materials have high melting and high boiling points.

The operation of the homopolar bond may also lead to the formation of discrete molecules as exemplified by the crystals of organic compounds. Such molecules, although electrically neutral, have distorted electron configurations, the centres of gravity of which do not quite coincide with the centres of gravity of the positive charges of the various nuclei. The molecules then act as minute electric dipoles which can exert weak attractive forces, known as *Van der Waals' forces*, upon each other. A relatively low temperature suffices to overcome the Van der Waals' attraction and pull the molecules apart from each other. Low temperatures of liquefaction and vaporization are thus characteristic of organic compounds, but in order to dissociate the molecules into discrete atoms, very much higher temperatures are required.

Finally, we have that class of substance, the true metal, which, in the solid state, consists entirely of electropositive ions held together by the neutralizing field of the detached valence electrons which can move freely between them. The valence electrons are too few in number to permit the completion of stable outer shells by the addition of further electrons from neighbouring atoms, a circumstance which rules out the possibility of the formation of stable positive and negative ions and prevents the occurrence of ionic linkages. The valence electrons are also too few in number to allow the formation of strong homopolar bonds between adjacent pairs of atoms. These lightly bound electrons which become stripped from the outermost shells of the atoms may be considered on the average as a highly mobile negative fluid spread continuously over the whole of the space between the ions. Thus, in the case of the *metallic bond*, the valence electrons may be considered *to belong to the lattice as a whole* and not to any individual atom or group of atoms.

Naturally, as the number of valence electrons in the outermost shell increases, the possibility of linkages other than the purely metallic bond becomes correspondingly greater. Gradually, as the atomic number increases, the non-directional interatomic forces characteristic of the true metal give place to a closer linking of certain atoms with their immediate neighbours, until finally we obtain the true homopolar link typified in the diatomic molecules of F_2, Cl_2, Br_2 and I_2.

The Crystal Structures of the Metals. The atomic arrangements in the elements are, as we have seen, considerably influenced by the structure of the outermost electron shells of the atoms. Where the non-directional type of metallic linkage is predominant, the atoms tend to pack together in the simplest possible manner after the fashion of spheres of similar size. This is singularly fortunate from the X-ray investigator's point of view, for it means that with few exceptions relatively simple atomic arrangements are possessed by the industrially important metals.

X-ray investigation has shown that copper, aluminium, nickel, silver and gold all possess face-centred cubic structures. Iron (ferrite) is body-centred cubic, while zinc, magnesium and cadmium have hexagonal close-packed structures. The atomic packing in these simple structures displays a high degree of symmetry which contributes in great measure to the ductility and the other physical properties shown by these metals. Their plasticity can be attributed to the ease in which movement in certain directions on specific crystallographic planes can take place. The planes of highest atomic density are able to slide over each other under the action of surprisingly small shearing forces, with the result that slip takes place in the direction of the line of closest packing of the atoms. Owing to the high symmetry displayed by the lattices of the common metals, these glide processes can be studied in great detail by the X-ray methods.

The three simple types of structure have been designated A1, A2, A3 in the *Strukturbericht of the Zeitschrift für Kristallographie*. A1 and A3 correspond to structures of closest packing, that is, to symmetrical ways in which spheres of equal radii can be packed together so as to occupy the minimum volume. These are the face-centred cubic and hexagonal close-packed arrangements described below. The third structure, that of the body-centred cube, which is not quite so tightly packed, is denoted by the symbol A2.

The Face–Centred Cubic Structure (A1 Type). The manner in which spheres can be most closely packed together in a plane is readily understood. The centre of each sphere in such a close packed arrangement will lie at the corner of an equilateral triangle and each sphere will be surrounded by a hexagon formed by six immediate neighbours in contact with it. These spheres are marked (*A*) in Fig. 59. We can now lay an identical sphere (*B*) on this layer so that it nestles in contact with three spheres below it. By continuing to lay similar spheres on the layer below, we finally build up a second layer, identical with the first one, and in doing so

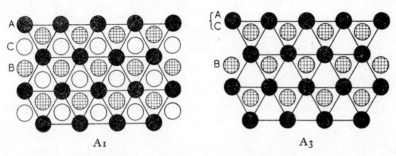

A1   A3

FIG. 59.—Close packing of spheres (Plan).

(A1) Superposition of layers in face-centred cubic form of closest packing.
(A3) Superposition of layers in hexagonal form of closest packing.

we cover the centre of every alternate triangle of the bottom layer by a sphere in layer (*B*). A third identical layer is now added above layer (*B*) but with its spheres (*C*) lying vertically above the centres of the unoccupied triangles of the nethermost layer, and the sequence is repeated indefinitely giving the series *ABCABCABCABC*. ...

The arrangement seen in plan is that of the *face-centred cubic lattice* when viewed in the direction of a cube diagonal. Fig. 60 shows the nature of the structure with one of the planes of closest packing exposed. Since each sphere is in contact with a ring of six neighbours in its own layer and with three in each of the layers immediately above and below it, the total number of closest neighbours, or *co-ordination number*, is twelve.

The closest packed planes form the octahedral faces {111}. There are only four series of {111} planes since the opposite faces of the octahedron are parallel to each other. The most densely packed lines of the structure run in the directions of the face diagonals, and are therefore $\langle 110 \rangle$ directions. These are twelve in number and are perpendicular in direction to the twelve faces of the regular dodecahedron which have the crystal form $\{110\}$. The face-centred

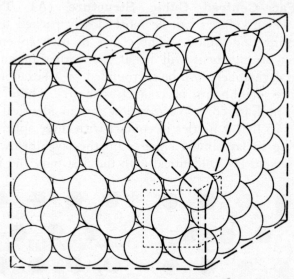

FIG. 60.—Face-centred cubic form of closest packing of spheres, showing (111) plane and unit cell.

cubic lattice, having four closely packed planes $\{111\}$ and twelve closely packed directions, has the highest degree of atomic concentration and symmetry to be found in any crystal structure. The metals with this type of lattice are very ductile and are good conductors of heat and electricity.

The Hexagonal Close–Packed Structure (A3). The hexagonal close-packed structure differs from the cubic form of close packing in the manner in which the layers of spheres are assembled. The first two layers overlap in the same way as in the cubic arrangement. The third layer is such that the spheres in it lie immediately above those in layer (A) instead of fitting over the unoccupied centres of layer (B) as in the cubic arrangement. The view shown in the drawing of Fig. 59b is the one obtained looking straight down the hexagonal axis of the

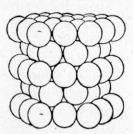

FIG. 61.—Hexagonal close packing of equal spheres. A3.

structure. A perspective view of the same structure is shown in Fig. 61. It will be appreciated at once that the hexagonal and cubic structures described above are equally close packed, having each a co-ordination number twelve, and that the hexagonal arrangement is at the same time the less symmetrical of the two.

The planes of closest packing are the basal planes {0001}, of which there is only one set as compared with the four sets of planes {111} parallel to the octahedral faces of the cubic crystal. The most closely packed directions in the hexagonal structure, $\langle 11\bar{2}0 \rangle$, are parallel to the first-order prism faces {10$\bar{1}$0}, and are only three in number as compared with the twelve $\langle 110 \rangle$ most closely packed directions of the face-centred cube. Glide takes place on the basal plane, perpendicular to the hexagonal axis and in the $\langle 11\bar{2}0 \rangle$ directions, but the freedom of slip is less than that of the face-centred cubic lattice by reason of the fewer equivalent directions in the structure.

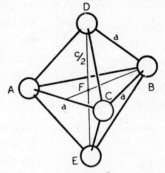

FIG. 62.— Derivation of axial ratio in hexagonal close-packed structure.

The axial ratio c/a for the hexagonal close packing of perfect spheres is equal to 1·633 : 1. This value is obtained as follows:

Let ABC in Fig. 62 represent the centres of three adjacent spheres in the basal plane, and let D and E be spheres in planes immediately above and below ABC, which nestle in contact with A, B and C.

We have $BC = a$, the edge of the unit cell of height

$$DE = 2DF = c.$$

The height of the tetrahedron $ABCD$ is clearly

$$DF = \sqrt{a^2 - \left(\frac{2}{3}\frac{a\sqrt{3}}{2}\right)^2} = a\sqrt{\frac{2}{3}}$$

Hence $c = 2DF = a\sqrt{\frac{8}{3}}$ and therefore the axial ratio

$$\frac{c}{a} = \sqrt{\frac{8}{3}} = 1\cdot633.$$

It is found that the axial ratios of the hexagonal close-packed elements deviate quite appreciably from this ideal value. For Be, Mg, Zn and Cd, the values of c/a are 1·584, 1·6236, 1·856 and 1·8859 respectively. The atoms in these cases are thus behaving as ellipsoids rather than as hard, incompressible spheres, and these deviations are connected with the nature of the electron grouping in the outer shells of the atoms.

E

The Body–Centred Cubic Structure (A2).   The body-centred cubic structure has atoms at cube corners and cube centres as illustrated in Fig. 63.

It is not quite as closely packed as structures A1 and A3, for each sphere has eight neighbours in contact with it compared with twelve in each of the close-packed lattices described above.   The closest packed planes have the form {110}, of which there are six

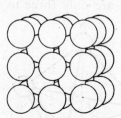

FIG. 63.— Body-centred cubic packing of equal spheres. A2. Eight-unit cells are stacked together in the illustration.

sets.   The atoms in these planes are clearly not as closely packed as those in the {111} planes of the face-centred cube.   It is this absence of an outstanding set of closely packed planes which enables a number of alternative sets of planes to function as planes of slip, namely {110}, {112} and {123}.   The most closely packed rows in the lattice, in which directions slip tends to take place are ⟨111⟩ which form a set of four, having directions perpendicular to the octahedral planes of the cube.

The slip processes described above are possible mainly because of the non-directional character of the metallic bond which gives the crystal a "self-healing" power as the atom planes slide over each other, for the interatomic linkages reform as soon as they are broken.   In crystals, where the interatomic forces are strongly directional and which often have a more complicated atomic pattern, there are no well-defined planes of closest packing, directions of slip, or deformation.   Under the action of external forces, the linkages between the atoms, once broken, remain permanently so.   Such crystals are therefore relatively brittle.

The "(8 – N)–Rule".   We have already described how there is a gradual loss of metallic properties as we approach the end of each Period in the classification of the elements.   The change in electronic structure which occurs in the outermost shells of the atoms reveals itself in a most interesting way.   Owing to the tendency to form homopolar linkages by the sharing of electrons between adjacent atoms, the crystal structures of the elements near the end of the Periods, namely those that fall in the B subgroups, are distinguished by the building up of characteristic groups of closest neighbours. In fact, so close do the atoms approach that in many cases their outer shells overlap to a considerable degree.   Examination of the elements in the B subgroups shows that the structures crystallize in such a manner that each atom has $(8 - N)$ closest neighbours, where N is the number of the Group to which the element belongs.

The elements in Group IVB, carbon (diamond), silicon, germanium and grey tin possess the well-known atomic arrangement of diamond which is illustrated in Fig. 64. Each atom lies at the centroid of a tetrahedron formed by four near neighbours. Here, then, the number of closest neighbours is 8 minus the group number 4.

The elements of Group VB, arsenic, antimony and bismuth have been found to crystallize with $(8 - 5)$ or three nearest neighbours.

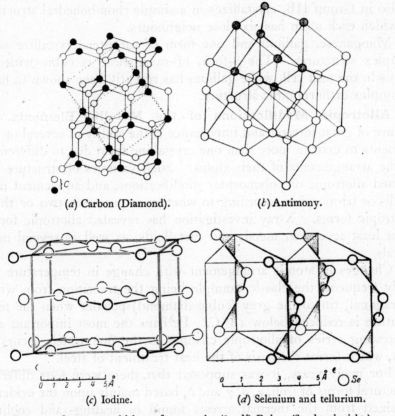

(a) Carbon (Diamond).   (b) Antimony.

(c) Iodine.   (d) Selenium and tellurium.

Fig. 64.—Structures which conform to the $(8-N)$-Rule. (Strukturbericht.)

In the antimony structure, illustrated in Fig. 64 (b), the atoms are arranged in double layers, each atom having three closest neighbours and another three at a rather greater distance of approach.

In Fig. 64 (d) is shown the structure of tellurium. This element and selenium, which fall in Group VIB, are characterized by spiral chains of atoms in which each atom has two close neighbours. Again, this is in accordance with the $(8 - N)$-Rule.

Finally, in Group VII, we have the iodine structure which is illustrated in Fig. 64 (c). This reveals the presence of pairs of atoms which correspond to the diatomic molecules of gaseous chlorine and bromine, so that in this instance each atom has one close neighbour.

We are now in a position to understand why the axial ratios of zinc and cadmium are not exactly equal to $1 \cdot 633$. The type of inter-atomic linkage which eventually leads to the $(8 - N)$-Rule of closest neighbours is just beginning to influence the elements in Group IIB, and in consequence the atoms in zinc and cadmium have six close neighbours and six at a slightly greater distance. Mercury, which is also in Group IIB, crystallizes in a simple rhombohedral structure in which each atom has six close neighbours.

Manganese, gallium and one form of tungsten crystallize with complex structures. The β-form of manganese is cubic with 58 atoms in the unit cell, while gallium has recently been shown to have a complex orthorhombic structure.

Allotropic Modifications of the Metallic Elements. A feature of great interest and importance is the ability of several of the elements to exist in more than one crystalline form due to differences in the arrangements of their atoms. Such varieties of structure are termed allotropic or polymorphic modifications, and an element may be di- or tri-morphic according to whether it possesses two or three allotropic forms. X-ray investigation has revealed allotropic forms of at least seventeen metals and metalloids, as well as several non-metals.

Changes in atomic arrangement with change in temperature are fairly frequent, the classic example being the transition from white (tetragonal) tin to the grey (cubic diamond) powder when the temperature is reduced below $18°$ C. Perhaps the most important and interesting series of allotropic changes is the one which occurs in iron, which forms the basis of the heat treatment of steel.

For many years, it was supposed that there were four different structural forms of iron, α, β, γ and δ, based mainly upon the evidence obtained from the thermal arrests found in heating- and cooling-curves. Thanks to the brilliant researches of Arne Westgren and G. Phragmén [21] who were among the first to apply X-ray diffraction methods to the study of metals and their alloys, the true nature of the thermal arrests in iron were discovered. They used a specially designed high-temperature Debye-Scherrer camera, in which the specimen was a filament of pure iron wire heated by an electric current.

Westgren and Phragmén made the interesting discovery that the Curie point at $768°$ C. was not marked by a change in atomic arrangement as had been inferred from the thermal arrests in the cooling curves of pure iron. Instead, the room-temperature body-centred cubic α-form (ferrite) persists right up to the temperature of 909° C. (the A_3 point) when the structure instantly transforms to γ-iron, or austenite, which the Debye-Scherrer photographs show to possess the face-centred cubic arrangement of atoms.   At 1403° C., an allotropic transformation back again to the original body-centred cubic arrangement was found to occur and persist up to the melting point.   The so-called β-iron is not a unique structural modification of the iron lattice but merely the α-form in a non-magnetic condition. The X-ray evidence shows quite clearly that only two genuine poly- morphic transformations occur, namely $α \rightleftharpoons γ$ at the A_3 point and $γ \rightleftharpoons δ(\equiv α)$ at A_4.

As the temperature rises, the thermal expansion of the iron is marked by an increase in the dimensions of the unit cell which

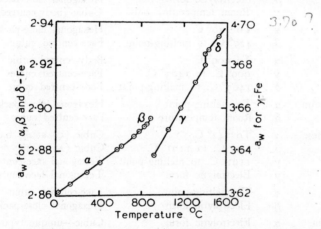

FIG. 65.—Lattice Parameters a_w of the polymorphic forms of iron according to W. Schmidt.

causes a slight movement of the lines in the diffraction spectrum. W. Schmidt has made a study of the changes in lattice parameters which accompany the rise in temperature of the metal.   His experimental results are recorded in Fig. 65.   The discontinuities in the curves reveal the temperatures at which the polymorphic changes are under- gone by the crystal structure.

Quite a number of elements when deposited electrolytically reveal polymorphic forms not found when prepared in the more orthodox manner.   Chromium and nickel are both hexagonal close packed when electrolytically deposited, although the former is body-centred cubic and the latter face-centred cubic in the normal room temper- ature form.   Table VI gives a list of polymorphic modifications in metals and metalloids.

TABLE VI

ALLOTROPIC MODIFICATIONS OF METALS AND METALLOIDS

Metal	Form	Stable Range	Crystal Structure	
Beryllium	α	To 630°	Hexagonal close-packed	A3
	β	630° to melting-point	Hexagonal	
Calcium	α	To 450° C.	Face-centred cubic	A1
	β	300° C. to 450° C.	Tending to face-centred cubic	A1
	γ	Above 450° C.	Hexagonal close-packed	A3
Carbon	Diamond		Cubic	A4
	α	Graphite ⎱ Both stable	Hexagonal	A9
	β	Graphite ⎰	Rhombohedral	*
Cerium	α	To melting-point	Hexagonal close-packed	A3
	β	Room temperature	Face-centred cubic	A1
Chromium	α	To melting-point	Body-centred cubic	A2
	β	Electrolytic form	Hexagonal close-packed	A3
	γ	Room temperature only	Cubic (body-centred)	A12
Cobalt	α	To 420° C.	Hexagonal close-packed	A3†
	β	420° C. to melting-point	Face-centred cubic	A1
Iron	α	To 909° C.	Body-centred cubic	A2
	γ	909° C. to 1403° C.	Face-centred cubic	A1
	δ	1403° C. to melting-point	Body-centred cubic	A2
Lanthanum	α	To melting-point	Hexagonal close-packed	A2
	β	Room temperature	Face-centred cubic	A1
Manganese	α	To 742° C.	Cubic (58 atoms b.c.)	A12
	β	742° C. to 1191° C.	Cubic (20 atoms)	A13
	⎰γ	1191° C. to melting-point	Tetragonal face-centred	A6
	⎱γ	Electrolytic form	Tetragonal face-centred	A6
Nickel	α	To melting-point	Face-centred cubic	A1
	β	Electrolytic form	Hexagonal close-packed	A3
Rhodium	α	Electrolytic form	Cubic—unique type	
	β	18° C. to melting-point	Face-centred cubic	A1
Selenium	α	Room temperature	Monoclinic—unique type	
	β	Room temperature	Monoclinic—unique type	
	γ	Room temperature	Hexagonal	A8
Thallium	α	To 231° C.	Hexagonal close-packed	A3
	β	231° C. to melting-point	Body-centred cubic	A2
Tin	α	To 18° C.	Diamond cubic	A4
	β	18° C. to 161° C.	Tetragonal	A5
	γ	161° C. to melting-point	Hexagonal close-packed	A3
Tungsten	α	To melting-point	Body-centred cubic	A2
	β	Electrolytic form	Cubic (eight atoms)	
Uranium	α	Room temperature	Monoclinic, face-centred cubic	
	β	To melting-point	Body-centred cubic	A2
Zirconium	α	To 862° C.	Hexagonal close-packed	A3
	β	862° C. to melting-point	Body-centred cubic	A2

* Closely related to A9.
† Often a mixture of A1 and A3 according to previous history.

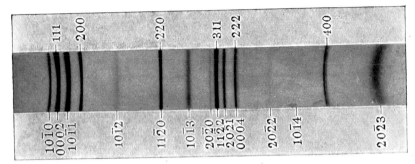

FIG. 66.—Powder photograph of pure cobalt showing mixture of sharp and diffuse spectra due to lattice "mistakes."

9-cm. diameter Debye-Scherrer camera, Van Arkel type. Ni Kα radiation, monochromatized by pentaerithritol.

(O. S. EDWARDS and H. LIPSON, *Proc. Roy. Soc.* (A) **180**, 268, 1942.)

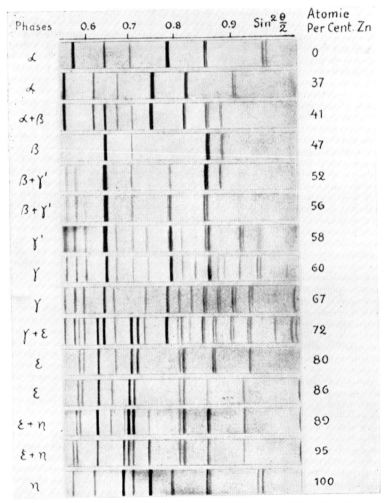

FIG. 69.—Powder Photograms of Copper-Zinc Alloys. FeK(α + β) radiation.

Phragmén type Seemann-Bohlin camera recording higher orders only.

(A. WESTGREN.) (See *page* 123).

Facing page 119.]

It is believed that hydrogen, or traces of impurity, are responsible for many of the polymorphic varieties which have been reported and which subsequent investigation has shown not to exist. P. W. Bridgeman,[22] in his experiments on the effects of high pressures, has claimed that he has obtained a new modification of zinc, but this discovery has not as yet been confirmed by X-ray methods.

Imperfections in the Structure of Cobalt. The structure of cobalt is somewhat anomalous as it often occurs as an intimate mixture of hexagonal and face-centred cubic forms. The Debye-Scherrer photograph gives a mixture of the hexagonal and cubic patterns, but some of the lines belonging to the hexagonal form are broadened by varying amounts as shown in Fig. 66.

The reason for the peculiar powder photograph lies in the close relationship between the cubic and hexagonal forms of closest packing. In cubic close packing, the sequence of spheres, as we have seen, is *ABCABCABC* ... while in hexagonal close packing the sequence is *ABABABABAB*. ... Actually we could have an infinite number of ways of close-packing spheres if we stacked up a few layers in cubic array, then a few more in hexagonal array, then back to cubic, then cubic again shifted by one interatomic distance, and so on, with each structural layer having a quite arbitrary thickness. The structure may be visualized as having a series of occasional faults which makes a sequence like *ABABAB* ... change into a sequence *BCBCBCBC* ..., *ABCABC* ..., and so on. Lipson and Edwards, and Wilson [23] estimate that the faults occur on the average between every ten planes or so.

From the way the two forms are derived, we see that the planes of closest packing are at one and the same time the (0001) planes of the hexagonal lattice and the (111) planes of the cubic forms. Reflexions from these planes will be perfectly sharp and overlap on the powder photograph, while among the other reflexions, those which are affected by the structural irregularity will be broadened. The full story of the X-ray effects is too complex to be related here, and reference must be made to the original literature. It should be noted, however, that the effect occurs in very pure cobalt and does not result from small amounts of contamination.

The Atomic Radii of the Elements. In the face-centred cube of lattice parameter a_w, the closest distance of approach of the atoms is half the length of the face diagonal or $a_w \sqrt{2}/2$. For the body-centred cube it is half the cube diagonal, $a_w \sqrt{3}/2$. In cubic structures with the diamond type of lattice, of which silicon is an

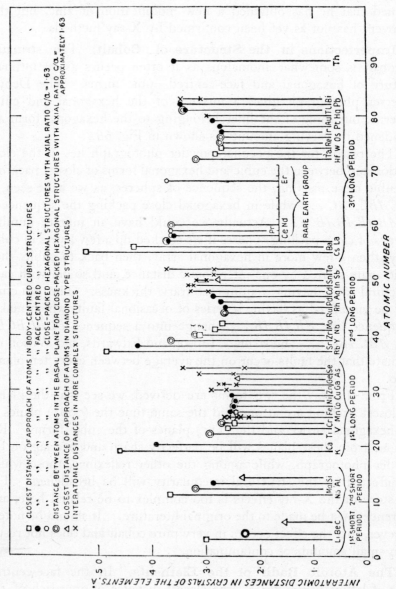

FIG. 67.—Inter-atomic distances in crystals of the elements.   (W. HUME-ROTHERY, *The Structure of Metals and Alloys*.)

example, the closest distance of approach becomes $a_w \sqrt{3}/4$. In a hexagonal close-packed structure such as zinc, the distance between an atom and its six nearest neighbours in the basal plane is a. The distance between an atom and its three neighbours in each of the layers immediately above and below works out as $\sqrt{\dfrac{a^2}{3} + \dfrac{c^2}{4}}$. Were the axial ratio c/a exactly equal to 1·633, this last expression would then equal a, and all the twelve neighbours would be at the same distance, which is the case in the face-centred cubic arrangement.

If we pack together spheres of radius r, each having a volume $\frac{4}{3}\pi r^3$ or $4\cdot18r^3$, we find that the *volume of structure* per sphere in the A1 and A3 forms of packing is $5\cdot66r^3$, and $6\cdot16r^3$ in A2. It sometimes happens that an element may have the polymorphic forms A2 and A1 (or A3). According to V. M. Goldschmidt, the atomic radius is about 3 per cent. smaller for the A2 structure where the co-ordination number is eight than for A1 or A3 in which the co-ordination number is twelve. The result is that the volume of structure per atom is almost the same for both types of co-ordination although the interatomic distances are different. An atom which enters into solid solution must therefore be given an ionic radius appropriate to the number of its nearest neighbours.

For completeness, a plot of the closest distance of approach for the elements is given in Fig. 67. The periodic dependence of the interatomic distance on atomic number is quite apparent. For a fuller discussion of the subject, the reader is referred to Hume-Rothery's excellent monograph *The Structure of Metals and Alloys*.

CHAPTER VIII

THE STUDY OF THERMAL EQUILIBRIUM DIAGRAMS BY X-RAY METHODS

The Nature of Alloys. The properties of the metallic elements are so limited in character that in the pure state they are quite unsuitable for the numerous functions required of metals in the modern world. It is a practice, familiar from earliest times, to improve the properties of metals by melting two or more of them together, by which means alloys are formed, having characteristics over which a high degree of control can be established. Melting, though still the most important method whereby alloys are produced, is not the only one. It is possible to produce alloys by the simultaneous deposition of component metals either from the vapour phase or by electrolysis from solution. A method of growing importance is that of "powder-metallurgy", in which intimate mixtures of carefully graded metal powders are compressed and sintered at an appropriate temperature. Such compacts are seldom in a state of true equilibrium.

With very few exceptions, the metals are completely miscible in the liquid state. Two metals which may be completely miscible when liquid do not necessarily remain so when the alloys have solidified. Complete solid-solubility is fairly common, examples being the gold-silver, tungsten-molybdenum and the copper-nickel binary systems. Much more frequent is the occurrence of partial solid-solubility of one element in another. The formation of intermediate phases and "intermetallic compounds" which are often accompanied by the violent evolution of heat is another feature encountered in the alloying process. Metals which are completely miscible as liquids occasionally segregate out from one another on cooling and become completely immiscible in the solid state.

Types of Solid Solution. We have already seen how each element possesses a characteristic atomic arrangement and how the majority of metals crystallize in one or other of the cubic or hexagonal forms of packing. If we take a sample of pure copper which has a face-centred cubic lattice and alloy with it a small amount of zinc, we find that a homogeneous alloy, α-brass, results. The appearance of the alloy under the microscope after the usual metallographic process of polishing and etching is very little different from that of pure copper, while the X-ray diffraction pattern obtained in a Debye-Scherrer camera from such an alloy is essentially the same as that of the parent metal, copper.

The zinc is said to have gone into solution in the copper. In the example we are discussing, atoms of zinc have replaced some of the copper atoms in the parent lattice and so formed a substitutional type of primary solid solution. The zinc atoms are slightly larger than those of copper, so that one of the consequences of the substitution is a slight distortion of the copper lattice in accommodating the atoms of zinc. The random distribution of the atoms of zinc is accompanied by an increase in the mean size of the unit cell which causes a slight displacement of the X-ray spectra.

The substitution does not go on indefinitely. Instead of zinc continuing to go into solution, a new structure which is body-centred cubic commences to form, and exists side by side with the original face-centred cubic structure. The occurrence of this new structure, or *intermediate phase*, is at once apparent as a new constituent in the microstructure or as a new pattern of lines in the Debye-Scherrer photographs. It increases with the addition of zinc until all the face-centred cubic structure has disappeared (Figs. 68 and 69).*

Continued addition of zinc results in the formation of new phase-structures, until finally we arrive at pure zinc which has a hexagonal close-packed lattice. Each of the separate phase-structures gives its own characteristic X-ray diffraction pattern, while alloys in the two-phase regions yield a spectrum containing the two overlapping diffraction patterns which belong to the single-phase alloys lying adjacent the two-phase regions.

Provided X-ray photographs of the separate phase-structures can be obtained for identification purposes, the application of Debye-Scherrer photographs to the study of phase diagrams entails a considerable simplification and saving of time. It is more certain than the classical method involving the use of the microscope, for this depends so much upon the etching characteristics of the various constituents.

In addition to the substitutional type of solid-solution which embraces by far the largest number of alloys, there are other but none the less important types. Elements such as carbon, boron, hydrogen or nitrogen have very small ionic radii and are capable of fitting in the interstices between the atoms in the lattice of the parent metal. These form the well-known interstitial type of solid solution. One of the most important alloys in this class is austenitic steel which is essentially γ-iron with only a very small percentage of carbon in solution.

* Fig. 69 facing p. 119.

Quite recently, a third type of solid solution in alloy systems has been discovered. It takes the form of a defect-lattice. Such a lattice results from the absence of atoms which would normally occupy lattice points, leaving vacant atomic sites distributed at random throughout the lattice. The first examples of alloy defect-lattices were found to occur among the β-nickel-aluminium alloys and soon afterwards in iron-nickel-aluminium, cobalt-aluminium and copper-

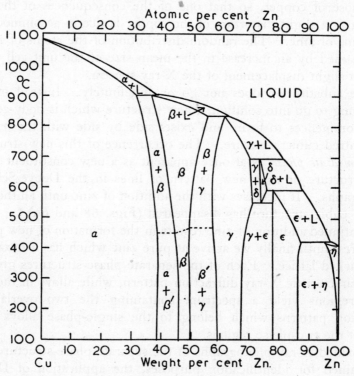

FIG. 68.—The system copper-zinc.

nickel-aluminium alloys. The existence of the defects causes local contractions in the lattice and considerable decreases in lattice parameters are readily observed.[24]

Defect and interstitial types can be discerned from substitutional solid solutions by means of the number of atoms per unit cell calculated from the lattice parameters, the densities, and the chemical constitutions of the alloys.

The Thermal Equilibrium Diagram—Underlying Principles. A thermal equilibrium diagram is a graphical means of displaying and correlating the dependence of the different phases of an alloy system upon temperature and composition. It contains a tremendous amount of useful information in compact form. As the name implies, the condition to which the diagram refers is one of strict thermodynamic equilibrium, a state which is seldom if ever completely attained in practice. Indeed, the most interesting and useful properties are often attained only when the alloy is far removed from its true equilibrium condition. Nevertheless, the properties can still be described in terms of the extent of the departure from the ideal state.

When a thermodynamic system tends towards equilibrium, the condition ultimately attained is one of lowest potential energy or of greatest entropy. In a chemical reaction, a quantity known as the *thermodynamic potential* is used which expresses the tendency to change from one state of combination to another.

According to J. Willard Gibbs,[25] a system formed by a number of component substances sets itself in equilibrium at a given temperature and pressure, so that the ζ-function

$$\zeta = \varepsilon - T\eta + pv$$

tends towards a minimum. ζ is the thermodynamic potential, ε the internal energy, T the absolute temperature, η the entropy, and p and v are the pressure and volumes respectively of the system under consideration. This principle was applied many years later by Ryn van Alkemade [26] to the equilibria existing between salt solutions and their crystalline solid phases.

In a two-component or binary system, each phase-state can be represented by a point which is fixed by giving the concentration of the phase, and the ζ-value at a given p and T. The values of ζ are plotted as ordinates and the compositions of the mixtures plotted as abscissæ. These latter should be expressed in terms of grams or gram-molecules per unit volume of mixture, but with certain reservations the composition may be expressed more simply in terms of molecular, atomic, or even weights per cent.[27] In the simplest case of all, when two components A and B are completely miscible, the ζ values for all compositions between 0 and 100 per cent. B form a continuous curve which is convex downwards.

H. W. B. Roozeboom [28] converted these theoretical ζ-curves into temperature-concentration diagrams which are the prototypes of the phase equilibrium diagrams used to-day by the practical metallurgist. He showed that there were five main types of binary temperature-concentration diagram, and that any type or combination of types could exist in any actual binary system. Among the first-fruits of his researches was the construction of the iron-carbon equilibrium diagram in which he reinterpreted the cooling curve data obtained by Roberts-Austen.

Basic Forms of the Thermal Equilibrium Diagram. We shall now describe the basic forms of binary diagram of which Type I is the simplest. Alloys belonging to Type I occur when the two components A and B, which are of the same crystal type, are miscible in all proportions in the solid and the liquid states, and when the freezing points of all the intermediate compositions lie between those of A and B. The copper-nickel system is an excellent example.

Let B have the higher melting-point. At temperatures above the melting-point of B, the ζ-curve of the solid state, S, must lie completely above L, the ζ-curve-liquid, because only the liquid state can exist. At the melting-point of B, both curves intersect the ζ-axis in a common point.

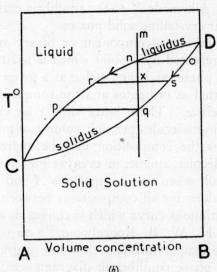

FIG. 70.—Derivation of Type I equilibrium diagram.

At lower temperatures, below the melting-point of B, solid crystals can deposit from the melt. For this to occur, it is necessary that a portion of the S-curve should come below the L-curve. The co-existing phases are now found by the points of contact of the common tangent which can be drawn to the two curves. Let the abscissæ values of the points of contact be a and b (Figs. 70, II). Then the stable states possible at the temperature considered are:

Liquid phases from the pure component A to a.

Liquid phase of composition a in equilibrium with solid of composition b, in which the proportions of a and b can vary
  according to the average composition of the alloy between
  them, and

Solid-solution ranging in composition from b to B.

As the temperature falls, the curve S falls more and more below L, so that a progressively larger region of stable solid solution occurs. Finally, at temperatures below that of the melting-point of A, only solid-solution in all proportions can exist.

If we associate the temperatures T at which solid and liquid co-exist with the concentrations of the phases, we obtain the *thermal-equilibrium* diagram shown in Fig. 70 (b).

All points above the upper curve, the liquidus, in this C-T plane indicate stable liquid phase. All points below the lower curve, the solidus, indicate stable solid solution. The extremities of horizontal lines drawn between both curves gives the compositions of the co-existing solid and liquid phases.

The freezing of an alloy of composition m occurs in the following way. It commences at the temperature of the point n, and the skeletal solid crystals or dendrites which first appear have the com-position o. The composition of the melt is changed, being less rich in B, and it continues to change from n to p, while the composition of the solid solution, which is evened up by diffusion processes, runs through all points from o to q. At the temperature of the line pq, the alloy is completely frozen to homogeneous solid solution of the same composition as the melt from which it originated.

By taking different curvatures of the S and L curves, it is possible to derive other types of temperature-concentration diagrams as shown in diagrams 71 a, b, c and d.

Figs. 71 (a) and 71 (b) represent Types II and III where a maxi-mum and a minimum occur in the solidus-liquidus curves.

Fig. 71 (c) shows the "peritectic" type of equilibrium diagram, Type IV. There is a miscibility-gap in the solid state so that two solid phases of different composition can coexist. All points above the curves CE and DE indicate homogeneous liquid. Coexisting with the liquid phases existing along the curve DE, we can have solid solutions belonging to the curve DG.

Below the temperature t of the point E, melt of compositions CE can coexist with the appropriate solid solutions along the line CF. There is thus a discontinuous change-over from solid solution G

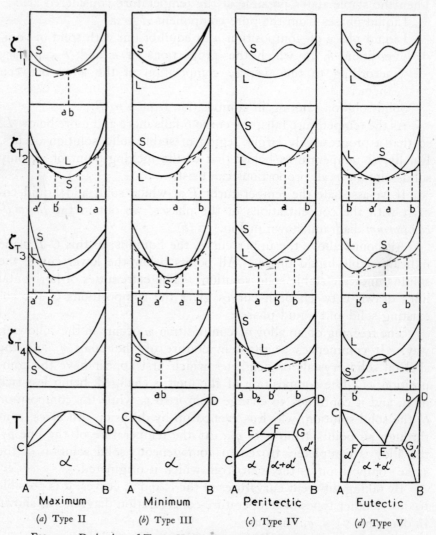

Maximum	Minimum	Peritectic	Eutectic
(a) Type II	(b) Type III	(c) Type IV	(d) Type V

FIG. 71.—Derivation of Types II, III, IV, and V binary equilibrium diagrams.

to solid solution F which can coexist together with the melt E. At the temperature of E, the following peritectic reaction will occur:

$$\text{Solid } G + \text{Liquid } E \longrightarrow \text{Solid } F.$$

Type V is the eutectic type shown in Fig. 71d. Here again we have a solubility gap in the solid state, but in this case the addition of B to A or A to B lowers the freezing-point of either of them. At the temperature of the eutectic point E, we can have solid of compositions F and G in equilibrium with liquid of composition E. Below the eutectic temperature, only two solid phases can coexist.

The same types of temperature-concentration diagram still apply, even when A and B form two different crystal types.   In these cases,
we merely have to use different ζ-curves corresponding to each crystal type.   If α and β are the two types, we can again obtain the peritectic and eutectic types of diagram.   Such a binary eutectic is shown in Fig. 72. Only one curve, ζ_L, is required because in the case considered the components are completely miscible in the liquid state.

Fig. 72b illustrates the splitting up of a homogeneous solid solution into two solid phases. This is a very simple example of a phase change which can occur in the solid state.   Changes in the solid state analogous to the peritectic and eutectic reactions can occur and are designated peritectoid and eutectoid. In these cases, instead of having to consider the common tangents to the S and L curves, we merely have to consider those to the $\zeta\alpha_s$, $\zeta\beta_s$ curves.

In practice, we meet quite complicated equilibrium diagrams which run through a large sequence of phases.   These may be looked upon as being com-

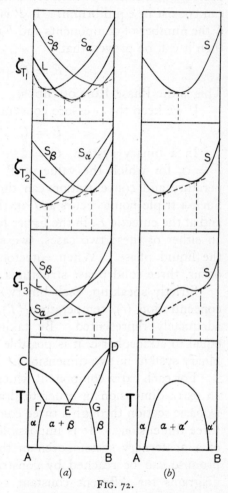

FIG. 72.

(a) Eutectic formed by two crystal types.
(b) Miscibility gap formed in the solid state.

posed of the more elementary types placed side by side so that one links naturally with the other, but the underlying principles are exactly the same as for the prototypes.

The relative quantities of the phases coexisting in equilibrium are given by the "lever principle". For example, in Fig. 70 (*b*), at temperature *t*, *r* and *s* are in equilibrium, and we have

$$\frac{\text{Amount of solid of composition } s}{\text{Amount of liquid of composition } r} = \frac{rx}{xs}.$$

The Gibbs Phase–Rule. The mode of variation of the ζ-values with the variables or "degrees of freedom", temperature, pressure and concentration, sets a limit to the number of phases which can coexist in equilibrium. If *P* is the number of coexisting phases, *C* the number of components and *F* the number of degrees of freedom, then it can be proved that

$$F = C + 2 - P.$$

This is the Phase Rule of Gibbs.

If we keep the pressure constant, we have one variable fewer, and

$$F = C + 1 - P.$$

In a binary system, $C = 2$. The system is "invariant" when $F = 0$, for which the value of *P* is 3. That is, at only one temperature and concentration can three phases coexist in equilibrium. Such a triple point occurs at *F* in the diagram for the peritectic type, and at the eutectic *E*, in the figure for the eutectic type of equilibrium. In either of these two cases, two solid phase-structures coexist with the liquid phase. When eutectoid and peritectoid transformations occur, three solid phase-structures coexist in equilibrium.

Strictly speaking, each binary system requires three dimensions, concentration (*c*), temperature (*T*) and pressure (*p*) in order to be adequately represented. By taking the pressure as constant and equal to atmospheric, it is possible to draw an isobaric section of the binary system in two dimensions.

For each extra component which we add to the system, we require an extra dimension in order to draw the equilibrium diagram. An isobaric section through a three component or ternary system requires three dimensions. It is impossible to represent the isobaric section of a quaternary system even in three dimensions, although a compromise can be reached by constructing separate three dimensional diagrams for different constant concentrations of one of the four components.

The Ternary System. The representation of the composition of an alloy formed by three components can be done in a number of ways. The two most generally used are due to Gibbs [29] and independently, to Stokes [30], and to Roozeboom. [31]

Gibbs makes use of an equilateral triangle of height equal to unity or to 100 (Fig. 73a). The corners A, B, C, represent the pure components. A point on the line AB represents a binary alloy of A and B, and so on for the sides AC and BC. Any point within the triangle corresponds to an alloy of the three components. The temperature axis is taken at right angles to the plane which represents the compositions of the alloys.

If we have a per cent. of A, b per cent. of B, c per cent. of C in an alloy, $a + b + c = 100$.

Now the sum of the perpendiculars drawn from any point to the sides of an equilateral triangle is equal to the height, in this case 100. We can, therefore, represent the composition of a ternary alloy such as o (Fig. 73a), by its perpendicular distances from the sides. In this case, the percentages of the components are $a = oa$, $b = ob$ and $c = oc$.

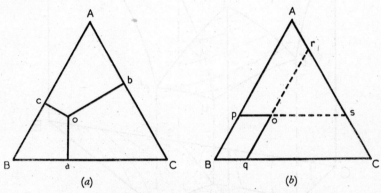

FIG. 73.—Representation of the composition of a ternary alloy.

(a) J. WILLARD-GIBBS and C. G. STOKES.
(b) H. W. B. ROOZEBOOM.

A somewhat more convenient method is that due to Roozeboom (Fig. 73b). Here the sides of the triangle are made unity or 100. It is evident that by drawing ps, qr through O parallel to the sides BC, BA, then

$$or + op + oq = 100.$$

That is, the percentages a, b, c of the components A, B and C are given by $a = oq$ or Bp, $b = or$ or os, $c = Bq$.

Ternary Eutectic. The solidus and liquidus lines of the binary systems forming the sides of the ternary prism spread into the prism as solidus and liquidus surfaces. Binary eutectic points become extended into ternary eutectic lines which intersect to give ternary eutectic points. A very simple case is chosen to give an example.

The three vertical planes bounding the ternary prism contain contiguous binary diagrams AB, BC, CA, each of the simple eutecti-ferous type. Fig. 74 shows that the addition of a third component to each of the binary eutectics lowers their temperatures along the curves $r'u'$, $s'u'$, $t'u'$, until finally the curves intersect at the point u', the ternary eutectic point.

The lower boundary of the liquid phase consists of the three curved surfaces $A_1t'u'r'$, $B_1s'u'r'$, $C_1t'u's'$, and it can be seen that the

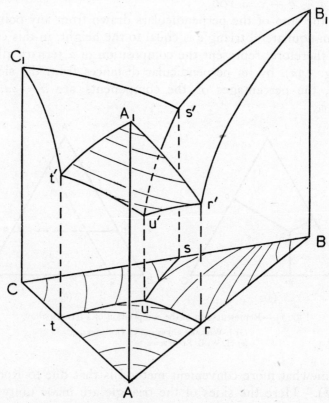

FIG. 74.—Partial representation of simple eutectiferous ternary system.
u' is the ternary eutectic point.

eutectic curves $r'u'$, $s'u'$, $t'u'$, are the intersections of these surfaces. Instead of making a three-dimensional drawing, isothermal contours of the surfaces can be drawn on the composition plane, along with the projections of the ternary eutectic lines.

Fig. 75 shows, schematically, the three eutectiferous binary systems, and an isothermal section taken through the ternary system formed by them. We can see that there are regions of homogeneous solid solution α, β and γ which terminate at the boundaries pv, vu; qw, wr; and sx, xt.

We have two-phase regions $pqwv$, $rsxw$, and $txvu$, which lie adjacent the three-phase region wxv.   Any alloy within this triangle will be composed of the three phase-structures w, v and x.

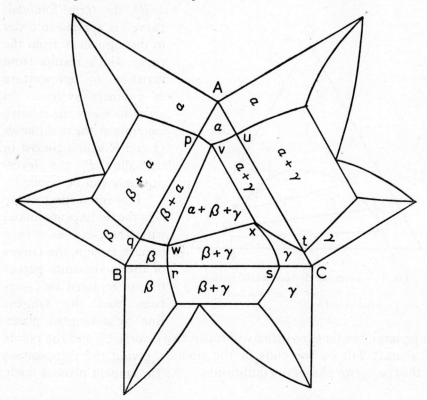

FIG. 75.—Isothermic section through simple ternary system.

The Isothermic–Isobaric Solubility Gap.   If we have a solubility gap represented by ab in the binary system AB, the addition of a third constituent C, which is completely soluble in A and B, will result in the distribution of C among the two according to the value of its partition coefficients (Fig. 76).

It thus produces two ternary conjugate solutions which can co-exist in equilibrium with each other.   Upon addition of more C, the intersolubility of A and B increases, until finally the two solutions become identical.   The point at which the two solutions become identical is a "critical point".

Certain of the conjugate solutions are indicated by ab, QR and ST; the lines joining them are called "tie-lines" by Stokes.   As a consequence of the fact that C does not distribute itself in the two phases equally, the tie-lines are not parallel to the base of the triangle.

As the two phases become more nearly the same, the tie-lines diminish in length, the limit occurring at the critical point.

Because there are always two related values of solubility on curve $aSRb$, the term "binodal-curve" is applied in order to distinguish it from the curve which results from variation of temperature in a binary system. In order to know the relative amounts of the two phases Q and R which coexist in the alloy P, the lever-principle can be applied.

It is interesting to see how the tie-lines are linked with the ζ-curves. In a ternary system, the curves of thermodynamic potential are replaced by ζ-surfaces, and the tangent line by a tangent plane.

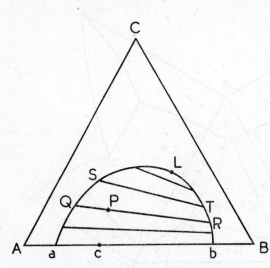

FIG. 76.—Isothermic-Isobaric Solubility Gap.

QR, ST are "tie-lines" or "co-nodal lines".
L is the "critical point".

In general, the tangent plane will touch two ζ-surfaces, and the points of contact will be the ends of the tie-lines giving the composition of the conjugate phases in equilibrium. As the tangent plane is made

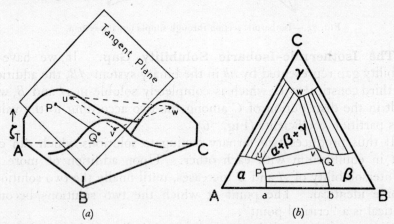

(a)   (b)

FIG. 77.—The derivation of Tie-Lines in simple ternary system.

(a) PQ is the tie-line joining the points of contact of the tangent plane rolling on the ζ-surfaces. U, V, W are the limiting points of contact when plane rests on all three ζ-surfaces, thus defining 3-phase triangle.

(b) The ternary diagram derived from (a). aPu is the locus of P projected on the composition plane A, B, C.

to roll over the ζ-surfaces, the locus of the points of contact trace out the phase boundaries and yield the extremities of the corresponding tie-lines. If the tangent plane comes in contact with a third ζ-surface, it is no longer free to roll and the three points of contact form the vertices of a triangle within which three phases can coexist in equilibrium. Any alloy with its composition lying within this area splits up into three phases whose compositions are those of the vertices of the triangle.

Binodal Surface. In Fig. 78, we see the extension of the binodal curve into a binodal surface. K_2 is called the critical solution point, and the point K_1 to which the binodal surface rises to a maximum is the true ternary critical point. The surface is dome-shaped, except for the flat portion cut away by the vertical plane, BCK_2. The isothermic contours are shown in Fig. 78. A variation of this case occurs when the temperature of the critical point K_2 is lowered with the addition of A. The ternary system does not then possess a true critical point.

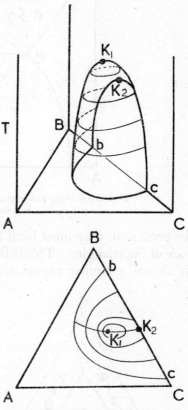

Fig. 78.—Binodal Surface. K_1 is the ternary critical point.

The Usefulness of the ζ-Function in Drawing Phase Diagrams. Many investigators have drawn equilibrium diagrams which have apparently obeyed the phase rule in that the correct number of phases have coexisted in equilibrium, but which have, in fact, violated the thermodynamic principles on which these diagrams are based. In Fig. 79, a simple eutectiferous binary system is drawn. As far as the eutectic point E is concerned, liquid phase γ is in equilibrium with the two solid phases α and β. There are thus three phases in equilibrium at E and apparently all is in agreement with the phase rule. However, a study of the derivation of the eutectic type of equilibrium diagram from the ζ-curves quickly shows that the construction of the diagram at P is correct while at Q it is definitely wrong.

In ternary systems, the three-phase regions are triangles. If the boundaries of the single phase area at one of the apexes of the triangle

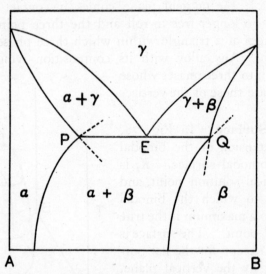

FIG. 79.—Possible (left) and impossible (right) relations between phase boundaries and eutectic horizontals.

be produced, they must both lie inside the triangle or lie one on each side of the triangle. This is illustrated in Fig. 80 (*a*). In Fig. 80 (*b*) is shown a similar region in which the construction of the phase

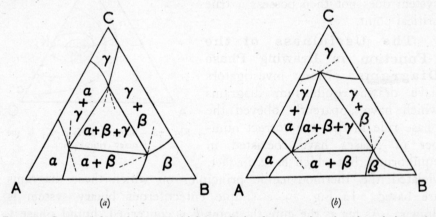

FIG. 80.—Correct (left) and incorrect (right) methods of constructing phase boundaries at the corners of three-phase triangles.

boundaries is incorrect, as consideration of a plane rolling upon the ζ-surfaces would quickly reveal.

A realization of the principles underlying the equilibrium diagram is of great assistance in the correct drawing of the phase boundaries from the experimental data and helps to avoid the mistakes which an uncritical application of the phase rule would entail.

The Preparation of Alloys for Equilibrium Diagram Studies. When commencing any systematic research on an alloy system, it is of paramount importance to use metals of the highest degree of purity obtainable. Very small amounts of impurity amounting to only a fraction of a per cent. can modify the physical properties of the alloy and influence the formation of the phases to a marked degree. Even when very pure materials are available, very special precautions must be taken at all stages in the preparation and heat treatment of the alloy in order to prevent the pick-up of small amounts of impurity. For example, the choice of crucible is very important as the crucible often reacts with its contents unless lined or made of a refractory material which is inert towards the charge.

In general, melting should be done *in vacuo* or in an inert atmosphere such as argon or hydrogen to prevent any oxidation taking place, and is to be preferred to melting in air under a flux, the latter being an all-too-common source of contamination. The most satisfactory type of furnace in which to make alloys in small amounts, say 30 or 40 grams in weight, is undoubtedly a high frequency induction furnace operated in conjunction with a valve oscillator or mercury spark. The heat is generated very rapidly in the charge itself, the crucible remaining relatively cool, so that very clean melting conditions are obtained, while the great turbulence set up by the eddy currents is very advantageous in producing a well-mixed alloy.

After carrying out the melting process in the inert atmosphere, the gas is then pumped off and the alloy is allowed to cool in a vacuum. This treatment leaves the alloy comparatively free from blowholes.

Heat Treatment — The Elimination of Coring. On page 126 we considered the freezing of an alloy of composition *m*, which was solidifying so that the liquid phase was always in thermodynamic equilibrium with the conjugate solid phase at every stage during the freezing. In order that such an equilibrium should be maintained, it is necessary for the rate of diffusion within the solid crystals which separate from the melt to be sufficiently rapid to equalize the composition and ensure homogeneous solid. In most cases, however, the rate of crystallization is more rapid than the rate of diffusion, and so, as the temperature of the solidifying alloy falls, crystals separating first which are rich in *B* become surrounded with shells of solid crystals which are progressively less rich in *B*. When the rate of cooling has not been slow enough to equalize the composition, each of the crystals of the solid-solution will, at the end of the freezing process, consist of a core of metal relatively rich in B, surrounded by successive layers decreasing in their content of B from the centre outward.

In order to render the alloy homogeneous, it may be necessary to anneal or "soak" the ingot at a high temperature for some time, preferably as near the solidus temperature as possible.   The higher the temperature of soaking, the greater is the rate of diffusion and the more rapidly does the alloy become homogeneous.   Fig. 81 shows the effect of such an annealing process on a nickel-aluminium alloy containing 54·5 atomic per cent. of nickel.   Lump annealing *in vacuo* for three days at 1,000° C. resulted in the blurred end-doublets, which is the result of large variations of lattice parameter and is in this instance indicative of coring.   A prolongation of the soaking period to six days sharpened the doublets, but still did not completely eliminate the coring.   Finally, half of the alloy, which had been kept in reserve, and which had had no previous heat treatment, was subjected to a three-day anneal *in vacuo* at a temperature of 1,300° C. The result was extremely sharp end-doublets, indicating the entire absence of a cored structure.   It is evident then that the temperature of soaking is more important than the time factor in the elimination of coring.

A type of inhomogeneity which proves very difficult to remove may arise at a composition where a peritectic reaction occurs, especially if it occurs at a low temperature, when the rate of diffusion is low.   Usually, a peritectic reaction proceeds so slowly, due to the formation of a layer of compound through which the reacting atoms must diffuse, that all the three phases which coexist in equilibrium at the peritectic reaction temperature in the initial stages of cooling the alloy continue to exist in metastable equilibrium down at room temperature.

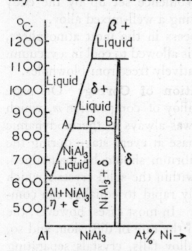

FIG. 82.—The Ni-Al equilibrium diagram in the region of NiAl₃.   Liquid of composition A reacts with solid phase δ of composition B to give the compound NiAl₃ at P,

The solidification of NiAl₃ presents such an example.   At the temperature of the peritectic reaction, NiAl₃ exists in equilibrium with Ni₂Al₃ and liquid.   As the temperature is lowered, the reaction:

$$\text{Liquid} + Ni_2Al_3 \rightarrow NiAl_3$$

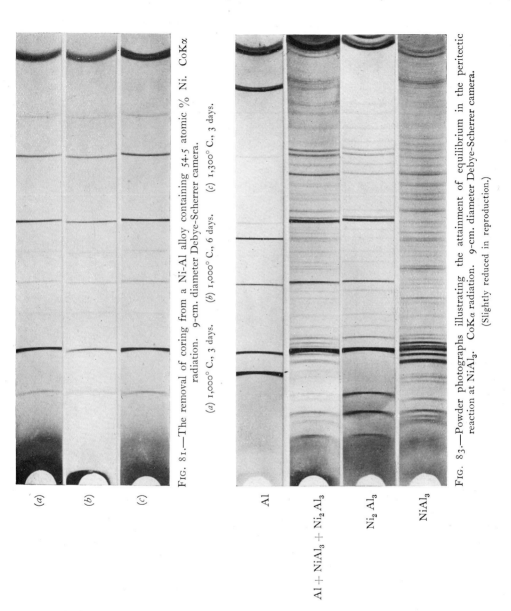

FIG. 81.—The removal of coring from a Ni-Al alloy containing 54.5 atomic % Ni. CoKα radiation. 9-cm. diameter Debye-Scherrer camera.

(a) 1,000° C., 3 days.　(b) 1,000° C., 6 days.　(c) 1,300° C., 3 days.

FIG. 83.—Powder photographs illustrating the attainment of equilibrium in the peritectic reaction at NiAl₃. CoKα radiation. 9-cm. diameter Debye-Scherrer camera.

(Slightly reduced in reproduction.)

(a)

(b)

(c)

Al

Al + NiAl₃ + Ni₂Al₃

Ni₂Al₃

NiAl₃

[Facing page 138.

proceeds extremely slowly. True equilibrium cannot be maintained with normal rates of cooling and so the composition of the melt moves down along the liquidus until the melt solidifies as a eutectic mixture of Al and $NiAl_3$ (see Fig. 82). Thus, the metastable alloy consists of the three phases Al, $NiAl_3$ and Ni_2Al_3.

Powder photographs in Fig. 83 show the three phase-patterns in the metastable alloy. Prolonged lump-annealing *in vacuo* at 830° C. just below the peritectic line for a period of three days enabled the reaction to proceed to completion.

Heat Treatment of the Powder Specimen. After the annealing of the ingot has been completed, a representative powder sample is obtained for Debye-Scherrer examination. Whether filing, drilling or crushing methods will be used will depend largely upon the relative toughness or brittleness of the alloy. In filing, only the highest grade jeweller's files should be used. They must be kept scrupulously clean by brushing with a fine wire brush or hard bristle tooth-brush and washed in toluene or trichlorethylene. Drillings are seldom very satisfactory, for it is difficult to obtain a powder specimen which will pass through a sufficiently fine sieve. Crushing in a hardened steel rock-crusher followed by grinding in an agate mortar under toluene is an excellent and rapid method of powdering the brittle alloys which often compose the intermediate phases of an equilibrium diagram.

If the alloy is to any degree malleable, the heavy cold work imparted during the powdering process leaves the crystal lattice with a high degree of plastic distortion. To remove this consequence of cold work, heat treatment must be resorted to or the lines of the Debye-Scherrer pattern will be broad and fuzzy and the photograph practically useless. Brittle phases do not suffer plastic deformation to anything like the same extent. The reason is to be found in the existence of ionic and covalent linkages in the crystal structures of the intermediate phases. Once the linkages are broken down under the application of exterior forces, they remain permanently so, and the piece of metal falls apart into fragments which are almost completely free from strain.

Heat treatment of the powder will, in general, have a two-fold object. The first will be to remove the lattice strains produced by cold work and the second to obtain a specimen which will be in thermal equilibrium at a particular temperature. The two objectives are sometimes reached by one and the same process, but if conditions do not permit this to happen, a dual heat treatment will have to be carried out, for the first essential is to remove the plastic deformation.

The powder should be sieved and then placed into small silica or hard glass tubes, approximately 2 in. long by $\frac{1}{8}$ in. diameter, which are evacuated by means of a rotary oil pump before being sealed off. The tubes from the various specimens which have to receive the same heat treatment should be very carefully marked before being placed in the furnace. Great emphasis must be placed upon accurate temperature control. Some form of programme regulator which automatically controls the temperature of the furnace to follow a prescribed time-temperature cycle should be used. Whenever possible, a pyrometric chart should also be obtained in order to procure concrete evidence as to the accuracy of the heat treatment.

One of the first objects in the investigation of a thermal equilibrium diagram is to determine the phases and the positions of phase boundaries at room temperature. The work is then extended to higher temperatures. The determination of the solidus and liquidus curves is, for the present, beyond the scope of X-ray work and can only be carried out by the older classical thermal methods.

To obtain conditions approximating to thermal equilibrium at room temperature, the powder should be taken to a reasonably high temperature when equilibrium will be rapidly achieved and then cooled very slowly, at 10° or less per hour, over a period of days if necessary, until room temperature is reached. To promote equilibrium conditions, the rate of cooling should be made much slower over the final stages of the treatment.

If the spectra still remain diffuse after the slow cooling process, we must carry out a check on the adequacy of the heat treatments. The usual fault is lack of homogeneity in the ingot, generally a legacy of too low an annealing temperature or too brief a period over which the heat treatment has been carried out. On the other hand, the fault may lie in the heat treatment of the powder, for which the initial temperature was insufficient to remove the effects of cold-work. In the majority of cases, repeating the ingot anneal or commencing the slow cooling treatment from a higher temperature is sufficient to give satisfactory diffraction patterns.

There will be instances when phase transformations occur in the process of cooling down. If these transformations take place at high temperatures when the atomic mobility is great, diffusion through the lattice to produce thermal equilibrium is rapid and the slowly cooled powder yields X-ray patterns with sharp end-doublets. But transformations sometimes occur at quite low temperatures when atomic diffusion is very sluggish. The method of slow cooling over a limited period of time then breaks down, for the approach to equilibrium during the transformation lags far behind the rate of fall in temperature. Consequently, the composition of the lattice is no longer homogeneous and the irregularities in the interplanar spacings produce blurred end-doublets in the diffraction spectra. In such cases, the only method which can be adopted is to give the alloy powder extremely long annealing periods just below the transformation temperature. A well-known example is to be found in the iron-nickel system. The region between 6 and 25 per cent. nickel, in which range the transformation takes place below 600° C., is particularly difficult to study on account of the great sluggishness of the change. Some of these alloys require annealing for years before conditions approaching true equilibrium are obtained. Age-hardening alloys of the "Duralumin" type present peculiar difficulties in that no obvious changes are to be observed in the Debye-Scherrer spectra corresponding to the period in which the mechanical properties are enhanced. We shall discuss this particular problem on page 295.

In order to examine high-temperature modifications of an alloy, two courses are open to us. We may use an X-ray camera designed specifically for high temperature work or we may quench the alloy after annealing it for some time at the desired temperature. At high temperatures, the thermal movements of the atoms are so large that equilibrium is soon obtained. If the rate of quenching is rapid enough, it will be possible to retain the high temperature phase and so we shall be able to examine it at room temperature.

In some cases, such as the change from γ to α-iron, the change-over from the face-centred to the body-centred cubic structure is so rapid that it is impossible to retain the high-temperature form. In these circumstances, only investigation with a high temperature camera is possible.

A quenching apparatus which has proved satisfactory is a modification of one designed by W. Rosenhain. It is shown in Fig. 84. The evacuated furnace tube is connected by means of a rubber tube and tap to a cylinder in which water can be maintained at a pressure of two atmospheres. The other end of the furnace tube is sealed by means of a rubber stopper held against a ground flat rim by the pressure of the atmosphere. Opening the tap between the cylinder and the furnace allows a considerable volume of cold water to rush through the evacuated furnace. The water sweeps the specimens along and the rubber stopper drops off enabling the water and the specimens to fall into a bucket.

The powder specimens are placed inside small silica dishes and covered over with fine Monel metal gauze. By this means, the quenching water comes into actual contact with the alloy powder, and because of the very small thermal capacity of the grains, quenching is exceedingly rapid. Alloys quenched by this means almost invariably give sharp end-doublets. In cases where the powder is readily

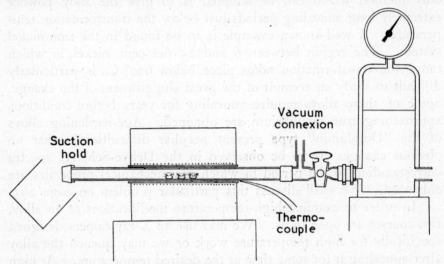

FIG. 84.—Modified Rosenhain Quenching Apparatus showing layout of furnace and water-pressure mains.

attacked by water, it is sealed inside thin-walled silica tubes but the efficiency of the quench is not quite as high. Very rapid quenching rates can be achieved by subjecting an alloy to a stream of cold hydrogen gas, but this technique has not been applied in any measure to equilibrium diagram studies.

The Determination of the Phase Boundaries. It has already been mentioned that the addition of a solute metal B may increase or decrease the lattice parameters of the solvent metal A by an amount depending on the relative magnitudes of the radii of the ions. In general, if the alloys are in a single-phase region in which the substitutional type of solid-solution is formed, the lattice parameters will continue to increase, or decrease, with the continued addition of B until the phase is saturated and a new phase structure commences to form. The solubility limit, or phase boundary, is marked by a discontinuity which takes place in the lattice parameter-composition curve.

In order to determine the position of the boundary with accuracy, a series of alloys with increasing amounts of B is made up, covering the single phase (α) and part of the two-phase ($\alpha + \beta$) region. These alloys are given a thorough ingot annealing, and then given a powder heat-treatment which produces an equilibrium condition approximating to that at room temperature.   After taking the necessary powder photographs, the lattice parameters of the alloys are plotted as ordinate against alloy composition as abscissæ.   In the single phase region a smooth curve, very often a straight line, is obtained until the phase boundary composition is reached.   Inside the two-phase region, the α-constituent of all the two-phase alloys will have the same room temperature composition, and therefore the same lattice parameters. It follows, then, that the lattice parameters of the α-constituent of all the two-phase alloys will plot as a horizontal line, and its point of

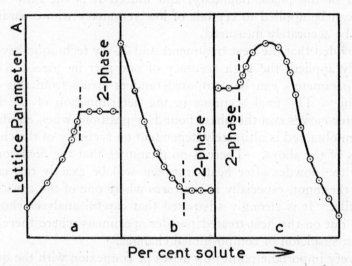

FIG. 85.—Determination of phase boundary (shown dotted) from lattice parameter curves.

(a) When lattice parameter is increased by added solute.   (b) Decreased.   The type of curve for the nickel-rich phase of the Fe-Ni system is shown in (c).

intersection with the curve obtained in the single phase region will yield the position of the phase boundary (Fig. 85).

At elevated temperatures the compositions of the α and β constituents in equilibrium with each other are changed to values predetermined by the run of the phase boundaries.   The high temperature state may be retained by quenching the powder.   It is clear, then, that if the two-phase alloys are all quenched at the same temperature, their lattice parameters will again lie on a horizontal line corresponding to the lattice parameter of a single-phase alloy on the phase boundary. The point of intersection of this horizontal with the extrapolated lattice parameter curve of the single-phase α-region now yields the phase boundary position corresponding to the temperature of quenching.

By quenching the two-phase alloys at successively higher temperatures, it is possible to plot the course of the phase boundary. The method is illustrated in Fig. 86 (*a*) and (*b*).

It will be noted that, if the phase boundary is suitably curved, alloys which lie just within the two-phase region may move out into the single phase region at elevated temperatures. Quenching will then retain the single-phase condition, and the lattice parameters will lie on the extrapolated curve drawn for the single-phase alloys X-rayed in the room temperature condition. Quenching to obtain a single phase specimen forms a very useful method of establishing the position of the phase boundary, and indeed it is the only method which can be applied to crystals of low symmetry whose parameters cannot be accurately measured.

Provided that the heat treatments and X-ray technique have been correctly applied, the high accuracy of one part in 30,000 whereby lattice parameters can be computed renders errors from this source negligible. The final accuracy in the determination of the lattice-parameter curves and the phase boundary positions when equilibrium has been obtained is ultimately dependent on accuracy of the chemical analysis of the alloys. There is no guarantee that the final composition of the powder after heat-treatment will be exactly the same as that of the ingot, especially in the cases where one of the constituents is volatile. It is strongly advocated that careful analyses should be carried out on the heat-treated powder specimens where there is the slightest suspicion of compositional changes.

A very important point now arises in connexion with the quenching process. We shall suppose that in the process of cooling down to room temperature the alloy has separated into two sharply defined coarse-grained phases, α and β. The effect of filing or crushing the ingot may be such that the powder sample now consists of fragments, some composed almost wholly of α and some of β. Raising the temperature of the powder fails to effect those diffusion processes which normally take place in the solid ingot between the now separated constituents. Consequently the quenching process will *not* in this instance lead to an X-ray pattern which is truly representative of the high temperature conditions.

It is clearly advisable to quench the ingot first at a temperature above that at which it is desired to quench the powder. The powder should then be taken up to the temperature at which the ingot was quenched, then slowly cooled to the desired quenching temperature, and finally maintained there until thermodynamic equilibrium is reached. By this means the correct balance of reacting phases will

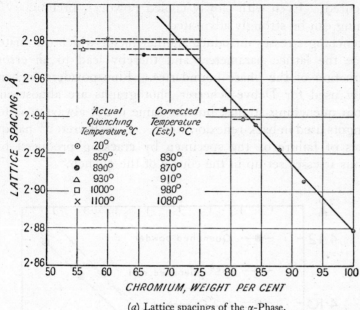

(a) Lattice spacings of the α-Phase.

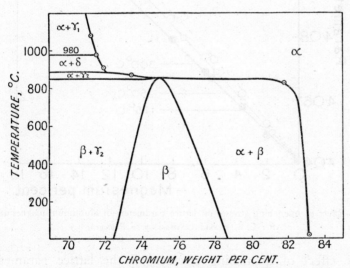

(b) Boundary of the α-Phase.

FIG. 86.—Determination of the phase boundary position at elevated temperatures by means of lattice parameters of quenched powders. Example taken from the α-phase boundary of the Cr-Al binary system. (A. J. BRADLEY S. LU, and S. *Journal Inst. Metals*, **60**, 319, 1937.)

be procured. Even with slowly cooled powders, preliminary ingot quenching can be strongly advocated.

Quenching stresses introduce another factor which can materially influence the lattice parameters and thereby lead to an erroneous determination of the phase boundaries. Fine powders such as are normally used for Debye-Scherrer photographs are almost entirely free from quenching strains, but the same is not always true for the small ingots used in back-reflexion work. C. S. Barrett [32] has quoted instances of failure of the specimen by cracking produced by the enormous stresses set up in the course of the quench.

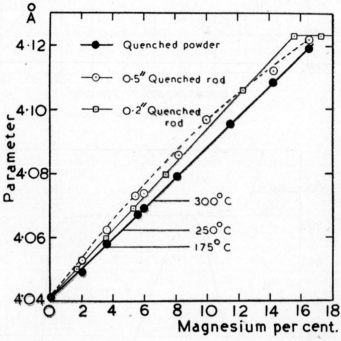

FIG. 87.—Effect of quenching stresses on lattice parameters of aluminium-magnesium alloys. (After C. S. BARRETT, *Symposium on Radiography*.)

The effect of quenching stresses on the lattice parameters of aluminium-magnesium alloys is clearly demonstrated in Fig. 87. The lowest curve representing alloys in powder form gives lattice parameters of alloys substantially free from strain. The results of Schmid and Siebel on quenched 0·2 in. diameter rods and results on quenched 0·5 in. rods are considerably higher, with the consequence that the phase boundary appears to be too near the aluminium-rich end of the diagram.

Anomalies in Lattice Parameter–Composition Curves. It was thought at one time that the variation of lattice parameter in a single-phase alloy was an exact linear function of the composition. This was known as Vegard's Law and was originally based upon the behaviour of solid solutions in ionic salts. The law would have implied that the lattice parameters were merely the result of simple addition of atomic radii which remained fixed in value whatever the compositions of the alloys. Researches on several alloy systems have

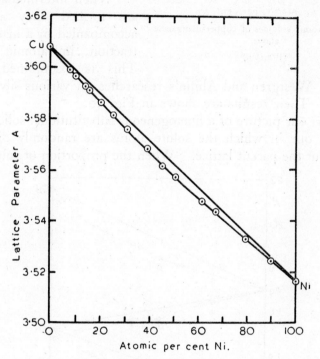

FIG. 88.—Lattice parameters of copper-nickel alloys.
(OWEN and PICKUP.)

revealed that Vegard's law is seldom obeyed, even in the most favourable cases where complete miscibility over all compositions is obtained.

In the copper-nickel system, the deviation from the theoretical values of lattice parameter obtained by joining those of pure copper and pure nickel is greatest at 32 atomic per cent. of nickel. At this point, the deviation, which is a contraction, is 0·11 per cent. This is illustrated in Fig. 88, the results being taken from the work of Owen and Pickup.

Generally speaking, all systems show a greater or lesser deviation from the law of Vegard. In the majority of cases this deviation is in the direction of lattice contraction, although there are a few known isolated examples where the divergence is in the other direction.   An

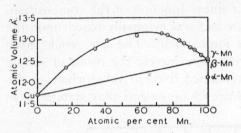

example of such a positive deviation is given by the copper-manganese alloys as shown in Fig. 89, in which atomic volumes are plotted against composition.

FIG. 89.—Atomic volumes of copper-manganese alloys.

(PERSSON.)

When intermediate phases are formed, they are often accompanied by a marked contraction in atomic volume. This is exemplified by the results of Westgren and Almin's researches on various silver binary systems.   Their results are shown in Fig. 90.

So far, our picture of a homogeneous substitutional solid-solution has been one in which the solute atoms are randomly distributed throughout the parent lattice.   When the proportion of solute atoms

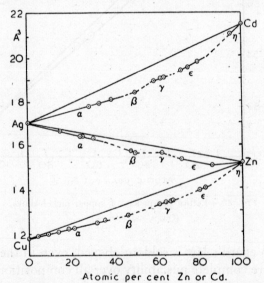

FIG. 90.—Volume per atom in Cu-Zn, Ag-Zn and Ag-Cd alloys.

(WESTGREN AND ALMIN.)

becomes sufficiently great, the effect of prolonged annealing at a suitable temperature, or of slow cooling, is to reshuffle the atoms into more ordered arrangements.   This is most marked at simple ratios of constituents, such as Cu_3Au, $CuAu$, $CuAu_3$, $FeNi_3$, $MgCd$ and Fe_3Al.   The change from the disordered to the ordered atomic array is known as "super-lattice" formation. For a more detailed discussion, the reader is referred to page 173 *et seq.*

Striking changes in lattice-parameter may accompany the formation of a superlattice. For example, in the region of Fe_3Al there is a sharp break in the lattice parameter-composition curve for fully annealed alloys. The curve remains horizontal over a considerable

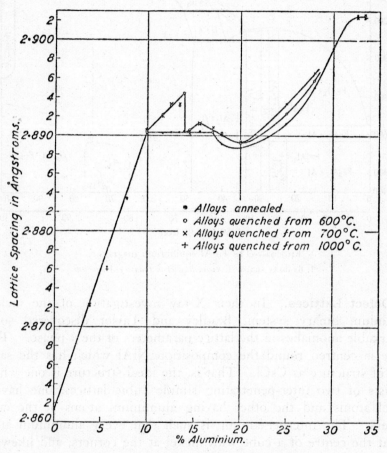

FIG. 91.—Lattice spacings of iron-aluminium alloys.

(A. J. BRADLEY and A. H. JAY, *Journal of Iron and Steel Institute,* 339, 1932.)

range of compositions. To the inexperienced investigator it would appear to herald the formation of a two-phase region, whereas in fact it is a consequence of atomic rearrangement within a range of homogeneous single phase alloys. The curve for iron-aluminium alloys obtained by Bradley and Jay is shown in Fig. 91, and is in itself an example of marked deviations from Vegard's law. The Fe-Al equilibrium diagram given in Fig. 92 illustrates the extent of the body-centred cubic phase.

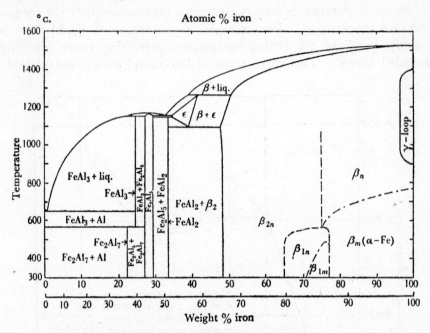

FIG. 92.—The Fe-Al equilibrium diagram.

(A. J. BRADLEY and A. TAYLOR, *Physics in Industry-Magnetism*.)

Defect Lattices. In their X-ray investigation of the nickel-aluminium binary system, Bradley and Taylor discovered some remarkable anomalies in the lattice parameters of the β-phase. This phase is centred round the composition NiAl which has the same type of structure as CsCl. That is, the ideal structure is one which consists of two inter-penetrating simple cubic lattices, one having nickel atoms and the other having aluminium atoms at the cube corners. The interpenetration is such that every aluminium atom lies at the centre of a cube with nickel at the corners, and likewise, every nickel atom can be considered as lying at the centre of a cube with aluminium atoms at the corners. The structure is often loosely termed body-centred cubic, although this would only apply to the case when cube corner is indistinguishable from cube centre (Fig. 93).

At the stoichiometric composition NiAl we have one nickel atom at each cube corner and one aluminium atom at each cube centre. On the nickel-rich side of the ideal composition NiAl, some of the aluminium atoms are replaced at random by those of nickel. Now the nickel atoms are both heavier and smaller than those of aluminium

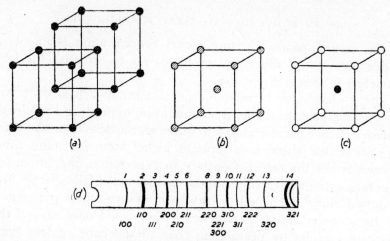

FIG. 93.—NiAl Superlattice.

(a) Interpenetration of two simple cubic lattices.
(b) Body-centred cube with atoms in disorder.
(c) Body-centred cube with ordered structure.
(d) Powder photograph of ordered body-centred cube.

(A. J. BRADLEY, W. L. BRAGG and C. SYKES, *Journal of Iron and Steel Institute*, 1940.)

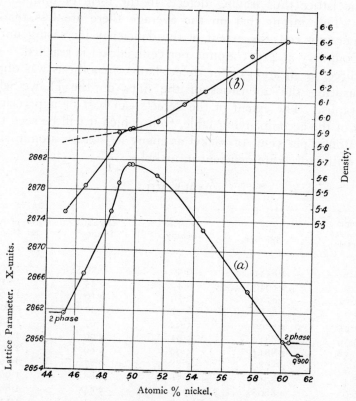

FIG. 94.—The lattice parameter (*a*), and density variations (*b*), in the body-centred cubic β-phase nickel-aluminium alloys.

(A. J. BRADLEY and A. TAYLOR, *Proc. Roy. Soc.*, **159**, 56, 1937.)

and the natural result of rising nickel concentration is to increase the densities of the alloys and progressively to diminish the lattice parameters as shown in Fig. 94.

The β-phase also extends to the aluminium-rich side of NiAl. One would expect the addition of aluminium to produce a progressive increase in lattice parameter and to diminish the density on the natural supposition that aluminium replaces nickel atom by atom. Such, however, is not the case. Contrary to expectation, the lattice parameter falls extremely rapidly and the density curve falls sharply below the dotted curve calculated on the basis of two atoms per unit cell and the observed lattice parameters. One could only explain these remarkable results by postulating that all the cube centres remain filled with aluminium atoms, and that all those nickel positions which would normally have been occupied by the excess of aluminium remain unfilled. In other words, the increase in the aluminium content of the alloys is really effected by the *subtraction* of nickel atoms at random from the lattice thus leaving defects in the form of unfilled lattice points. This means that on the average there are less than two atoms per unit cell, the extent of the deficiency increasing until the phase boundary at 42·25 atomic per cent. nickel is reached.

A direct verification of the defect-lattice hypothesis was obtained by measuring the intensities of the lines on the Debye-Scherrer photographs. The extent of the defects can best be appreciated by a study of the accompanying table, from which it will be seen that at 45·25 atomic per cent. of nickel as many as sixteen atomic sites in every two hundred are deficient in nickel.

TABLE VII

Atomic Percentage Nickel	Lattice Spacing	Observed Density	Calculated Density *	No. of Atoms per Unit Cell
60·1	2·8581	6·50	6·50	2·00
57·7	2·8646₅	6·40	6·35	2·01₅
54·5₅	2·8726₅	6·16	6·16	2·00
53·2	2·8766	6·07	6·07	2·00
51·45	2·8799	5·95	5·97	1·99
49·79	2·8812₅	5·91	5·90	2·00
49·58	2·8814	5·90	5·89	2·00
48·9	2·8789	5·88	5·87	2·00
48·4	2·8750₅	5·76	5·88	1·96
46·6	2·8668	5·52	5·84	1·89
45·25	2·8615	5·35	5·82	1·84

* Assuming two atoms per unit cell for simple replacement theory.

From what has been said in the preceding pages concerning the departures from Vegard's law, it will now be apparent that linear interpolation between the parameters of widely separated alloys in a single phase region has little justification and would be extremely dangerous to apply in the determination of phase boundaries. It is absolutely essential to obtain a sufficient number of alloys near the boundary in order to know the precise values of the lattice parameters in that region.

Procedure to be Adopted in Examining a Binary System by X-rays. It is not possible to lay down any hard-and-fast rules as to the exact procedure to be adopted in the X-ray investigation of a binary system, as so much will depend on the precise nature of the system itself and whether a rough survey or an accurate determination is the object of the research. A thorough search should be made of the literature for information on the alloy system to be investigated, as it will prove to be of inestimable value as a guide as to which alloys to make up first. Two books of great value may be mentioned in this connexion which summarize researches on alloy systems to a comparatively recent date, namely *Der Aufbau der Zweistofflegierungen*, by M. Hansen, and *Handbuch aller Legierungen*, by Jähnecke.

We shall assume that the system to be investigated has been chosen, that the Debye-Scherrer method is to be used in conjunction with 9- and 19-cm. diameter cameras, and an X-ray set which gives a wide choice of characteristic radiations is to be employed. All alloy compositions will be given in atomic per cent. as this method of presentation is more informative from the academic point of view. First of all we need photographs of the component elements. We then use the published data to make up a minimum number of alloys in what are supposed to be single-phase regions, in order to obtain the simplest patterns on the identification photographs. The method of slow cooling would be used in the opening stages in order to approximate to room temperature equilibrium. Then an alloy would be made in each of the two-phase regions which should yield the interwoven patterns of the single phases lying on each side of the two-phase region.

Where no data at all are available, the investigator must proceed by methods of trial and error to establish the simplest possible patterns whereby the single-phase regions can be identified. This procedure is not as formidable as it sounds, as a careful visual inspection of the intensities of the individual lines on the powder-photographs of the various alloys arranged in sequence will often act as a sure guide as to which new alloys to make. This method is to be preferred to

F*

making up a whole series of alloys at regular intervals of say 2 per cent. right across the system, for the trial-and-error method ensures that only those alloys which are necessary are made up, and enables one to concentrate on the most interesting and informative compositions.

Having decided from the X-ray patterns the positions of the single-phase regions, the precise positions of the phase boundaries should now be sought. This is done by the methods already described, namely by looking for the appearance of new patterns in the photographs and by determining the composition at which a sharp discontinuity occurs in the lattice parameter-composition curves. Quenching the alloys will yield the run of the phase boundaries and will often reveal the existence of unsuspected high-temperature phases. All these data should then be linked as far as possible with any existing thermal data on the solidus-liquidus curves.

The Nickel–Aluminium System. As an example, we shall discuss the nickel-aluminium system. This was first investigated by

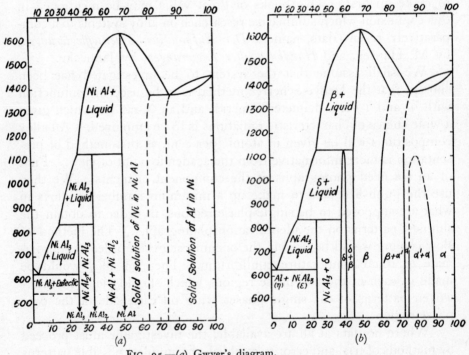

FIG. 95.—(a) Gwyer's diagram.
(b) The modification of Gwyer's diagram.

(A. J. BRADLEY and A. TAYLOR, *Proc. Roy. Soc.*, **159**, 56, 1937.)

C. G. Gwyer in 1908 by thermal and microscopic methods and the resulting diagram is given in Fig. 95 (a). Early X-ray work by Becker and Ebert (1923) and Westgren and Almin (1929) on the crystal structure of the NiAl-phase showed it to have the same type of ordered cubic arrangement as the atoms in CsCl. In addition, Westgren and Ekman in 1930 showed that an alloy with the composition Ni_3Al was face-centred cubic like pure nickel, but that the structure was ordered so that nickel atoms occupied centres of cube faces and aluminium atoms cube corners.

Subsequent work was carried out, using the X-ray technique by Bradley and Taylor [33]. They made use of the data given in Gwyer's diagram and made up alloys corresponding to single-phase regions.

It was first of all discovered that the region designated "solid solution of Al in Ni" was in reality much more complex and contained the face-centred cubic nickel-rich α-phase and the face-centred cubic α'-phase which had the ordered arrangement of Ni_3Al. This was first revealed by the two-phase alloy with 80·4 per cent. (atomic) nickel, powder photographs of which are shown in Fig. 96. The slowly cooled alloy yields photographs with two well-defined overlapping face-centred cubic patterns, one of which shows extra lines due to the superlattice of the α'-phase. Quenching the alloys at successively higher temperatures influenced the lattice parameters and caused the patterns to merge together until at 1,100° C it appeared as if only a single phase-structure remained. From the lattice parameters of alloys in the single-phase α and α' regions and in the two-phase $\alpha + \alpha'$ region it was possible to determine the run of the phase boundaries as shown in Fig. 95 (b).

Alloys made in the region of NiAl, the β-phase, substantially confirmed the findings of Gwyer, although modifications of the phase boundaries determined by him had to be made. The β-phase was shown to extend as far as 45·25 per cent. (atomic) nickel, and it was in this region that the existence of a defect lattice in alloys was first discovered.

The phase with the stoichiometric composition $NiAl_2$ shown in Gwyer's original diagram gave a very complex pattern and a search was made to see if alloys in its neighbourhood would yield simpler powder photographs. It was very quickly established that the alloy Ni_2Al_3 gave a much simpler pattern which could not be further modified by compositions in its immediate neighbourhood. This pattern was shown to extend from 37·3 to 41·35 per cent. (atomic) of nickel, and any alloys falling outside this region resulted in photographs with faint extra lines belonging to the adjacent phases. Conclusive proof that the region was single phase was obtained by determining the actual crystal structure of Ni_2Al_3, which was shown to be hexagonal or "trigonal" on account of its having only threefold symmetry.   One of the features of Ni_2Al_3 must be emphasized.   The strongest lines of its powder photograph overlap those of the body centred cubic β-phase and from this it was immediately inferred that δ was a distorted form of β.   The structure may be looked upon as an extension of the defect lattice of the β-phase in which every third sheet of nickel atoms perpendicular to the trigonal axis of the cube is removed (Fig. 97).

The region of $NiAl_3$ was then explored.   Although $NiAl_3$ proved difficult to obtain in perfect equilibrium as explained on page 138, and when finally isolated yielded a very complex diffraction pattern, this pattern proved to be simpler than those yielded by compositions on either side of it.   Those alloys containing excess of nickel yielded the patterns of $NiAl_3$ (ε) and Ni_2Al_3 (δ), while those with excess aluminium yielded the pattern of $NiAl_3$ (ε) and Al (η).   Because $NiAl_3$ will not tolerate any excess of Ni or Al, it can be looked upon as an "intermetallic compound". The crystal structure of $NiAl_3$ was also determined and shown to be orthorhombic.

Finally, no new pattern could be established between pure Al and $NiAl_3$.   Any alloy made up in this region merely gave the superimposed patterns of Al and $NiAl_3$, and in addition, since the lattice parameter of the η-phase remained totally unaffected, it was concluded that there was no appreciable solid-solution of nickel in aluminium.   A selection of Debye-Scherrer photographs covering the entire range from nickel to aluminium is given in Fig. 98.

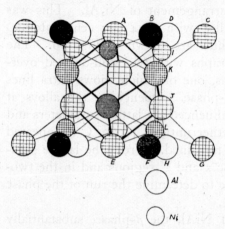

FIG. 97.—The structure of Ni_2Al_3 showing pseudo-cubic unit with vacant centre.
(A. J. BRADLEY and A. TAYLOR, *Phil. Mag.*, 23, 1049, 1937.)

It was then necessary to dovetail the X-ray findings with the thermal and microscopic work of Gwyer.   This was achieved with little difficulty, as shown in diagram 95 (b), but uncertainties still remained as to the exact run of the phase boundaries at the highest temperatures, particularly in the region of Ni_3Al.   The system was shortly re-investigated by W. O. Alexander and N. B. Vaughan,[34] who followed the classical methods of thermal analysis, microscopical examination and hardness measurements.   Their work is in almost complete agreement with that of Bradley and Taylor.   They showed

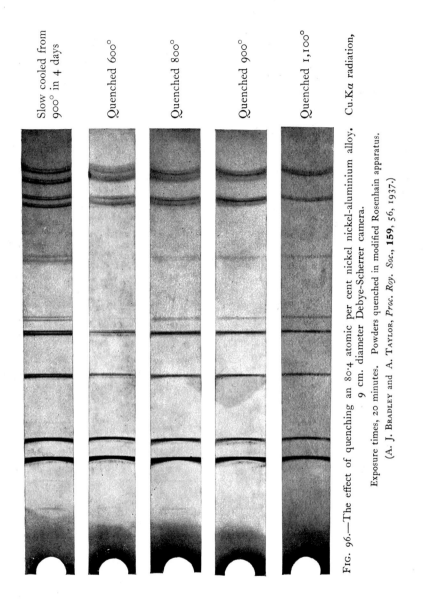

Slow cooled from 900° in 4 days

Quenched 600°

Quenched 800°

Quenched 900°

Quenched 1,100°

Fig. 96.—The effect of quenching an 80·4 atomic per cent nickel nickel-aluminium alloy. Cu.Kα radiation, 9 cm. diameter Debye-Scherrer camera. Exposure times, 20 minutes. Powders quenched in modified Rosenhain apparatus.

(A. J. Bradley and A. Taylor, *Proc. Roy. Soc.*, **159**, 56, 1937.)

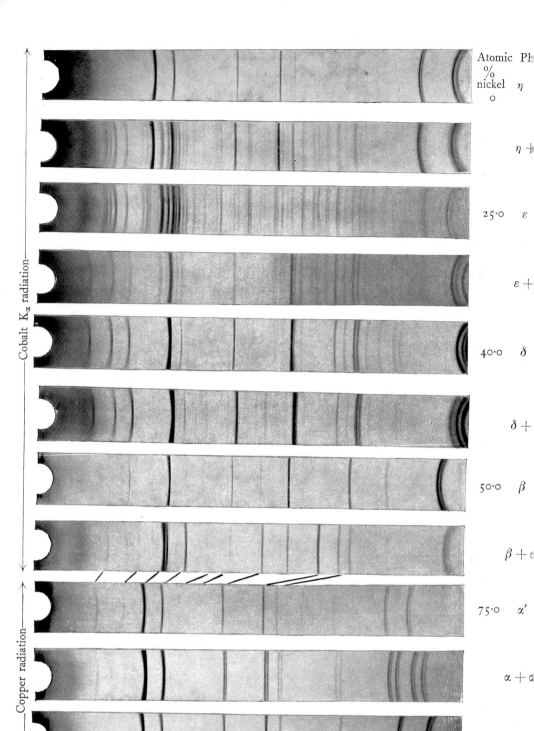

Atomic Ph
%
nickel η
0

η +

25·0 ε

ε +

40·0 δ

δ +

50·0 β

β + α

75·0 α'

α + α

100 α

FIG. 98.—Debye-Scherrer Photographs of Nickel-Aluminium Alloys, 9 cm. diameter camera.

Note change from CoKα to CuKα radiation to bring end-doublets of α-phase near to the knife edge for accurate lattice parameter work. (A. J. BRADLEY and A. TAYLOR, *Proc. Roy. Soc.*, **159**, 56, 1937.)

that the Ni₃Al region was slightly more complex than was revealed by the X-ray methods, namely that the α and α′ face-centred cubic phases do not merge together, but that α reacts peritectically with β to form α′.

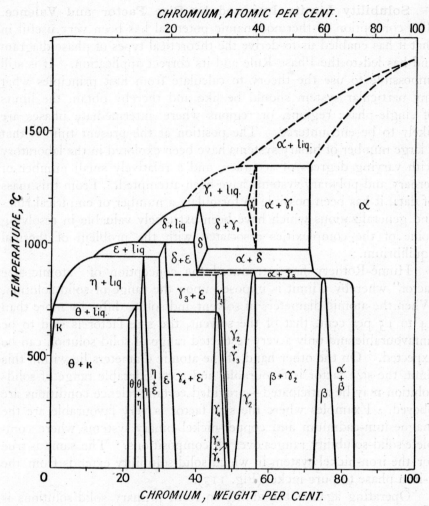

FIG. 99.—The Chromium-aluminium System.

(A. J. BRADLEY and S. S. LU, *J. Inst. Met.*, **60**, 319, 1937.)

As an example of what can be achieved when very little thermal and microscopic data are available, the chromium-aluminium phase diagram determined by Bradley and Lu [35] must be considered an outstanding accomplishment. It is given in Fig. 99 and is based on Debye-Scherrer patterns from slowly cooled and quenched powders. Over 70 alloys were prepared, this being necessitated by the great complexity the system revealed. The composition intervals did not exceed 1 per cent. except where there were no features of special interest. For full details the reader must be referred to the original paper.

Solubility Limits Imposed by Size Factor and Valence. The conception of thermodynamic potential has been very useful in that it has enabled us to derive the theoretical types of phase diagram and has led to the Phase Rule and its correct application. It is still impossible to use the theory to calculate from first principles what any particular system should be like and thereby obtain the limits of single-phase regions, or regions where intermediate phases are likely to be encountered. The position at the present time is that a large number of binary systems have been explored in the laboratory with varying degrees of accuracy, and a relatively small number of ternary and polynary systems have been attempted. From this mass of data, it has been possible to formulate a number of empirical rules and generalizations which have been extremely valuable in resolving some of the complexities associated with the problem of thermal equilibrium.

Hume-Rothery has introduced the conception of "atomic size factor" whereby a limit is imposed upon the range of solid solution. When the atomic diameters of solvent and solute differ by more than 14 to 15 per cent. that of the solvent, the size factor is said to be unfavourable and only a very restricted range of solid solution can be expected. On the other hand, if the atomic diameters lie within this limit, the size factor is favourable, and a considerable range of solid-solution may be anticipated—provided certain valence conditions are obeyed. Examples where the size factor is very favourable are the magnesium-cadmium and copper-nickel binary systems where complete solid-solubility ranges over all compositions. The same is true for the iron-nickel system in which solid-solubility extends from the γ-iron phase to pure nickel (Fig. 117).

Operating against the ability to form primary solid-solutions is the tendency to form stable intermediate phases which have a much lower thermodynamic potential. The more electronegative the solute element and the more electropositive the solvent (or vice versa), the more pronounced is the tendency to form stable intermediate phases. This has been termed the "electronegative valence" effect. One of the very many examples is to be found in the system magnesium-antimony, shown in Fig. 100. Although the size factor is favourable, the mutual solid-solubilities of magnesium and antimony in each other is almost zero. The reason is to be found in the

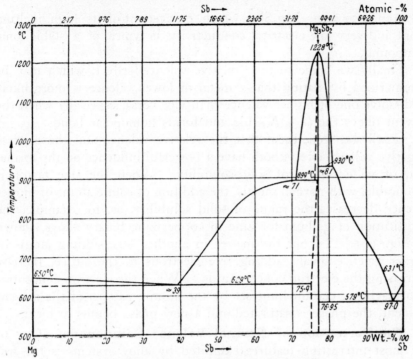

FIG. 100.—The magnesium-antimony equilibrium diagram.
(GRUBE and BORNHAK, *Zeits. Elektrochemie*, **40**, 140, 1934.)

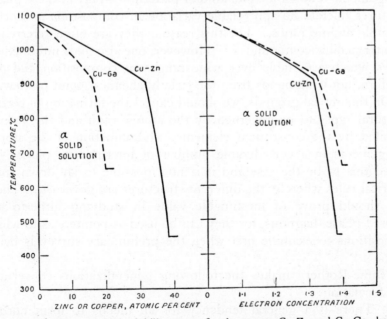

FIG. 101.—Solidus and solid-solubility curves for the systems Cu-Zn and Cu-Ga, drawn
(*a*) in terms of atomic percentages, (*b*) electron concentration.

(W. HUME-ROTHERY, *The Structure of Metals and Alloys.* Published by The Institute of Metals.)

preference to form Mg_3Sb_2, which, on account of its high melting point and very low electrical conductivity, is typical of a stable ionic compound.

Finally we come to the "relative valence" effect, which may be summarized by stating that a metal of lower valence is more likely to dissolve one of higher valence than vice versa, especially when the solvent obeys the $(8 - N)$-rule and forms homopolar bonds.

It will be seen, then, that the relative valence and the electronegative valence effects both have a powerful influence on the formation of wide ranges of solid-solubility. When the size factor is favourable, with normal metals, the addition of solute atoms of higher valence decreases the range of solid solubility, as, for example, the substitution of gallium for zinc in copper-zinc binary alloys, shown in Fig. 101. To put the matter in another way, adding atoms of higher valence means adding free electrons to the lattice, thereby increasing the electron concentration. When the electron concentration reaches a certain limit set by the atomic pattern of the solvent element, the phase is saturated and a new phase begins to form.

The Formation of Normal Valence Compounds. One of the most interesting features exhibited by alloy systems is the frequency with which intermediate phases appear in which the atomic arrangements follow the same kind of pattern. Many of these phase-structures tolerate no appreciable variation in composition and occur at simple atomic ratios. For this reason, they are often referred to as "intermetallic compounds". However, one also finds intermediate phases which are stable over wide ranges of composition and are, therefore, not compounds from the strictly chemical point of view.

On theoretical grounds, we should expect the formation of certain structural types to be governed by the atomic radii and the valence exhibited by the constituent elements. Examination of the atomic arrangements in a considerable number of intermediate phases has proved this to be the case and it is now possible to lay down some empirical rules whereby the different structures are governed. These rules should prove of inestimable value in studying hitherto unexplored phase diagrams, for they can be used as pointers as to which compositions to examine first when the preliminary survey is being made.

Hume-Rothery makes the following generalizations concerning alloy formation:

   1. There is a general tendency for all metals to form normal valence compounds with the elements of Groups IVB, VB, and VIB.

2. This tendency, and also the stability of the compound, is greater the more electropositive the metal and the more electronegative the element from Groups IVB, VB or VIB.

In these particular cases, one is led to expect, and indeed one finds, that the intermetallic compounds have the same types of crystal structures as the simple ionic or homopolar compounds with the formulæ AB, A_2B, A_3B_2.

The simplest type of atomic configuration possessed by an ionic compound of the form AB is the structure of NaCl. Taken as a whole, the structure is face-centred cubic, but we may look on it as having a simple cubic lattice with half the true cell edge, on which positive Na and negative Cl ions alternately occupy the lattice points (Fig. 28). Alloys with the NaCl type of lattice are listed below in Table VIII.

TABLE VIII

Sodium Chloride Structure	Calcium Fluoride Structure
MgSe	Mg_2Si
CaSe	Mg_2Ge
SrSe	Mg_2Sn
BaSe	Mg_2Pb
CaTe	Cu_2Se
SrTe	
BaTe	
MnSe	
SnTe	
PbSe	
PbTe	

The CaF_2 structure shown in Fig. 102 (a) is one of the commonest ionic structures of the type AB_2. Alloys which possess this atomic arrangement are listed in Table VIII. It is of interest to observe that in CaF_2 there are two non-metallic ions to each ion of the metal, whereas in compounds such as Mg_2Si there are two metal ions to each one of the metalloid. Since the metal ions in CaF_2 occupy the structurally equivalent positions of the metalloid ions in the compounds, the two structures are said to be anti-isomorphous.

Similar cases of anti-isomorphism occur with compounds of the form Mg_3Sb_2 and Mg_3Bi_2 which have the same types of structure as La_2O_3, and Mg_3As_2 and Mg_3P_2 which have the structure of Sc_2O_3.

We have already discussed the tetrahedral arrangement of the atoms in carbon (diamond) and its connexion with the $(8 - N)$-rule, and how the same type of lattice is possessed by the tetravalent elements, silicon, germanium, and grey tin. It is not surprising, therefore, in alloy compositions where the same ratio of four valence electrons per atom is attained, that we should discover the same type of atomic packing as that which exists in the diamond.

When equal numbers of the two kinds of atom are present, the tetrahedral arrangement can be achieved in a number of ways. The simplest arrangement is that of zinc-blende ZnS, in which the pattern would be exactly the same as diamond if all the atoms were identical.

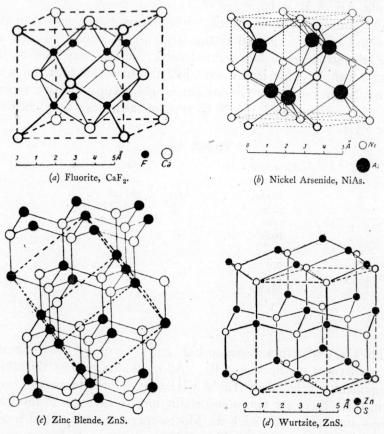

(a) Fluorite, CaF$_2$.

(b) Nickel Arsenide, NiAs.

(c) Zinc Blende, ZnS.

(d) Wurtzite, ZnS.

FIG. 102.—Compounds simulated by alloys (*Strukturbericht*).

The tetrahedra may be looked upon as lying in sheets parallel to the (111) planes of the cube, with their apexes pointing in the direction of the cube diagonal or trigonal axis. If we rotate the tetrahedra of alternate sheets through an angle of 180° about an axis parallel to the cube diagonal, we obtain the hexagonal structure of wurtzite (ZnS), the *c*-axis of which lies parallel to the diagonal of the cube from which the wurtzite structure was derived. Each atom is still surrounded by a tetrahedron of four atoms of the other kind, but the symmetry of the lattice has been debased.

The structures of blende and wurtzite are shown in Fig. 102 (c) and (d). Alloys possessing these types of atomic arrangements are listed in Table IX.

TABLE IX

Zinc Blende Structure			Wurtzite Structure
BeS	BeSe	BeTe	MgTe
ZnS	ZnSe	ZnTe	CdSe
CdS	CdSe	CdTe	
HgS	HgSe	HgTe	
AlP	AlAs	AlSb	
GaP	GaAs	GaSb	
		InSb	

Yet another structural type which is frequently recurring in alloy systems is that of NiAs. This hexagonal structure is illustrated in Fig. 102 (b), in which three unit cells are shown stacked together. Layers of metal and metalloid atoms alternate in separate sheets, and the grouping is such that each atom has six nearest neighbours of the other kind. This type of structure is formed chiefly by the transition elements with the metalloids. A list of such compounds is given in Table X.

TABLE X

NICKEL ARSENIDE STRUCTURE

CrS	CoTe	AuSn	MnSb
CoS	FeTe	CuSn	PdSb
FeS	NiTe	PtSn	PtSb
NiS	CrTe	NiSn	MnAs
CoSe	MnTe	CoSb	NiAs
FeSe	PdTe	FeSb	NiBi
NiSe	PtTe	NiSb	
CrSe	FeSn	CrSb	

The Formation of Electron Compounds and the Hume-Rothery Rule. We now pass on to a series of structural types which are constantly recurring among the intermediate phases of alloy systems when the electron concentration reaches particular values. In the copper-zinc system which we have already mentioned, illustrated in Figs. 68 and 69, the α-phase is a primary solid-solution which has the face-centred cubic structure of the parent metal copper. The β-phase is body-centred cubic CsCl type, the γ-phase has a complex cubic structure with 52 atoms in the unit cell, ε is nearly hexagonal close-packed and η is a primary solid solution of copper in hexagonal close-packed zinc.

The same type of phase sequence is to be found in other equilibrium diagrams where copper, silver and gold are alloyed with the elements of the B-subgroups. Hume-Rothery points out that the higher the valence of the added subgroup element, the less is the atomic percentage which need be added to reach a corresponding position in the equilibrium diagram, and moreover these intermediate phases continually occur when a definite ratio of valence electrons to atoms is attained.

For example, when univalent copper is alloyed with divalent zinc, the β-phase occurs in the region of 50 atomic per cent. of zinc (CuZn). When alloyed with trivalent aluminium, the β-phase occurs in the region of 25 atomic per cent. of aluminium (Cu_3Al), and with tetravalent tin, the β-phase falls in the neighbourhood of 16 atomic per cent. of tin ($Cu_5Sn = 16\cdot7$ atomic per cent. of tin). All these β-phases were shown by Hume-Rothery to have a characteristic in common by all possessing the same electron concentration. In CuZn there are two atoms and three valence electrons, one from the copper and two from the zinc atom. In Cu_3Al there are four atoms and a total of six valence electrons, one from each copper atom and three from the aluminium atom. Again, in Cu_5Sn, there are six atoms and nine valence electrons, one from each copper atom and four from the atom of tin. In other words, if we take the ratio of valence electrons to atoms we find it has the constant value of $3/2$ whenever the β-phase is formed.

This important conclusion was reached without reference to the crystal structures of the phases, but added confirmation was received when these alloys were shown by X-ray methods to have the same body-centred cubic atomic arrangement. It was also shown that when the electron-atom ratio was $21 : 13$, the γ-phases were formed having the same type of complicated atomic arrangement possessed by γ-brass, while the ε phases which occur with an electron-atom ratio of $7 : 4$ all possess a hexagonal crystal structure. Bernal has suggested calling these phase-structures "electron compounds" in order to stress the principle of the dependence of the atomic pattern on the electron concentration, a principle now universally known as the Hume-Rothery Rule.

A list of these electron compounds is given in Table XI. There it will be seen that in addition to the alloys formed by copper, silver and gold with the elements of the B-subgroups, similar structures are also to be found in alloys of the transition elements. It will also be found that alloys in which the electron-atom ratio is $3 : 2$ do not always crystallize with the CsCl structure but possess the complicated atomic arrangement of β-manganese.

In order to reconcile the transition elements in the scheme of electron compound formation, it is necessary to make the assumption that they contribute no electrons to the structure and thereby behave as if they have zero valence. This peculiar behaviour is connected in some way with the incomplete outer shells which is a characteristic feature of the transition elements. The other elements must be regarded as exerting their normal valencies and supplying the following number of free electrons to the system:

Cu, Ag, Au 1
Be, Mg, Zn, Cd, Hg 2
Al, In, Ga 3
Sn, Si, Ge, Pb 4
As, Sb, Bi, P 5
Fe, Co, Ni ⎫
Ru, Rh, Pd ⎬ 0
Os, Ir, Pt ⎭

TABLE XI
HUME-ROTHERY ELECTRON COMPOUNDS

Electron : Atom Ratio = 3 : 2		Electron : Atom Ratio = 21 : 13	Electron : Atom Ratio = 7 : 4
Body-centred Cubic Structure	Complex Cubic ("β-Manganese") Structure	"γ-Brass" Structure	Close-packed Hexagonal Structure
CuBe	Ag_3Al	Cu_5Zn_8	$CuZn_3$
CuZn	Au_3Al	Cu_5Cd_8	$CuCd_3$
AgMg	Cu_5Si	Cu_9Al_4	Cu_3Sn
AgZn	$CoZn_3$	Cu_9Ga_4	Cu_3Ge
AgCd		Cu_9In_4	Cu_3Si
AuZn		$Cu_{31}Si_8$	$AgZn_3$
AuCd		$Cu_{31}Sn_8$	$AgCd_3$
Cu_3Al		Fe_5Zn_{21}	Ag_3Sn
Cu_3Ga		Co_5Zn_{21}	Ag_5Al_3
Cu_5Sn		Ni_5Zn_{21}	Au_5Al_3
CoAl		Rh_5Zn_{21}	$AuZn_3$
NiAl		Pd_5Zn_{21}	$AuCd_3$
FeAl		Pt_5Zn_{21}	Au_3Sn
		Ni_5Cd_{21}	
Possibly also MgTl, CaTl, and SrTl as compounds of univalent Tl		$Na_{31}Pb_8$ Ag_5Zn_8 Au_5Zn_8 Ag_5Hg_8	Cu_3Sb and Ag_3Sb are sometimes erroneously included in this list although their electron : atom ratio is really 8 : 4

Note. High temperature X-ray work by Hume-Rothery shows that in the system copper-indium, the β-phase has a simple body-centred cubic structure. This phase is a solid solution of which the mean composition is more nearly Cu_4In than Cu_3In, but on the indium-rich side the solid solution extends nearly to the composition Cu_3In required by the 3 : 2 electron/atom ratio.

A diagram indicating some of the homogeneous phases in various alloy systems and their connexion with the electron-atom ratio is given in Fig. 103. It will be seen that some of the phases do not include the stoichiometric composition representative of the phase. For example, the intermediate phase "CuZn" does not appear at exactly 50 atomic per cent. of zinc. X-ray analysis shows that the atomic arrangement is undoubtedly based on an ideal CuZn structure for with suitable heat treatment the alloy possesses the CsCl type of lattice with a small excess of copper atoms in solution. The same phenomenon is to be observed in the copper-aluminium system where

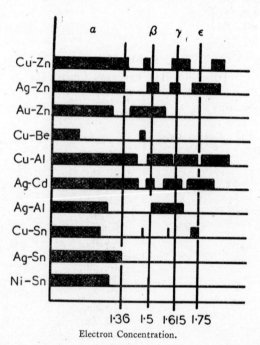

FIG. 103.—Formation of Intermediate Electron Compounds.

the θ-phase is based upon the atomic arrangement of an ideal $CuAl_2$. The very accurate work of Stockdale using thermal and microscopic methods and of Bradley, who used the X-ray technique, definitely shows that the phase lies to the aluminium-rich side of this composition and does not include it.

This phenomenon is difficult to comprehend on the basis of the Hume-Rothery rules alone, and it is here that a purely qualitative application of thermodynamic principles is of great assistance. Reference to Fig. 104 will make the matter clear. The extent of a phase depends entirely upon the manner in which the tangents to its

ζ-curve come in contact with the ζ-curves of the adjacent phases. In the case of CuZn, one of the common tangents between adjacent ζ-curves is so placed that the stoichiometric composition typifying the β-phase actually lies within a two-phase region. Only a small

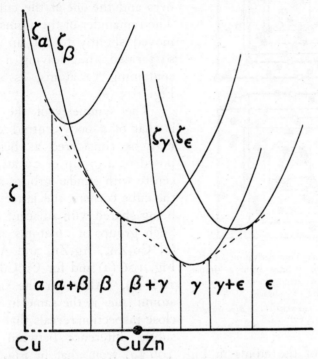

FIG. 104.—Hypothetical ζ-curves to illustrate the anomalous position of phases. Although ζ_β is a minimum at CuZn, CuZn cannot exist because it lies between the points of contact of the tangent to ζ_β and ζ_γ.

portion of the β-phase ζ-curve lying to the copper-rich side of CuZn is operative in producing the single phase. The same sort of argument can be applied to the θ-phase based on $CuAl_2$ and to numerous examples in other alloy systems.

The γ-Structure. The phases with γ-brass-like structures are an interesting and theoretically important series of alloys. They are hard and brittle, break with a conchoidal fracture and all possess a typical lustre which makes it difficult to distinguish one from the other. The atomic arrangement was first worked out for Cu_5Zn_8 by Bradley and Thewliss.[36] The derivation of the structure is illustrated in Fig. 105. It is based upon the simple body-centred cube which contains two atoms per unit cell. Let us suppose that we have stacked 27 of these cubes together to get a large cube with three times the cell edge and containing a total of 54 atoms as shown

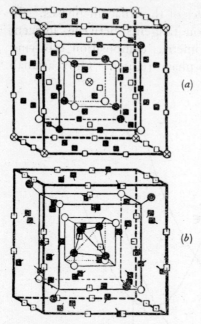

FIG. 105.—(a) The derivation of the structure of γ-brass from a simple cube-centred arrangement of atoms. (b) Structure of γ-brass.

(BRADLEY and THEWLISS, *Proc. Roy. Soc.*, A. **112**, 678, 1926.)

in Fig. 105 (*a*). We derive the γ-structure by removing two atoms from the large cube by taking away the crossed atoms at the cube corners and the one at the cube centre. The remainder of the atoms are then moved slightly to fill up the gaps so formed, thus leaving a structure containing 52 atoms, as shown in Fig. 105 (*b*).

The symmetry of the structure is that of a body-centred cube and may be considered as being composed of a group of 26 atoms at its centre with similar groups at each of the cube corners, the latter naturally being shared with adjacent unit cells. Such groups of 26 atoms are shown for Cu_5Zn_8, Ag_5Zn_8 and Au_5Zn_8 in Fig. 106 (*a*) and for Cu_5Cd_8 in Fig. 106 (*b*). Although the pattern of atomic *sites* is the same in all cases, close inspection reveals that there is a subtle difference between the distribution of the atoms in Fig. 106 (*a*) from that in Fig. 106 (*b*).

It is here that we find a marked distinction between alloy phase structures and chemical compounds. In the latter, it is invariably

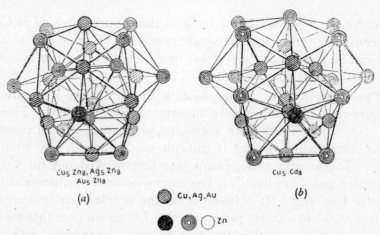

FIG. 106.—Typical groups of 26 atoms at lattice points of γ-structure.
(W. L. BRAGG, *J. Inst. Met.*, **56**, 275, 1935.)

found that in isomorphous compounds, corresponding elements occupy corresponding places.   But with the γ-structure, we see that although Cu_5Zn_8 and Cu_5Cd_8 are built on the same pattern, the substitution of cadmium for zinc causes a reshuffle of the atoms among the atomic sites and so the cadmium atoms of Fig. 106 (b) have quite different neighbours from the zinc atoms of γ-brass.   The phase-structure in an electron compound is thus independent of the distribution of the atoms among the pattern of atomic sites, and must be considered as being independent of any direct bonds between neighbouring atoms such as those which occur in normal valence compounds.

The Jones Theory.   The Hume-Rothery rule merely tells us that we may expect certain closely related phases at particular values of the electron concentration.   In itself it tells us nothing about the atomic arrangements, such information having to be obtained by X-ray analysis.   An explanation of the electron concentration rules, of which only the barest outline can be given here, has been offered by H. Jones,[37] using the wave theory of the electron originally developed by Sommerfeld and de Broglie.

On the basis of the older physical theories, the electron had been regarded as an elementary particle of mass m carrying a negative charge of magnitude $-e$.   It was later found to exhibit many of the characteristics which are normally attributed to a wave motion. According to de Broglie, we can associate a definite wavelength λ with each electron moving with velocity v, given by the relation $\lambda = \dfrac{h}{mv}$, where h is Planck's constant.   The kinetic energy E in electron-volts associated with the moving electron will therefore be given by the equation

$$E = \tfrac{1}{2}mv^2$$
$$= h^2/2m\lambda^2 \qquad . \qquad . \qquad . \qquad . \quad (1)$$

from which it is apparent that the shortest wavelengths are associated with electrons of highest kinetic energy.

To a first approximation we may neglect the periodic field of the atoms and treat the crystal as a box partitioned into a large number of energy levels in which we put increasing numbers of freely moving valence electrons.   When their number is small, the electrons naturally fill up the levels of lowest energy first, not more than two electrons of opposite spin being permitted by the Pauli "Exclusion Principle" to occupy each energy level.   These electrons with lowest energy will be the ones with the longest wavelengths.   With continued addition, the energy of the electrons rises in a smooth continuous curve as the wavelength diminishes, thus giving a whole series of wavelengths down to λ_{minimum} which can be obtained from the relation

$$N = \frac{8\pi}{3} \cdot \frac{1}{\lambda^3_{\text{min.}}} \qquad . \qquad . \qquad . \qquad . \qquad (2)$$

where N is the number of free electrons in unit volume of the crystal.

It is not difficult to show from equation (2) that if sufficient electrons are added, $\lambda_{\text{min.}}$ will become of the same order as the inter-

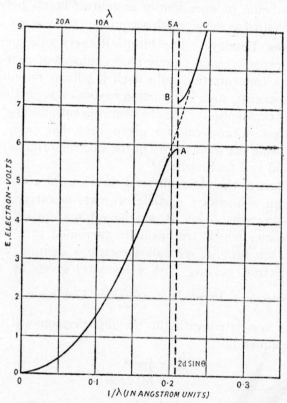

FIG. 107.—Variation of energy E of free electrons with their wavelength λ.
(W. L. BRAGG, *J. Inst. Met.*, **56**, 275, 1935.)

atomic distances in the crystal, and, ultimately, it will be possible for the electrons to be reflected by the atomic array according to the Bragg relation $2d \sin \theta = n\lambda$ in very much the same manner as X-rays when λ becomes smaller than $2d$. When this critical wavelength is reached for a set of strongly reflecting planes, the electrons travelling normal to them will be totally reflected straight back along their incident path. In general, there will be a family of these planes belonging to the same "form" so that there will be several possible

directions in the lattice in which the electron waves will be reflected
back.   The crystal planes will then act as impassable barriers and
prevent the electron waves from travelling in specific directions
through the crystal lattice.   Only electrons with a very much higher
energy can travel in these particular directions and so we get a gap
in the smooth curve connecting E with λ, of the order of an electron-
volt, which is a considerable amount (Fig. 107).

As the number of electrons continues to increase, other sets of
strongly reflecting planes belonging to different forms become effective
and the energy gap affects more and more directions.   The first of
the strongly reflecting sets of planes which make up the forms can be
thought of as outlining a polyhedron or zone within the crystal lattice.
When the electrons assume wavelengths such that they can be
reflected from all the possible simple forms with high reflectivity, it
is said that the first Brillouin zone has been filled and additional
electrons must go into higher zones.*

FIG. 108. — Brillouin
Zone for γ-brass type
of structure.
(H. JONES.)

The values of the interplanar spacing d which
determines at what value of λ the energy gap
occurs is primarily dependent on the atomic
arrangement.   For the metal or alloy to assume a
stable atomic pattern, the Jones' theory requires
that all the electrons should be accommodated
on the lowest portion of the (E, λ)-curve, that is,
the electrons should occupy the lowest energy
states when the zone is just completely filled.
This implies that the *atomic pattern* assumed
by an alloy depends upon the ratio of valence electrons to atoms in
the structure which is merely another way of formulating the Hume-
Rothery rule.

The first atomic pattern to which the theory of Jones was applied
was the γ-structure which we have described above.   The X-ray work
of Bradley and Thewliss showed that the most strongly reflecting
planes in the crystal were those with the forms $\{411\}$ and $\{330\}$.
These both have the same value of $h^2 + k^2 + l^2$ ($= 18$) and therefore overlap on the Debye-Scherrer photograph because the interplanar spacings belonging to each set of indices is 2·08 Å.   The zone
enclosed by these two forms is almost spherical in shape as shown in
Fig. 108, so that whatever the direction in which an electron wave is
travelling, it must fall almost normally on one or other of these planes.
The critical wavelength given by the Bragg law for normal reflection

* The discussion is usually carried out using the concept of "reciprocal" or "k" space,
but this treatment is beyond the scope of the present work.

must be $2d = \lambda$, or $\lambda = 4\cdot16$Å. Using equation (2) and $\lambda_{min.}$ to evaluate the number of electrons per unit volume, we find that it corresponds to an electron-atom ratio of 80 electrons to 52 atoms when reflexion just begins to occur on the {411} and {330} planes. When all possible directions of the electron waves, including those which can be reflected obliquely, are taken into account, a total number of 90 electrons for each 52 atoms can just be accommodated on the lower branch OA of the energy curve. The Jones' theory, then, predicts that the γ-structure should occur when there is a ratio of between 80 and 90 valence electrons to 54 atoms. This is in excellent agreement with the Hume-Rothery value of $21 : 13$ or $84 : 52$ valence electrons to atoms.

It will now be apparent that the atoms must take up such configurations that the 411 and 330 planes are very strong reflectors. It is a consequence of crowding the maximum possible number of electrons into the OA branch of the energy curve in order to produce a structure with the lowest possible energy. It is permissible to vary the electron-atom ratio within limits by changing the composition, but should the limit be exceeded, a new set of planes must be provided if the structure is to remain stable and this is achieved by the formation of a new phase-structure with suitable planes.

As long as the atomic sites remain unchanged, the 411 and 330 planes will still remain strong reflectors no matter how the atoms are distributed among them, and so the stability of the γ-structure is in no way influenced by the preciseness of the atomic arrangement. The same reasoning applies to the other "electron compounds" which are the result of the interaction between the atomic pattern on the one hand and the common system of valence electrons on the other. The position has been aptly summarized by W. L. Bragg, who defines a phase-structure simply *as a pattern of atomic sites*.

The Formation of Interstitial Solid Solutions and Compounds. When valence conditions and atomic size factors are favourable, wide ranges of substitutional solid solution can be expected in the primary and intermediate phases of alloy systems. On the other hand, carbon, boron, nitrogen and hydrogen, which have small atomic radii, have the unique property of being able to fit in the interstices between the atoms of the transition metals thereby forming interstitial solid solutions and "interstitial compounds". These nitrides, carbides, borides and hydrides all possess metallic properties.

Gunnar Hägg has made a comprehensive study of the formation of these interstitial compounds and has been successful in arranging them in an ordered scheme. He has shown that if we denote the atomic radius of the transition metal by R_M and the radius of the metalloid atom by R_X, then the ratio R_X/R_M determines the type of interstitial compound to be formed. The most commonly occurring types have compositions ranging about the stoichiometric formulæ M_2X and MX. These types are to be found when the ratio R_X/R_M $<$0·59 and are based principally upon the face-centred cubic or hexagonal close-packed arrangements. Cubic close packing of the metal atoms exists in the compounds ZrH, TiH, CrN, ScN, ZrN, VN, TiN, TiC, TaC and VC, while some of those based on the hexagonal close packing of metal atoms are Ti_2H, Ta_2H, Zr_2H, Mn_2N, Cr_2N, Fe_2N, Ta_2C, W_2C and Mo_2C. Pd_2H, Mo_2N and W_2N are cubic, while WC has a simple hexagonal arrangement.

It is difficult to place the positions of the interstitial atoms by X-ray methods owing to their relatively small scattering factors and their positions have to be inferred from the nature of the structures. When $R_X/R_M$$>$0·59, the structures are more complex and few have been analysed as yet. The structure of cementite Fe_3C has recently been established by Lipson and Petch [38] and shown to have a complicated orthorhombic atomic arrangement.

In steels, both the substitutional and interstitial types of solid solution may exist at one and the same time. In an austenitic manganese steel, it is possible to have manganese substituting iron atoms on the face-centred cubic lattice while carbon atoms fit in the interstices. This dual type of solid solution is contributory to the extraordinarily interesting and important properties which can be conferred upon alloy steels by suitable heat treatment.

The Formation of Superlattices. In our discussion on solid-solutions and intermediate phases, we gave a more or less static picture of the crystalline arrangement. In actual fact, the atoms are in a continual state of thermal agitation which gives them a certain amount of mobility at the higher temperatures. So weak is the metallic linkage and so "empty" is the atomic core that it is relatively easy for the atoms to be continually changing places by sliding past each other and thereby to diffuse through the solid structure at an appreciable rate. As the temperature falls and the amplitude of vibration diminishes, the energy of vibration becomes smaller than that required to produce an exchange of places, and so the atoms settle down to oscillate with a limited amplitude about fixed mean positions in the crystal lattice.

At high temperatures, we should expect the atoms to be arranged perfectly at random among the atomic sites, a condition that could be retained by quenching or cooling sufficiently rapidly. Complete randomness can not only be retained by rapid cooling in primary substitutional solid solutions with stoichiometric proportions such as Fe_3Al, or CuAu, but also in certain intermediate phase structures, of which CuZn may be quoted as an example.

If the rate of cooling is slow enough, or if the alloy is maintained at a suitable temperature for a sufficiently long period of time, the different sorts of atoms gradually settle down into regular positions in the lattice and the distribution of atoms now becomes one in which it is possible to distinguish between the different atomic positions. An "ordered" structure of this type is termed a *superlattice*, and its formation is accompanied by marked changes in the physical and

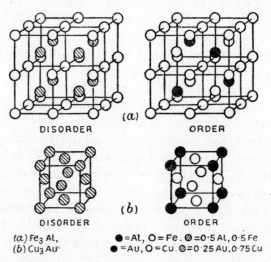

DISORDER   (a)   ORDER

DISORDER   (b)   ORDER

(a) Fe_3Al,   ● = Al, O = Fe. ⊘ = 0·5 Al, 0·5 Fe
(b) Cu_3Au ● = Au, O = Cu. ⊘ = 0·25 Au, 0·75 Cu

FIG. 109.—Superlattice formation in Fe_3Al and Cu_3Au. The Heusler alloy Cu_2MnAl has a superlattice analogous to the ordered Fe_3Al arrangement.

(W. L. BRAGG, *J. Inst. Met.*, **56**, 275, 1935.)

mechanical properties of the alloy. It is important to realize that in the ordering process no change of phase is involved, for the *pattern of atomic sites* remains unaffected.

Changes in the electrical resistance of alloys on prolonged annealing had been observed by Tammann in 1919 [39], changes which he interpreted as being due to atomic rearrangement. Conclusive evidence for the existence of superlattices was obtained some years later when Johansonn and Linde [40] conducted their classical X-ray investigations on the copper-gold system. The type of changes which take place are illustrated in Fig. 109.

Cu_3Au. Fig. 109 (b) represents the unit cell of the face-centred cubic structure Cu_3Au in which the copper atoms represented by white circles occupy the cube faces and the gold atoms shown as black circles are stationed at cube corners. The structure is fully ordered. The disordered high temperature form is a face-centred cubic structure in which it is impossible to distinguish the gold from the copper atoms.

The Debye-Scherrer photograph of the ordered structure illustrated in Fig. 110 (*b*) shows a number of extra "superlattice lines" over and above those normally obtained from a face-centred cubic lattice. The intensity of these superlattice lines gives us a direct measure of the degree of order which the crystal lattice has attained.

In Chapter VI, we showed that the intensity I of an X-ray reflexion was directly proportional to the square of the structure factor, $F(hkl)$. In the fully ordered Cu_3Au structure, the co-ordinates of the atoms are

$$Au \qquad 000$$
$$Cu \qquad \tfrac{1}{2}\tfrac{1}{2}0, \ \tfrac{1}{2}0\tfrac{1}{2}, \ 0\tfrac{1}{2}\tfrac{1}{2}.$$

The structure factor may therefore be written

$$F(hkl) = f_{Au}e^{2\pi i(0.h+0.k+0.l)} + f_{Cu}\{e^{2\pi i(\frac{1}{2}h+\frac{1}{2}k)} + e^{2\pi i(\frac{1}{2}k+\frac{1}{2}l)} + e^{2\pi i(\frac{1}{2}h+\frac{1}{2}l)}\}$$

$$= f_{Au} + f_{Cu}(\cos \pi(h+k) + \cos \pi(k+l) + \cos \pi(h+l)).$$

The main lattice lines with intensity I_m occur when hkl are all odd or all even. In these cases, then, we have

$$F(hkl)_m = f_{Au} + 3f_{Cu} \qquad (\Sigma h^2 = 3, 4 \ldots 8 \ldots 11, 12 \ldots)$$

or

$$I_m \propto (f_{Au} + 3f_{Cu})^2.$$

The superlattice lines occur when the indices are a mixture of odd and even numbers. For these, the structure factor reduces to

$$F(hkl)_s = f_{Au} - f_{Cu} \qquad (\Sigma h^2 = 1, 2 \ldots 5, 6 \ldots 9, 10 \ldots)$$

and their intensities

$$I_s \propto (f_{Au} - f_{Cu})^2$$

Thus the superlattice lines will tend to be very much weaker than the lines of the main pattern unless the difference between the atomic scattering factors is sufficiently large. Since f is roughly proportional to the atomic number of the scattering element, we see that the copper-gold example is a particularly favourable one which gives strong superlattice lines.

In the completely disordered state, the atoms are distributed at random among the lattice sites and it is therefore impossible to distinguish one atom from the other. The effective scattering powers of the atoms at the lattice points must then take the average value $f = \tfrac{1}{4}(f_{Au} + 3f_{Cu})$ and the structure factor now becomes the same as for a face-centred cube in which the atoms at cube corners and face centres are identical.   For complete disorder

$$F(hkl) = 4f \quad \text{when } hkl \text{ are all odd or all even, i.e. } \Sigma h^2 = 3,$$
$$4 \ldots 8 \ldots 11, 12 \ldots \text{etc.}$$

and $F(hkl) = 0$ when indices are a mixture of odd and even integers, i.e. $\Sigma h^2 = 1, 2 \ldots 5, 6 \ldots 9, 10 \ldots \text{etc.}$

The superlattice lines must therefore vanish entirely, when complete disorder sets in.

The degree of order may be defined by a parameter S which varies from 1 for perfect order to 0 for a completely random arrangement. The structure-factor of a superlattice line for any intermediate degree of order may therefore be written

$$F(hkl)_s = (f_{Au} - f_{Cu}).S$$

and the intensity becomes

$$I_s \propto (f_{Au} - f_{Cu})^2.S^2.$$

The main lattice lines belonging to the normal face-centred cube will, of course, remain totally unaffected throughout all the order-disorder changes.

CuAu.   The order-disorder transformations in the equi-atomic copper-gold alloy, CuAu, have been extensively studied by Dehlinger and Graf [41]. When quenched from high temperatures, this alloy possesses a face-centred cubic structure in which the atoms are randomly arranged.

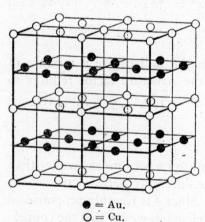

● = Au.
O = Cu.

FIG. 111.—The CuAu Superlattice.

When this alloy is annealed at a low temperature, the atoms segregate out into alternating copper and gold lattice planes as shown in Fig. 111. The structure is fully ordered, but on account of the different atomic radii the structure is no longer cubic but face-centred-tetragonal with an axial ratio which is very nearly unity. The change in symmetry is so slight that it is not looked upon as a phase transformation but as a genuine case of superlattice formation.

CuZn.   The change of β' into β-brass (CuZn) at 470°, once thought to be a definite phase change, has been shown by X-ray methods to be nothing more than an order-disorder transformation.

$\Sigma h^2 = 3$ 4   8   11 12   16   19 20

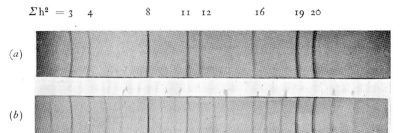

(a)

(b)

FIG. 110.—X-ray diffraction patterns of Cu₃Au. 9-cm. diameter Debye-Scherrer camera CuKα radiation. Wire specimens 0·4 mm. in diameter.

(a) Quenched 450° C. Complete disorder.
(b) Annealed 380° C. for 50 hours. Complete order.

(C. Sykes and F. W. Jones, *Proc. Roy. Soc.*, **157**, 213, 1936.)

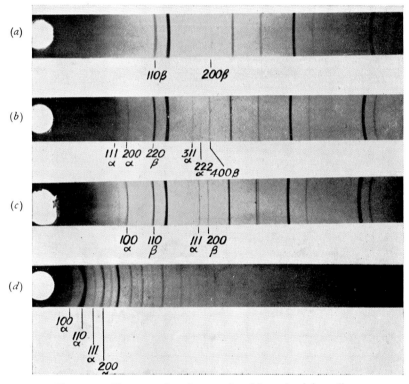

FIG. 112.—X-ray powder photographs of iron-aluminium-alloys.

(a) Pure iron.   FeKα and Kβ radiation.
(b) Fe₃Al type. FeKα and Kβ radiation.
(c) FeAl type.   FeKα and Kβ radiation.
(d) FeAl type.   MoKα radiation.

Note how the use of a short wavelength (MoKα) crowds the lines towards the low angle end of the film, and also how the high orders fade out due to the thermal motion of the lattice and heavy back-scatter. 9-cm. diameter Debye-Scherrer camera.

(A. J. Bradley and A. H. Jay, *Proc. Roy. Soc.*, **136**, 210, 1932.)

[*Facing page* 176.

When completely disordered at the higher temperatures, the structure is indistinguishable from that of a simple body-centred cube, and the corresponding powder photograph has lines which only appear when $(h + k + l)$ is even (see Fig. 93).

When completely ordered, below 470°, the structure is essentially the CsCl type. The atomic co-ordinates are then

$$\text{Zn} \quad 000$$
$$\text{Cu} \quad \tfrac{1}{2}\tfrac{1}{2}\tfrac{1}{2}.$$

The structure factor is therefore

$$F(hkl) = f_{Zn}e^{2\pi i(0.h + 0.k + 0.l)} + f_{Cu}e^{2\pi i(\frac{1}{2}h + \frac{1}{2}k + \frac{1}{2}l)}.$$

Hence

$$F(hkl)_m = f_{Zn} + f_{Cu} \quad \text{when } h + k + l \text{ is even}$$
$$(\Sigma h^2 = 2 \ 4 \ 6 \ 8 \ .. \text{ etc.})$$

and

$$F(hkl)_s = f_{Zn} - f_{Cu} \quad \text{when } h + k + l \text{ is odd.}$$
$$(\Sigma h^2 = 1, 3, 5, \cdots 9, 11 .. \text{ etc.}).$$

The diffraction photograph of the ordered structure takes on the appearance similar to NiAl shown in Fig. 98. The superlattice lines of CuZn, however, are extremely feeble, since f_{Zn} is very nearly the same as f_{Cu}. Only by employing a suitable radiation, namely zinc Kα and a 19-cm. diameter camera were Sykes and Jones [42] able to make them strong enough for measurement.

The alloys NiAl, CoAl and FeAl have similar structures to CuZn and give quite strong superlattice lines with Co Kα radiation. In these cases, however, the structures are completely ordered at very high temperatures and probably remain so right up to the melting-points of the alloys.

Cobalt Kα is also suitable for studying the superlattice in the highly magnetically permeable face-centred cubic alloy FeNi$_3$. With long annealing, this alloy eventually becomes fully ordered, but so small is the difference in scattering factor between iron and nickel that the superlattice lines are only just visible even under the best conditions.

Fe$_3$Al. The Fe$_3$Al type of superlattice which was first investigated by Bradley and Jay [43] is shown in Fig. 109 (a), the black circles corresponding to Al atoms and the white circles to Fe. The full regularity of the superlattice is brought out by stacking together eight elementary body-centred cubes. It will then be seen that aluminium and iron atoms alternate regularly at the cube centres. If the alloy is quenched above 700° C., the structure obtained is the

G

completely disordered one shown in Fig. 109. Powder photographs of Fe_3Al in the disordered and ordered condition are illustrated in Fig. 112. The superlattice lines occur at positions which correspond to doubling the cell edge of the elementary body-centred cube.

There is a transition to the CsCl type of superlattice in the region of Fe_2Al. This is marked by a definite minimum in the lattice-parameter curve (Fig. 91), and is probably connected with a change in valence of the iron atoms which falls to zero at the stoichiometric composition FeAl where the electron : atom ratio is 3 : 2.

The Heusler Alloys. A whole series of ferromagnetic alloys containing for the most part only the elements copper, manganese and aluminium was discovered by Heusler towards the close of the last century. The most ferromagnetic of these has a composition corresponding closely to Cu_2MnAl. When heated for six hours at 500° C. and slowly cooled to room temperature, the structure is very similar to that of γ-brass and, in this condition, the alloy is non-magnetic. On the other hand, when the same alloy is quenched from 800° C., the alloy becomes strongly ferromagnetic.

Bradley and Rodgers [44] investigated the alloy in the ferromagnetic condition by taking Debye-Scherrer photographs. They were able to show conclusively that the structure was very similar to the super-lattice possessed by Fe_3Al. If for a moment we consider the structure shown in Fig. 109, the Heusler alloy would have alternate cube-centres filled with Al and Mn atoms, while the rest of the lattice points would be occupied by Cu atoms. We thus have the interesting phenomenon of a ternary superlattice existing at a high temperature, which, on being retained by quenching, is ferromagnetic at normal temperatures. Slow cooling, instead of promoting a structure with a higher degree of order, results in the formation of the more stable though more complicated γ-structure.

An Outline of the Order–Disorder Transformation Theory. The literature on the mechanism of the order-disorder transformation, now very extensive, is comprehensively reviewed in a paper by Nix and Shockley.[45] The method of approach adopted by Bragg and Williams [46] based upon very simple assumptions about the energy of different atomic configurations leads to results of great practical and theoretical importance. We shall only attempt to give a brief outline of the theory and some of the consequences which flow therefrom.

Thermodynamical reasoning leads to the conclusion that the most stable structure is the one with the lowest thermodynamic potential or lowest internal energy. Now an ordered arrangement has lower internal energy than one of disorder and so the superlattice must represent the most stable condition at the lower temperatures. The effects of thermal agitation at higher temperatures is to shuffle the atoms and to destroy the ordered arrangement.

Let us suppose that two kinds of atom, A and B, form a structure which can be obtained in states of perfect equilibrium at all temperatures. At the lowest temperature, the structure will be perfectly ordered and the atoms will be readily distinguished from one another. Thus A and B atoms will alternate in proper sequence since they will all be in their "right" places. To move an A atom from its right place into a "wrong" position, which should really be occupied by an atom of B, will require a certain amount of work V_0 which can only be done by supplying energy in the form of heat. As the temperature of the alloy is raised, more and more A atoms move into "wrong" places, and, of course, the equal number of B atoms which take their places must now be in wrong positions. The structure loses its perfection of order and eventually becomes completely random as the temperature continues to rise.

We shall define the degree of order by a parameter S which varies from 1 for perfect order to 0 for a completely random arrangement. In the Bragg-Williams theory, S is a linear function of the probability of finding a given atom in a "right" place, that is, a place which is normally occupied by an atom of the same kind in the perfectly ordered structure. We wish to know how the equilibrium degree of order varies with the temperature, or what is very much the same thing, how many atoms will be in "wrong" places at a given instant.

As we apply heat to the fully ordered alloy, one of the A atoms will acquire sufficient energy V_0 to jump into a "wrong" place. The structure will now be slightly less ordered, and so the next atom to jump into a wrong place will need a slightly smaller energy V. Indeed, the more disordered the structure, the smaller becomes the energy to move into a "wrong" position, until finally, when disorder is complete and all distinction between "right" and "wrong" places has disappeared, no extra work is required to move an atom from one place to another. As a first approximation, we may assume that the work required to move an atom from a "right" to a "wrong" place is a linear function of the degree of order, or, expressed mathematically, $V = V_0 S$. If all the heat is used in producing disorder, the transformation takes place isothermally.

For every particular temperature T, there is an equilibrium degree of order $S = f(T)$ which decreases as the temperature is raised. We therefore have the interplay of two processes, one depending upon

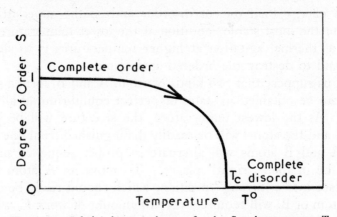

FIG. 113.—Relation between degree of order S and temperature T.

At temperatures above T_c the alloy is completely disordered. The order-disorder transformation is completely reversible. Note the sudden collapse of order when $T \longrightarrow T_c$.

the temperature alone and the other on the degree of order. First of all, the degree of order diminishes on account of $S = f(T)$, and secondly, the attainment of disorder is rendered easier on account of $V = V_0(S)$, which makes the required energy change smaller, the smaller the degree of order. These two mutually assisting effects act together, and as the temperature is raised, the disordering process, which begins slowly at first, gathers momentum like an avalanche until there is a complete collapse of the ordered state. The equilibrium thus follows the type of curve illustrated in Fig. 113.

The rapid collapse of the ordered state occurs at a *critical temperature* T_c which is characteristic of the alloy. It is important to

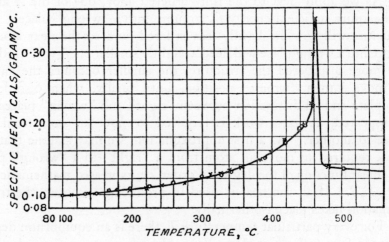

FIG. 114.—Specific heat of β-brass, 49·06% Zn.

(C. SYKES, *Proc. Roy. Soc.*, **148**, 422, 1935.)

realize that the process is strictly reversible provided conditions of thermodynamic equilibrium are maintained, so that on cooling down, the onset of order will be equally sudden when the critical temperature is reached.

The heat energy required to produce the change varies continuously with the degree of order and therefore with the temperature. Over the range of temperature in which the structure is becoming disordered, the alloy will show an abnormal specific heat which will be greater than the value given by Dulong and Petit's law. When the critical temperature is reached, no more disorder can take place and the value of the specific heat falls sharply to the normal value. The $\beta - \beta'$ transformation in CuZn gives a thermal arrest due to the changing specific heat of the alloy which retards the rate of cooling over an appreciable temperature range. The actual variation has been closely studied by Sykes, and his results are shown in Fig. 114.

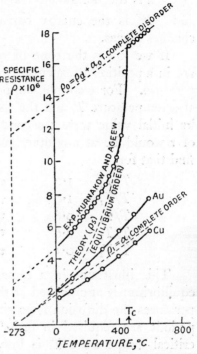

FIG. 115.—Resistivity curves of CuAu. (W. L. BRAGG, *J. Inst. Met.*, **56**, 275, 1935.)

The order-disorder transformation may also be studied by observing the changes of electrical resistivity with the temperature, for the resistance due to disorder will be superimposed upon the resistance promoted by the thermal vibrations of the lattice. The excellent accord between theory and experiment is borne out by the resistivity curve of CuAu illustrated in Fig. 115.

The Influence of Temperature on the Annealing Time. When the alloy is in thermodynamic equilibrium, as many atoms will be moving from ordered to disordered positions as in the reverse direction. If at this particular temperature the alloy is not in equilibrium, it will, if left to itself, relax towards the equilibrium state of order. This process takes time, and how long it takes will depend upon the temperature of the alloy as well as upon other factors which are practically independent of the temperature.

Let us suppose that we have an alloy at a temperature T whose equilibrium balance has been disturbed, and that it takes a time τ

for the departure from equilibrium to be reduced to $1/e$ of its initial value.   The "time of relaxation" is given by the approximate relation

$$\tau = Ae^{\frac{W}{kT}} \qquad . \qquad . \qquad . \qquad . \qquad (1)$$

where $A = 10^{-12 \pm 2}$

k is the Boltzmann constant

and W is the energy barrier to be surmounted when an atom changes places.

If we know the time of relaxation at any one temperature, we are in a position to calculate the time of relaxation at any other temperature.   For example, suppose the alloy were out of equilibrium at a temperature T_1 and the time, τ, taken for it to recover to $1/e$ of its initial value were 1 second, we require to know what the value of τ would be at any other temperature T.   From equation (1) we find that for

$T/T_1 = 1\cdot2$	$\tau = 0\cdot01$ second.
$T/T_1 = 1\cdot0$	$\tau = 1\cdot0$ second by definition.
$T/T_1 = 0\cdot8$	$\tau = 17$ minutes.
$T/T_1 = 0\cdot6$	$\tau = 3$ years.
$T/T_1 = 0\cdot5$	$\tau = 30{,}000$ years.

This illustrates in a remarkable way how rapidly the state of equilibrium is approached at the higher temperatures.   At low temperatures the diffusion is so sluggish that impossibly long annealing periods are required in order to obtain true equilibrium.   If the critical temperature T_c is low, atomic movement will have slowed down to such an extent that it will be virtually impossible to obtain the alloy in a state of complete order whatever the period of annealing. On the other hand, with T_c high, the alloy will pass into a state of order however rapidly it may be quenched.   To study a superlattice transformation necessitates the critical temperature of ordering to lie within a narrow range.   This accounts for the comparative rarity of cases like Fe_3Al, $CuAu$, Cu_3Au, where the alloy can be preserved at any predetermined degree of order by heat treatment.

Long Range and Short Range Order—Out of Step Domains. The order-disorder theory as originally put forward by Bragg and Williams makes the tacit assumption that the degree of order in the whole crystal is the same as the degree of order over short distances. This assumption of long-range order is perfectly sound when the alloy is cooled slowly enough to ensure perfect thermodynamic equilibrium at each stage.   However, when we study the transformation more closely, we find that it is much more complicated than we first of all supposed. The first stage in the transition from disorder to order involves the formation of nuclei or small volumes within the crystal which have a degree of order corresponding to the equilibrium degree of order at the temperature of the specimen. If we maintain the temperature constant, these nuclei grow until they become of the same order of size as the crystals themselves. The superlattice lines in the powder photographs are created by the ordered array which extends through the crystal as a whole and are therefore just as sharp as the main lattice lines, although their intensities vary in strength in proportion to the degree of order then prevailing.

If, now, the alloy is cooled faster than the rate at which it can come into equilibrium, two processes take place at the same time; the nuclei tend to grow, and at the same time the degree of order *in the nuclei* increases rapidly owing to the lowering of the temperature. We then arrive at a stage when nuclei, having rapidly attained a high degree of internal order, grow sufficiently large to come in contact with each other, being separated by more or less disordered boundaries only two or three atoms wide.

Within each individual grain, the lattice consists, as it were, of a "foam" of nuclei, each of which is perfectly ordered within itself but out of step with its adjacent neighbours. Expressed pictorially, we may write down the long-distance order which extends throughout the entire single crystal as:

A B A B A B A B A B A B A B A B A B A B A B A B A B,

while the order in the foam structure with its disordered boundaries may be expressed as:

A B A B : B : B A B A B : B : B A B A B A : A : A B A B A B A

Since the crystal has been cooled too rapidly, there is not sufficient time available for that dynamic interchange of atoms which would give rise to the long-distance order. The crystal becomes perfectly ordered, but only over short distances.

Such a "foam" structure as we have described above is revealed by a broadening of the superlattice lines in the powder photographs. The line broadening comes about from lack of resolving power of the crystal grating when the size of the diffracting unit becomes somewhat less than 10^{-4} cm. This is considered in detail in Chapter IX. By measuring the increase in breadth of the superlattice lines, it is possible to calculate the average size, ε, of the nuclei in addition to the degree of order prevailing for the different rates of cooling.

Some typical Debye-Scherrer patterns of Cu_3Au taken by F. W. Jones and C. Sykes are illustrated in Fig. 116. The great increase in line sharpness with increasing size of nuclei is brought out in a most striking manner by these very beautiful photographs.

Phase Changes at Liquid Air Temperature. Since Osmond and Cartaud's work on meteoritic irons in 1904, a vast amount of research has been carried out on the iron-nickel system, but despite all efforts a satisfactory equilibrium diagram has not yet been drawn. The difficulties lie mainly in the iron-rich portion of the system where the alloys are extremely difficult to produce in a condition of true equilibrium. The change from face-centred cubic γ solid solution to body-centred cubic α produced by normal slow cooling rates cannot be reversed on heating until a very much higher temperature is reached. A marked hysteresis in the physical properties with temperature follows as a natural consequence. This difficulty is demonstrated by the type of diagram proposed by Honda and Miura, and by Merica,[47] shown in Fig. 117, in which they attempt to reconcile two sets of conditions, one for cooling and one for heating. Clearly such a diagram is definitely in conflict with the laws of thermodynamics, and would not be followed if the rates of cooling or heating could be made sufficiently slow.

An alloy with a composition in the region of 15 per cent. Ni at 700° will have a single-phase face-centred cubic structure. As it cools through the α + γ range, it tends to precipitate α-phase of varying composition at the crystal boundaries. Such precipitation necessitates atomic diffusion to take place over several atomic distances, but since the difference between iron and nickel atoms is so very small, the thermodynamic potential for the state of equilibrium is very little different from the out-of-equilibrium potential at that particular temperature. The result is that the alloys are "sluggish" and only prolonged annealing over several weeks produces conditions even remotely resembling true equilibrium. The very broad lines in the powder photographs produced by the lack of thermal equilibrium in the alloys begin to sharpen up following the protracted annealing periods.

However, when such an alloy which has retained its face-centred cubic structure is plunged into liquid air (— 200° C.) for a few moments it transforms immediately into the body-centred cubic form. The phase transformation takes place under thermal conditions in which diffusion processes over long distances are clearly impossible. The change from the face-centred cubic to the body-centred cubic structure can be achieved by a very slight local rearrangement of the atoms, for the two structures are almost as closely packed. When the temperature drops to such a value that the thermodynamic poten-

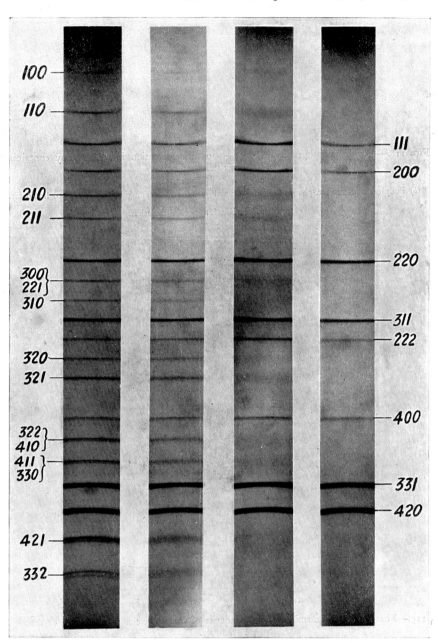

FIG. 116.—Effect of Nuclei size ε on breadth of superlattice lines of Cu₃Au. 9 cm. diameter camera. Copper Kα radiation. Wire specimen, 0·4 mm. diameter. (F. W. JONES and C. SYKES, *Proc. Roy. Soc.*, **166**, 376, 1938.)

[*Facing page* 184.

FIG. 118.—Powder photographs of the $\gamma \longrightarrow \alpha$ transformation in Fe-Ni alloy containing 28·9 atomic per cent Ni.

(a) Face-centred cubic γ-phase.
(b) Body-centred cubic α-phase + some residual γ-phase after plunging specimen into liquid air.

9-cm. diameter camera.   CoKα radiation.

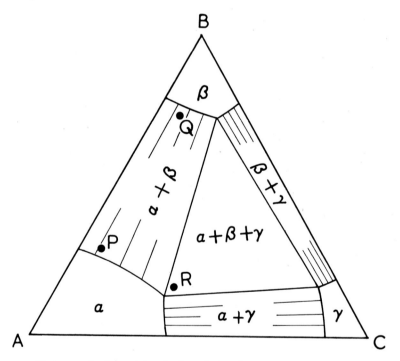

FIG. 119.—First stages in determining the boundaries of two-phase fields and corners of three-phase triangles.

Alloys P and Q yield the first approximations to the boundaries of the α and β phase fields.   An alloy such as R locates a corner of the three-phase triangle.

tial of the body-centred cubic structure is sufficiently below that for the face-centred cube, the whole crystal automatically goes over into

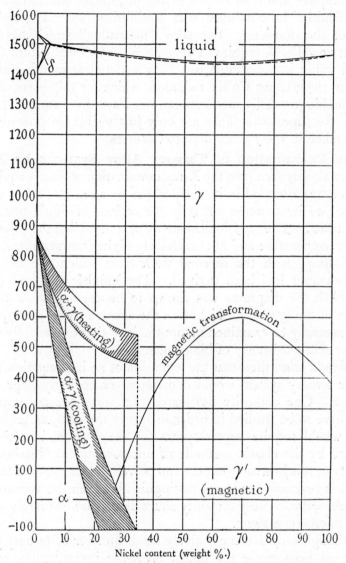

FIG. 117.—The Iron-Nickel Equilibrium Diagram (Merica).
(A. J. BRADLEY and A. TAYLOR, *Proc. Roy. Soc.*, **166**, 353, 1938.)

its equilibrium structure without the need of long-range thermal diffusion processes to occur.

When the alloys are duplex, treatment in liquid air always increases the amount of body-centred cubic phase. In Fig. 118 we show the change which has taken place in a single-phase alloy containing 28·9 atomic per cent. of nickel. Here the transformation has not been quite complete and a small proportion of γ-phase still remains.

Difficulties in obtaining true equilibrium extend over a large range of the diagram. The alloy "permalloy" which has a composition near Fe_3Ni requires a very prolonged anneal before the face-centred cubic lattice develops a fully ordered structure like Ni_3Al and even then, using Co Kα radiation, which for this particular alloy gives the biggest difference between the Fe and Ni atomic scattering factors, the superlattice lines are only just visible on powder photographs taken in the 19 cm. diameter camera.

The Examination of Ternary Alloy Systems by X-rays. We have already seen how the X-ray examination of binary equilibrium diagrams was attended in its early stages by a search for the simplest possible powder patterns whereby the regions of single phase could be identified. The next logical step was to establish the phase limits at room temperature and at successively higher temperatures, linking these findings with the thermal work from which the solidus and liquidus curves had been derived. The number of alloys required to establish the diagrams was shown to be dependent on the complexities of the system itself, but on the average some 40 or 50 alloys would normally be examined before the investigator was fully satisfied with the self-consistency of his results.

It would seem then that the extension of an investigation to cover a whole ternary system would demand an exceedingly large number of alloys. One authority has stated that some 1,250 compositions would have to be studied in order to survey the field, an undertaking which would require several years for the average investigator to complete by the classic methods of microscopic examination. It is precisely at this juncture that the full power and elegance of the X-ray method is revealed, for it can distinguish between the various phase-structures with absolute certainty and with an ease but rarely achieved by the microscope alone.

Although only a comparatively small number of ternary systems has as yet been made the object of X-ray investigation, one very important fact has emerged, namely that the formation of new ternary single-phase regions *is a comparatively rare event*, and their occurrence will be instantly recognized by the appearance of a fresh type of diffraction pattern. This is important because preliminary investigations covering the three binary systems, which form the sides of the composition triangle, will have established *in advance* most of the structural types likely to be encountered, and a comprehensive file of X-ray identification patterns belonging to the different binary phase-structures will already be to hand. The problem of investigating the interior of the composition triangle is thereby considerably simplified, so much so that only a relatively small number of ternary alloys is required to map out the entire area.

With all this binary diagram information at our disposal, it is now an easy matter to decide whether a ternary alloy consists of one, two or three phases in equilibrium, and with a little experience it is possible to make a good estimate of their relative amounts by visual inspection of the powder diagrams. Experience has shown that the phase boundaries are most easily located by examining the two- and three-phase regions first and then by studying single-phase ternary alloys.

Thus in a two-phase region (Fig. 119), the alloy P splits up into two conjugate solid solutions along a tie-line. Which phases are in equilibrium are immediately established from the simple binary patterns, and so the direction of the tie-line is very roughly fixed. That P is close to the α-phase boundary is readily inferred from the intensities of the α- and β-phase patterns, and the approximate position of the β-phase boundary is obtained. An alloy Q is then made up in order to confirm the position of the β-boundary and at the same time the phase proportions confirm the general run of the α-phase boundary. A few alloys made inside the α and β areas of single phase yield a series of lattice parameters, which, when compared with those of P, immediately determines the compositions of the two conjugate solid solutions and accurately fixes the direction of the tie-line. Repeating this process for a few alloys such as P and Q not only establishes the limits to the single-phase regions but also establishes the run of the tie-lines in a manner impossible by any other method of investigation.

The extent of the three-phase regions is just as easily mapped out. Any alloy made within a three-phase region splits up into three phases of fixed composition whose relative amounts are readily assessed by inspection of the powder photograph. If we make an alloy lying just within one of the apexes of a three-phase triangle, it yields a strong pattern belonging to the phase field nearest to it, and a weaker pattern belonging to each of the two phases at the other corners of the triangle. As before, by estimating the intensities of these two patterns, it is possible to ascertain with fair accuracy the compositions of the two minor constituents. Verification is obtained by making up alloys with compositions judged to lie just within the other two apexes. Further verification will be had from the run of the tie-lines, for the side of a three-phase triangle is the limiting tie-line of a two-phase field.   Lattice parameter measurements will then be used to give the final touch of accuracy to positioning the apexes of the triangle.

In general, the phase diagram will be roughed out by visual inspection long before lattice parameter measurements are made.   It is very helpful to make up alloys which will lie just within a two-phase region, thereby establishing the single-phase boundary, the two-phase region, and the tie-line directions simultaneously.   Also those alloys which lie just within the apexes of the three-phase regions will establish the limiting tie-lines and the compositions of the three co-existing phases.   These three-phase triangles, it is most important to note, give the key to the whole diagram.   By drawing hypothetical single-phase boundaries, which conform to the rules of direction at the triangle corners, vast areas of the ternary system can be rapidly mapped out in a provisional yet convincing fashion, to await the further refinements which confirmatory alloys and lattice parameter measurements will bring.   An interesting method of approach to the subject is also given by Anderson and Jette [48] who trace the boundaries by the discontinuities in the lattice parameters.

Nomenclature for the Single–Phase Regions.   The only really satisfactory system of phase nomenclature would be one based upon the crystal structures of the phases, but unfortunately most of the accepted symbols for well-known binary diagrams were adopted long before the application of X-ray methods.   When an attempt is made to carry these symbols over into ternary and polynary systems generally, difficulties arise, for those phases which have the same crystal structure must be given the same nomenclature or else a hopeless state of confusion would develop.

The following conventions have been tentatively adopted.[49] Face-centred cubic structures in the phase fields containing nickel and copper are called α, in accordance with the standard metallurgical terminology in binary systems containing a large region of copper-rich solid solution.   The symbol β is used for the body-centred cube. This also is in accord with the generally accepted nomenclature for the systems in which this structure follows the α-solid solution, but unfortunately it clashes with the symbol for ferrite which is usually termed α-iron.   However, for ternary systems, the enormous simplification in nomenclature resulting from labelling ferrite β, makes departure from older practice well worth while.   The symbol γ is reserved for the structures which have the same type of atomic pattern as γ-brass.   So far it has not been found practicable to extend the notation to other ternary structures, as they are considered to be of minor importance.

When a phase-structure develops a superlattice, it is indicated by the addition of a suffix rather than by the use of an additional symbol. For example, a face-centred cubic superlattice like Ni_3Al is denoted by α_1, the body-centred cubic superlattice of the Fe_3Al type by β_1 and that of the $FeAl$ type by β_2. When two structures of the same type are in equilibrium, a superscript is added to one of them for the purposes of differentiation, as for example in the two-phase region $\alpha_1 + \alpha_1'$ in the system Fe-Ni-Al.

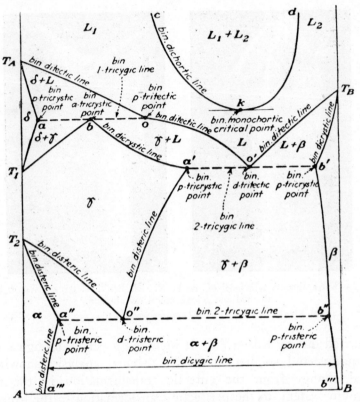

FIG. 120.—Illustration of a new system of nomenclature.

(J. S. MARSH, *Principles of Phase Diagrams.*)

Marsh [50] has pointed out the urgent necessity for a satisfactory notation which can be applied to the various transformations found in binary and polynary systems. His proposed nomenclature for binary systems is reproduced in Fig. 120. It is felt that the adoption of this scheme will do much to simplify the description of complicated polynary systems.

In the next section we shall describe some typical results of X-ray investigations on ternary systems which have been carried out according to the general methods described above.

The Ternary System Fe–Ni–Al.   The discovery of a new permanent magnet material by Mishima [51] having a composition in the region of Fe_2NiAl focused attention on the iron-nickel-aluminium ternary alloys.   An important pioneer investigation into the metallography of the system which attempted to explain the relationship between the face-centred cubic and body-centred cubic phase fields

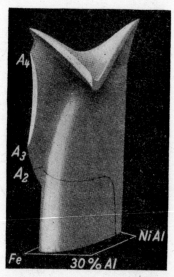

FIG. 121.—Three-dimensional model of the Fe-Ni rich Fe-Ni-Al ternary system based on thermal and microscopical examination.

(W. KÖSTER, *Archiv. für das Eisenhüttenwesen*, Heft 4, 257, 1933/4.)

was carried out by Köster.[51]   It included a very thorough study of the liquidus and solidus curves by thermal analysis, showing the gradual change from the eutectic transformation in the nickel-aluminium system, to the peritectic transformation in the iron-nickel system (see Fig. 95 (Ni-Al) and Fig. 117 (Fe-Ni)).   A microscopic study fixed the boundaries in the solid state and indicated the existence of a wide area of solid solubility stretching from pure iron to the compound NiAl.   The Curie points were also determined.

Three-dimensional views of the iron-rich portion of the system derived by Köster are given in Fig. 121.   An isothermal phase diagram for room temperatures taken from Köster's paper is given in Fig. 122 on the basis of atomic percentages.   The phases have been re-lettered in the present instance, α representing the face-centred cubic nickel-rich phase, while β denotes the body-centred cubic phase field which extends from Fe to NiAl.   The microscope could not determine the tie-line directions and it was naturally, albeit erroneously, assumed that they linked straight across the $\alpha + \beta$ two-phase field.

The whole ternary area was mapped out by Bradley and Taylor[52] using X-ray methods. In all, they required less than 150 alloys to cover the entire region apart from the alloys used in studying the three binary systems. Their final results for slowly cooled alloys are shown in Fig. 123 (a) and an enlargement of the aluminium-rich corner in Fig. 123 (b). Attention is specially

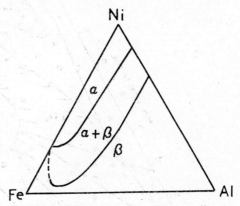

FIG. 122.—The Fe-Ni-Al equilibrium diagram according to W. KÖSTER.

Note the new nomenclature: α = face-centred cubic phase field, β = body-centred cubic phase field.

drawn to the few alloys required by the trial and error methods to establish the limits of the two- and three-phase fields and the directions of the tie-lines.

Along the Ni-Al edge there is a two-phase region which separates the α and α_1' alloys which are both face-centred cubic, but with slightly different spacings. This two-phase region narrows and finally vanishes as iron is added. The extensive α area is shown divided by a dotted line into the regions α and α_1, the latter having the same superlattice structure as α_1' in the binary Ni-Al system. The exact position of the dotted line is dependent on the heat treatment, for, as Sykes has shown, the alloy Ni_3Fe can be made to develop a completely ordered structure if the heat treatment is sufficiently prolonged.

The body-centred cubic β area which extends from pure Fe to FeAl and right across the diagram to NiAl exhibits complex superlattice variations. β is simple body-centred, like iron, with a random replacement of iron by aluminium atoms. β_1 has a superlattice based on Fe_3Al, while β_2, which stretches across the triangle including FeAl to NiAl, has the CsCl type of superlattice. The dotted boundary divides the area β_{2m} which is ferromagnetic at room temperature, from the area β_{2n}, which is not ferromagnetic.

The region shown by Köster to be $\alpha + \beta$ was discovered to be much more complicated and to consist of the four separate areas, $\alpha_1 + \beta_2$, $\alpha + \beta$, $\beta + \beta_{2m}$ and $\alpha + \beta + \beta_{2m}$. The two-phase field

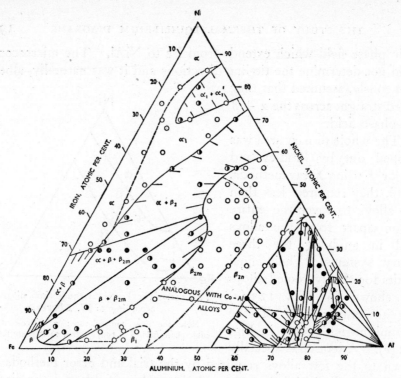

(a) The Iron-Nickel-Aluminium constitutional Diagram.

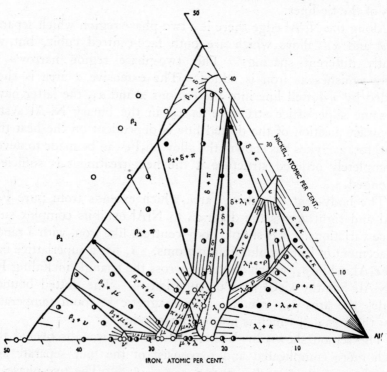

(b) The constitutional Diagram of the Aluminium-Rich Iron-Nickel-Aluminium Alloys.

FIG. 123.—The Fe-Ni-Al equilibrium Diagram for slowly-cooled Alloys.

○ Single-Phase Alloys.　◐ 2-Phase Alloys.　● 3-Phase Alloys.

(A. J. BRADLEY and A. TAYLOR, *J. Inst. Met.*, **66**, 53, 1940.)

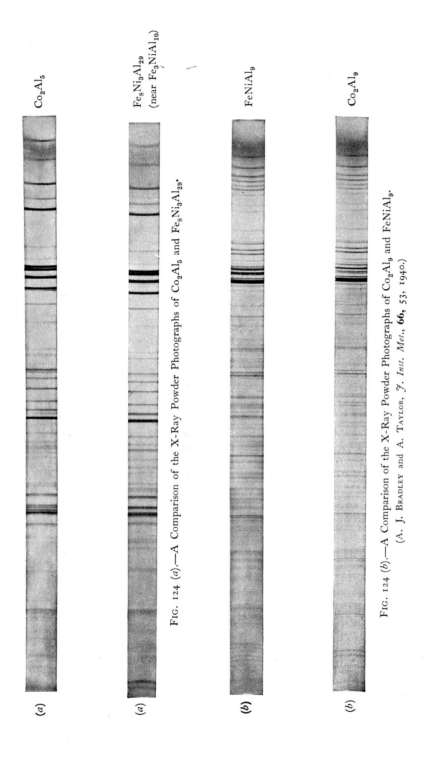

Co_2Al_5

$Fe_8Ni_3Al_{29}$
(near Fe_3NiAl_{10})

FeNiAl$_9$

Co_2Al_9

(a)

(a)

(b)

(b)

FIG. 124 (a).—A Comparison of the X-Ray Powder Photographs of Co_2Al_5 and $Fe_8Ni_3Al_{29}$.

FIG. 124 (b).—A Comparison of the X-Ray Powder Photographs of Co_2Al_9 and FeNiAl$_9$.
(A. J. BRADLEY and A. TAYLOR, *J. Inst. Met.*, **66**, 53, 1940.)

[*Facing page* 192.

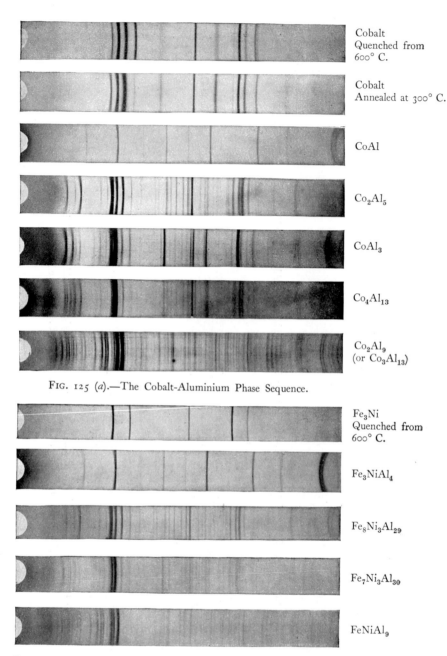

Cobalt
Quenched from
600° C.

Cobalt
Annealed at 300° C.

CoAl

Co_2Al_5

$CoAl_3$

Co_4Al_{13}

Co_2Al_9
(or Co_3Al_{13})

FIG. 125 (a).—The Cobalt-Aluminium Phase Sequence.

Fe_3Ni
Quenched from
600° C.

Fe_3NiAl_4

$Fe_8Ni_3Al_{29}$

$Fe_7Ni_3Al_{30}$

$FeNiAl_9$

FIG. 125 (b).—X-ray powder photographs of alloys on section across the Iron-Nickel-Aluminium Diagram, showing analogy with alloys of Cobalt-Aluminium System.

Compare these photographs with Fig. 124 and note the great improvement in resolution shown by the large camera.

(A. J. BRADLEY and A. TAYLOR, *J. Inst. Met.*, **66**, 52, 1940).

$\beta + \beta_{2m}$ includes all the compositions which are suitable for the manufacture of permanent magnets. Fe_2NiAl, which is indicated on the diagram, is typical. This alloy is single phase at high temperatures, but on slow cooling it breaks up into $Fe_{38}NiAl$ near pure iron and $Fe_6Ni_7Al_7$ near the centre of the diagram. We shall return to this point later, when we discuss the heat treatment required to produce an alloy with the best permanent magnet properties.

As we leave the β phase-field and approach the aluminium corner of the composition triangle, the system grows exceedingly complex. The enlargement of the area shown in Fig. 123 (b) reveals the existence of two ternary intermetallic compounds denoted by the symbols π and ρ, which, as far as the iron-nickel-aluminium system is concerned, comprise entirely new structural types. Their presence was first revealed by the appearance of extra patterns of lines which could not be reconciled with any of the powder diagrams of the binary iron-aluminium and nickel-aluminium alloys.

Once they were isolated, the π and ρ phases were found to have their counterparts in the cobalt-aluminium binary system. The π phase-field centred round Fe_3NiAl_{10} is isomorphous with Co_2Al_5 which contains 8 cobalt atoms and 20 aluminium atoms in a hexagonal unit cell.[53] Again, the ρ phase-field centred round $FeNiAl_9$ is isomorphous with the structure of Co_2Al_9. The analogies are brought out by the similarity of powder photographs in Fig. 124, taken with Co Kα radiation in a 19-cm. camera.

The dotted line in Fig. 123 (a) shows which compositions in the ternary system as a whole are most like the cobalt-aluminium alloys. A selection of powder photographs of alloys taken from the neighbourhood of this line is shown in Fig. 125 (b) for comparison with photographs of cobalt-aluminium alloys in Fig. 125 (a). Four phases are analogous, α, β_2, π, and ρ. Although there is another phase in the cobalt-aluminium system containing about the same amount of aluminium as does λ, its structure is different and the analogy can no longer be considered perfect.

The Crystal Structure of the Permanent Magnetic State.
The new iron-nickel-aluminium diagram described above removes the difficulties encountered by earlier X-ray workers on magnetic alloys. Burgers and Snoek[54] investigated the effect on the magnetic properties of cooling at different rates from 1,200° to 700° C. Their results are given in Fig. 126 which shows the coercive force H_c of an iron-nickel-aluminium alloy single crystal in relation to the time of cooling. The rapidly cooled material has a very low coercivity,

and is therefore useless as a permanent magnet. A very slowly cooled specimen gives only moderately high values of the coercive force. The best results are obtained by cooling at a definite rate. Burgers and Snoek found that the state of maximum coercivity corresponds to a condition of the specimen when the 310 reflexion begins to broaden.

The X-ray researches of Bradley and Taylor [55] carried these investigations a stage further. In Fig. 127 is shown their photographs from the same 310 reflexion, but from a powder instead of a single crystal, and after different heat treatments. Fe_2NiAl was

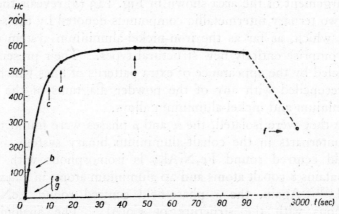

FIG. 126.—Coercive force (H_c) of a nickel-iron-aluminium single crystal in relation to the time t, required for cooling from 1,200 to 700° C.

(Reproduced by permission from *Physica*.)

quenched successively from 900°, 800°, 700° and 600° C. and finally it was slow-cooled. The powder photographs show a gradual broadening of the lines as the quenching temperature is reduced, culminating in a definite doubling of each line in the slowly cooled state.

The doubling of the lines can be understood from the phase diagram given in Fig. 123. The slowly cooled alloy consists of two constituents of slightly different lattice parameter. The X-ray patterns of the two constituents almost but not quite overlap. There are, therefore, four lines belonging to the 310 reflexion instead of the usual Kα-doublet. One pair of lines belongs to the pattern of the iron-rich constituent β, which has a lattice parameter slightly smaller than the rest of the alloy. The other pair belongs to a constituent $β_{2m}$ much richer in nickel and aluminium. The superlattice line which is present on the photograph also belongs to this constituent, and not to the iron-rich one.

Combining the evidence obtained by Burgers and Snoek with their own, Bradley and Taylor were able to picture the process which leads to the formation of the magnetically "hard" alloy. In the original high temperature state there is only one single type of lattice

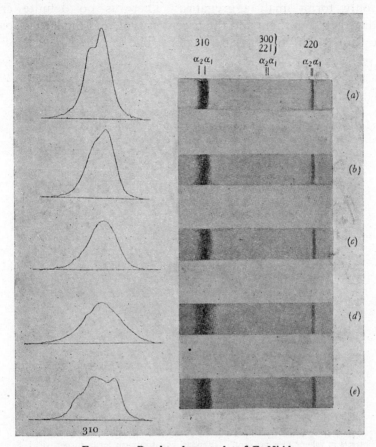

FIG. 127.—Powder photographs of Fe$_2$NiAl.

End doublets only shown. Photographs taken with CoKα radiation in 19-cm. diameter camera. Photometry carried out with manually-operated photometer of the Dobson type similar to the one illustrated in Fig. 54.

(BRADLEY and TAYLOR, *Physics in Industry-Magnetism.*)

which is body-centred cubic with a clear distinction between cube centres and cube corners. This is pictured in Fig. 128 (a). The nickel atoms are completely sorted out from the aluminium atoms, but the iron atoms are distributed at random, some replacing nickel, others replacing aluminium. In Fig. 128 (b) is shown the state of the alloy after slow cooling. The crystal has split into two portions. The smaller contains almost pure iron; the larger is very like the original lattice but contains fewer iron atoms.

In Fig. 128 (*c*) we show an intermediate state in which the coherence of the original lattice has not been lost, but the atomic distribution is no longer uniform throughout the crystal. The iron atoms have begun to separate from the rest of the atoms, but at first they only form small aggregates. There is no definite crystal boundary between them and the parent crystal, and the lattice spacing is the same as in the original state. The small "islands" of iron

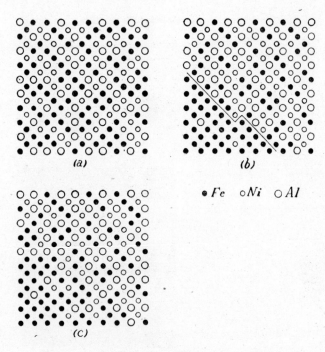

(a)   (b)

• *Fe*   o *Ni*   o *Al*

(c)

FIG. 128.—Fe₂NiAl after different heat-treatments.

(*a*) Quenched 1,200°, one crystal; Fe atoms at random.   (*b*) Slow cooled, two crystals; Fe-rich crystal contracts in volume by 1 per cent.   (*c*) Special heat-treatment for high coercivity; Fe atoms in "island"; no sharp boundary.

(BRADLEY and TAYLOR, *Physics in Industry-Magnetism.*)

cannot break away to form separate crystals once the alloy has been cooled down to room temperature.

In the permanent magnetic state the alloy has the structure represented in Fig. 128 (*c*). This state is obtained by cooling the alloy at such a rate that the "islands" have not time to grow before the material has cooled down. Being still forced to conform to the dimensions of the parent lattice, the iron atoms are held apart under a condition of immense strain. This is the cause of the remarkable magnetic properties of Fe₂NiAl.

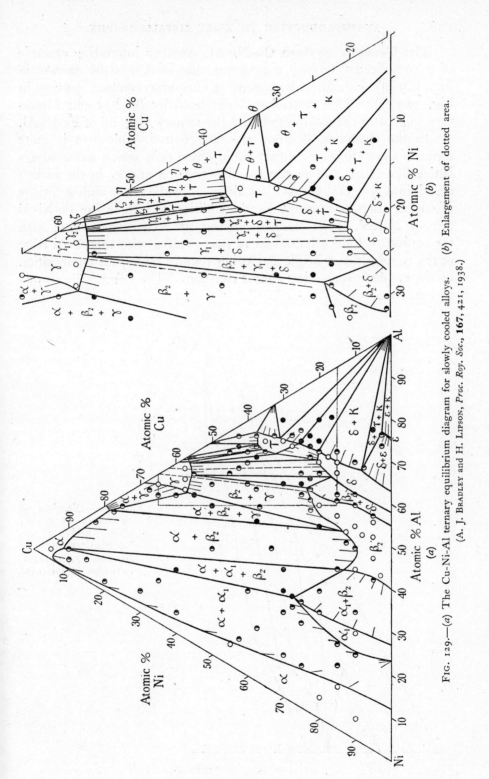

FIG. 129.—(a) The Cu–Ni–Al ternary equilibrium diagram for slowly cooled alloys. (b) Enlargement of dotted area.

(A. J. BRADLEY and H. LIPSON, *Proc. Roy. Soc.*, **167**, 421, 1938.)

The Ternary System Cu–Ni–Al. Another interesting example of a complicated ternary diagram is that of Cu–Ni–Al shown in Fig. 129 (*a*) with an enlargement of the most complex portion in Fig. 129 (*b*). This system was completed by Bradley and Lipson very soon after the establishment of the ternary diagram of Fe–Ni–Al.

In the Cu–Ni–Al diagram the face-centred cubic area is quite separate from the face-centred cubic phase field which has a super-lattice like Ni_3Al. The gap found between α and α_1 in the nickel-aluminium system does not close along a binodal curve with additions of copper such as accompanies the addition of iron in the Fe–Ni–Al ternary system. The tie-lines linking the extensive α-phase with the conjugate solid solutions in α_1 start parallel with the Ni–Al edge of the composition triangle and swing round rapidly, the composition of the α_1-phase remaining almost constant. The effect is illustrated in Fig. 130.

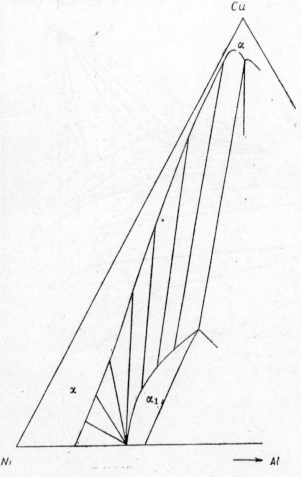

FIG. 130.—Directions of tie-lines in the $\alpha + \alpha_1$ phase field of the Cu–Ni–Al system.

(H. LIPSON, *Reports on Progress in Physics*, **6**, 361, 1939.)

The β_2-phase, which in Fe-Ni-Al extends from FeAl to NiAl, only reaches a short distance into the composition triangle of Cu-Ni-Al. In contrast, the δ phase-field is much larger. The γ-phase of the copper aluminium binary system, which in reality consists of three closely allied phase structures γ_1, γ_2 and γ_3 in rapid sequence, extends into the composition triangle to be linked with the tie-lines to the related structures β_2 and δ. There also exists a ternary intermetallic compound τ, which possesses a deformed body-centred cubic structure. The reader should note carefully the marked economy of alloys and the correct application of the rules of direction at the corners of the three-phase triangles.

Defect Lattices in Fe–Ni–Al and Cu–Ni–Al Ternary Alloys. It will be remembered how in the Ni-Al binary system the lattice parameters of the β-phase rose to a maximum at NiAl as the aluminium content was progressively increased only to decline to the accompaniment of a disproportionate fall in the densities associated with the formation of lattice defects. In Fig. 131 we show an extension of the lattice parameter measurements into the β-phase field of the ternary system Fe-Ni-Al.

At NiAl the Brillouin zone bounded by the planes {110} is just filled, so that the addition of extra electrons would be marked with the formation of a new phase, but in the Ni-Al system the increase is avoided by the omission of atoms which keeps the number of valence electrons per unit cell constant at 3·00. Although on spacial grounds we should expect copper and nickel to behave in much the same way since they have almost the same atomic radius, they do not do so because copper carries one valence electron, while nickel is effectively zero-valent. Thus in the copper-nickel-aluminium system the loss of atoms in the ternary β-phase field begins in alloys which have a maximum number of 3·0 electrons per unit cell, but since some of these electrons come from the copper atoms, the defects set in at compositions with less than 50 atomic per cent. of aluminium.

The Structure of Steel. Of all the alloys in use to-day, the steels form by far the largest and most important group. We may conveniently subdivide the steels into two main classes, the first embracing plain carbon steels, the essential constituents of which are iron and carbon. A number of minor constituents, namely silicon, manganese, sulphur, phosphorus and nickel are commonly present, which amount to approximately 1 per cent. and exert quite an appreciable effect upon the physical properties of the alloy.

Alloy steels form the second class. In them, nickel, chromium, molybdenum and tungsten are present as major additions and confer

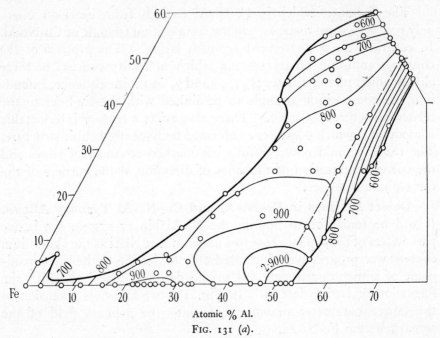

FIG. 131 (a).

Contours of constant lattice spacing in the β Fe-Ni-Al phase-field. The contours are all above 2·8 Å, and are identified by the three figures succeeding this, except in the case when the value rises above 2·9 Å. The broken line is that of electron/atom ratio = 1·50.

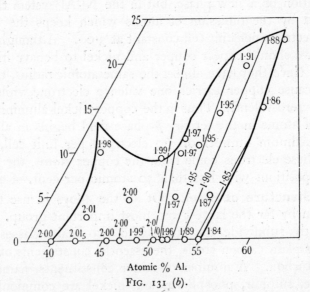

FIG. 131 (b).

Numbers of atoms per unit cell in the β Cu-Ni-Al phase-field. Approximate contours of constant number of atoms per unit cell are shown. The broken line is that of electron/atom ratio = 1·50.

FIG. 131.—Lattice parameters of Fe-Ni-Al β-phase alloys and numbers of atoms per unit cell in the β Cu-Ni-Al phase-field.

(H. LIPSON and A. TAYLOR, Proc. Roy. Soc., 173, 232, 1939.)

upon the finished alloy such properties as resistance to oxidation, or strength at high temperatures, etc.   In a sense, the term steel applied to some ferrous alloys is a definite misnomer, for the presence of carbon can be definitely harmful and rigorous steps are taken to see that it is excluded.   The permanent magnet alloys based on Fe_2NiAl are quite often erroneously referred to as "magnet steels" although their carbon content is almost zero.

The iron-carbon equilibrium diagram shown in Fig. 132 gives the key to the metallography of steel.   It is based almost entirely upon thermal and microscopic studies, but despite the vast number of intensive researches carried out during the last half-century, very

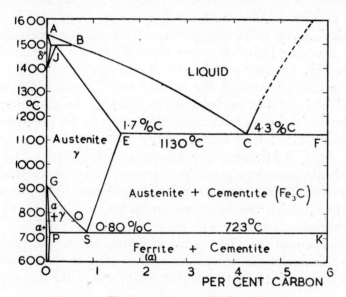

FIG. 132.—The Iron-carbon equilibrium diagram.

little is known about the system beyond 5 per cent. carbon.   The classical X-ray work of Westgren and Phragmén [56] on the structural changes in pure iron has paved the way to a deeper understanding of the crystallographic changes which take place during the various transformations that occur.

At 1,494° C., a peritectic reaction takes place between body-centred cubic δ-iron and liquid to form face-centred cubic austenite (γ-phase) with a composition of 0·07 per cent. carbon.   The austenitic region is one of considerable extent, reaching as far across the diagram as the point E at 1130° C. where a maximum of 1·7 per cent. of carbon by weight is held interstitially within the lattice, and as far down as 723° C. at the eutectoid point S at 0·80 per cent. of carbon.

At the eutectoid, on slow cooling the austenite decomposes into a two-phase mixture of almost carbon-free body-centred cubic α-iron, ferrite, and cementite, Fe_3C, which possesses a complicated orthorhombic structure. The two structures deposit side by side in fine lamellæ to give a characteristic microstructure known as "pearlite" after the mother of pearl which it so strongly resembles when illuminated by oblique illumination. Alloys in the range from 0 to 0·80 per cent. carbon break up into a mixture of ferrite and austenite on being slowly cooled below the line GS. At 723° C., the austenite, which now has the composition 0·80 per cent. carbon, immediately transforms into pearlite. The microstructure of a hypoeutectoid steel consists of an assemblage of ferrite grains set in a matrix of lamellar pearlite as shown in Fig. 133.

Typical X-ray diffraction patterns from various steels, taken in a 9-cm. diameter Debye-Scherrer camera with Co Kα radiation are shown in Fig. 134 (see also Figs. 138 and 139).

If the cooling through the *critical range* between GS and the eutectoid horizontal is carried out too quickly, the austenite, which cannot be retained even with quenching, may yet be prevented from decomposing into ferrite and cementite and made to form an intermediate, hard, brittle structure known as martensite. The highly dispersed microstructure given by martensite may be resolved under high powers into intersections of parallel straight lines as shown in Fig. 133 (*b*), which can be shown to be traces of the {111} planes of the original austenite. On tempering, martensite changes into ferrite plus cementite. The names troostite, sorbite and pearlite are given to this ferrite-cementite mixture according to the etching characteristics determined by the degree of fineness of the decomposition products.

With varied rates of cooling and suitable reheating or "tempering" temperatures, the ferrite and cementite constituents in the microstructures can be made to aggregate in several different ways with marked alterations in the physical and mechanical properties of the steel. For a full account of these changes, the reader should consult a standard work, such as *Practical Microscopical Metallography*, by Greaves and Wrighton.

The Structure of Austenite. Austenite is often referred to as a solution of cementite in γ-iron. This loose phraseology is definitely misleading, since it implies that the cementite retains its identity in the form of Fe_3C molecules within the austenite lattice. When the cementite dissolves in γ-iron, an atomic rearrangement takes place such that all the iron atoms, whether derived from the

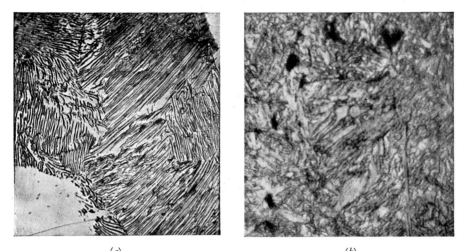

(a)   (b)

FIG. 133.—(a) Pearlite + ferrite in 0·45 C steel.   × 1000.
(b) Martensite × 2000.

(From GREAVES and WRIGHTON, *Practical Microscopical Metallography*.)

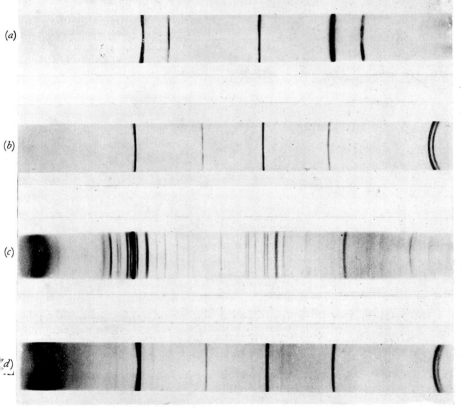

FIG. 134.—(a) Austenite face-centred cubic γ phase.   Manganese steel rod composed of large
grains.   (b) Ferrite body-centred cubic α phase in 1·0% C steel.   (c) Cementite (Fe_3C).
(d) Ferrite and Cementite.   Cf. Fig. 138.

CoKα radiation.   9-cm. Diameter Camera.

(Courtesy, Dr. A. J. BRADLEY and Miss AUDREY M. B. PARKER.)

FIG. 138.—X-ray powder photographs (19-cm. camera, *CoKα* radiation) of (*a*) pure annealed iron; (*b*) Martensite, 1·0 per cent. carbon; (*c*) Martensite heated at 350° C., showing precipitation of cementite Fe_3C .

(H. P. ROOKSBY, *Cantor Lectures*, Royal Society of Arts, 1942.)

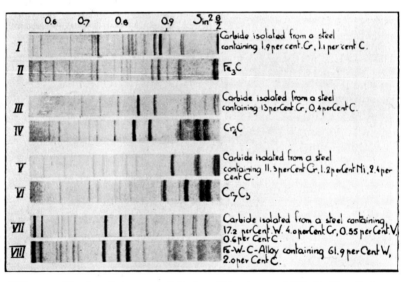

FIG. 139.—Powder photograms of Steel carbide phases. I–VI, Cr-K radiation; VII–VIII, Fe-K radiation.

(A. WESTGREN, *American Inst. Min. & Met. Eng.*, *Inst. Met. Div. B.*, 1931.)

cementite or the ferrite, now situate themselves on a face-centred lattice. The carbon atoms arrange themselves interstitially among the iron atoms but exactly where is difficult to determine by X-rays on account of the low scattering power of carbon.

N. J. Petch [57] has recently carried out a new investigation of the austenite structure by means of the powder method. Employing a very accurate photometric technique, minute changes in the intensities of the spectrum lines were found which enabled the location of the carbon atoms to be effected with a reasonable degree of certainty. They were found to lie at the centres of the unit cells and at the mid-points of the edges as illustrated in Fig. 135, these positions being the centres of the largest spaces between the iron atoms in the austenite structure.

There is never enough carbon in solution for every one of these positions to be filled. At the most, only one possible position in twelve can be occupied, since the number of carbon atoms per unit cell varies from zero for pure iron to 0·32 for a 1·7 per cent. carbon steel.

The austenite structure as determined by Petch now falls in line with the interstitial structures of TaC, CrN, etc., mentioned earlier, in which the small atoms occupy the centres of the octahedral spaces in the face-centred cubic metallic lattice.

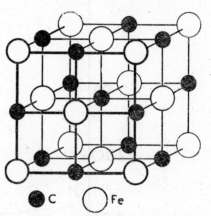

● C   ○ Fe

FIG. 135.—The crystal structure of austenite.

(N. J. PETCH, *J. Iron and Steel Inst.*)

The Formation and Decomposition of Martensite. Many X-ray investigations have shown that the martensitic constituent of hardened carbon steels is a phase with a tetragonal crystal structure which may be looked upon as a deformation of the body-centred cubic structure of α-iron. To retain the structure, it is necessary to quench the austenitic steel with a sufficiently high cooling rate. This leaves the nuclei of the newly formed martensite with insufficient time to coalesce into grains larger than 10^{-4} cm. with the consequential broadening of the X-ray reflexions which renders interpretation of the X-ray patterns very difficult unless a first-class experimental technique is employed.

Probably the most satisfactory investigations on the nature of martensite have been carried out by Kurdjumow and Kaminsky and by Öhman.[58]   The latter employed a Seemann-Bohlin focusing camera constructed by G. Phragmén which gave a much higher dispersion than the ordinary Debye-Scherrer cameras.   By employing Cr K radiation he was able to obtain a sufficiently high resolution of the spectra to enable him to compute the lattice dimensions of martensite with varying carbon content.   Öhman's results, which are in complete accord with those of Kurdjumow and Kaminsky, are illustrated in Fig. 136.   The two curves giving the axial dimensions of the tetragonal unit cell as a function of carbon content converge to a point corresponding to the cell edge of the elementary cube of

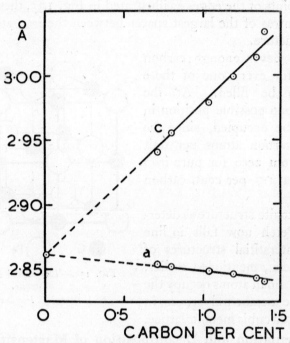

Fig. 136.—Lattice dimensions of the tetragonal martensite phase as functions of the carbon content.

pure α-iron.   This may be taken as conclusive evidence in favour of the belief that tetragonal martensite is a metastable super-saturated solution of carbon in α-iron, and we may therefore consider ferrite and martensite to be one and the same phase.

    Hägg has shown that when tetragonal martensite is annealed, its carbon content diminishes, causing a decrease in the lattice parameters.   According to this work, the cubic variety, β-martensite, accepted by Honda, is more probably tetragonal martensite in which the deviation from cubic symmetry is not observable owing to its low carbon content and diffuse X-ray reflexions.

The position of the carbon atoms in martensite has been the subject of a considerable amount of work. The suggestion has been made that the carbon atoms are situated at random in the interstices between the iron atoms. Based on careful density measurements, Öhman has concluded that a complex substitution occurs, in which a group of two carbon atoms is substituted for one iron atom of the parent lattice. This view is not substantiated by the recent findings of Lipson and Parker [58a]. These workers have shown that the iron atoms in the tetragonal lattice suffer small random displacements of about 0.18 Å in the direction of the c-axis The octahedral interstices between the iron atoms are thereby sufficiently enlarged to accommodate the carbon atoms.

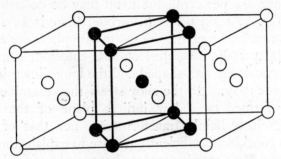

FIG. 137.—Bain's γ-α transformation in steel.

Two adjacent unit cells of the face-centred cubic γ-phase are shown with an alternative body-centred tetragonal unit cell heavily outlined. The α-phase is supposed to be formed by a compression along the tetragonal axis. The carbon atoms are not shown but would be present in interstitial solid solution.

The mechanism of the $\gamma \rightarrow \alpha$ transformation has been described in various ways. Bain has pointed out that the face-centred cubic structure might be considered as a body-centred tetragonal structure with the axial ratio 1·414, as may be seen from Fig. 137. The transformation would then consist in changing this axial ratio from 1·414 to unity by compressing the tetragonal axis. Though very simple to understand, it must be realized that it involves an enormous deformation of the face-centred cubic lattice.

Kurdjumow and Sachs have shown how the transformation from γ to α may be conceived to take place by a series of simple local displacements of the atoms which achieve the same final result as Bain's method but which at the same time involve a much greater economy of movement. They considered tetragonal martensite to constitute an intermediate stage in the transformation. The α-iron crystallites as well as the martensitic needles were found to be oriented in a regular way in relation to the crystal planes of the original austenite. The (101) planes of ferrite or martensite were shown to form upon the (111) planes of austenite in such a way that the [111] direction of the derived structure lay parallel to [101] of the original austenite lattice, that is, the most closely packed planes and rows of the two lattices took the same orientation.   These findings were later substantiated by the microscopic work of Mehl, Barrett and Smith on the formation of the Widmannstätten structure in steel (page 294).

In a detailed study of the austenite decomposition, A. B. Greninger and A. R. Troiano [59] have found that in a 0·35 per cent. carbon steel, the martensite crystals are needle-shaped and these crystals form a plate-like array delineating the (111) planes of austenite.   This agrees with the previous workers.   On the other hand, the precipitation is much more complex at higher carbon contents.   For carbon contents above 1·4 per cent., the habit may be described as parallel to {4 10 18}γ.   At 1·4 per cent. carbon, there is an abrupt change and for lower carbon contents the martensite plates are approximately parallel to {4 4 10}γ.   In steel of near-eutectoid composition, the martensite crystals are lath-shaped and the long dimension of the lath is parallel to ⟨110⟩γ.   In the alloy steels they examined, martensite plates *never* formed on a low indices plane of the decomposing austenite.   Neither Bain's transformation nor that of Kurdjumow and Sachs is considered sufficiently precise to explain these new facts.

In Fig. 138 * are shown powder photographs of ferrite, martensite with 1·0 per cent. carbon, and of the same martensite annealed at 350° C. showing the precipitation of cementite, Fe_3C.   The growth in crystal dimensions of the relieved ferrite lattice in (c) is shown by the remarkable sharpness of the end-doublets which are so broad as to be almost invisible in (b).

The Structure of Cementite Fe_3C.   Recent work by Lipson and Petch [60] has verified the structure of Fe_3C proposed by Westgren. The structure is orthorhombic, the dimensions of the unit cell being

$$a = 4 \cdot 5144 \text{ Å}$$
$$b = 5 \cdot 0787 \text{ Å}$$
$$c = 6 \cdot 7297 \text{ Å}.$$

These workers noticed that annealing cementite at 600° C. or higher always resulted in partial decomposition mostly into ferrite, but sometimes into another structure which was probably Fe_2C.   The existence of Fe_2C, which has been the subject of a great deal of controversy, must therefore still be regarded as an open question, and much more work is required to clarify this region of the iron carbon diagram.

* Figs. 138, 139 face page 203.

In order to obtain carbide samples in sufficient concentration from ferrous alloys, Westgren [61] uses a method of partial dissolution in acids, and thereby retains the larger proportion of the less soluble carbides. Some of Westgren's Seemann-Bohlin powder diagrams of carbide powders isolated from certain steels are given in Fig. 139.

A comparison of these photographs with patterns of known carbides, also shown in Fig. 139,* made it possible to determine the exact character of the carbide phases present in the steels. For example, the carbide of a ball-bearing steel containing 1·1 per cent. C, 1·9 per cent. Cr, is cementite. From the displacement of the high order lines, it could be inferred that the iron atoms had been partly substituted by chromium atoms.

The carbide phase of the stainless steel with 13 per cent. Cr, 0·4 per cent. C consists of a cubic chromium carbide, Cr_4C, in which approximately one-third of the chromium atoms have been replaced by iron. It was also proved that a steel containing about 11 per cent. Cr, 1·2 per cent. Ni and 2·4 per cent. C contained a rhombo-hedral carbide Cr_7C_3 in which more than one-half the chromium content was replaced by iron. The residue method used on a high-speed steel gave the same photograph as an iron-tungsten-carbon alloy, the composition of which corresponds closely to the formula Fe_4W_2C.

This residue method of Westgren should prove of inestimable value for artificially concentrating the amounts of phases which normally can only be obtained in minute quantities. It has the advantage of producing the substance in a form admirably suited to the technique of powder photography, and, according to Westgren, it can be applied with success to alloys other than steel.

CHAPTER IX

THE MEASUREMENT OF GRAIN SIZE

The Importance of Grain Size.* Single crystals of metals, being anisotropic, behave quite differently from polycrystalline aggregates. They are extraordinarily weak and plastic, suffering permanent distortion under the influence of relatively minute shearing forces. Deformation takes place by whole sections or "glide lamellæ" of the crystal slipping *en masse* along certain crystallographic planes in preferred lattice directions, a process often referred to as "block slip". In a single crystal of copper, a favourably oriented stress of as little as 150 grams/mm.^{2} is sufficient to cause permanent set. Once the crystal has been extended in tension by 50 per cent., its mechanical strength is found to have increased almost fifty-fold owing to the strain hardening effects set up within the crystal lattice. The hardening influence of impurities and of alloying constituents is also very marked. For example, single crystals of impure cadmium containing 0·11 per cent. lead and 0·03 per cent. zinc have double the critical shear stress of the spectroscopically pure variety.

In a polycrystalline metal, some crystals will be oriented in a direction favourable to the inception of slip, since for them the direction of the maximum resolved shear stress upon the block will be in a lattice direction of "easy glide". However, the glide processes are considerably hampered by less favourably oriented neighbours which function as constraints upon the edges of the glide lamellæ. As the bulk of metal is deformed as, for example, by rolling or drawing, the crystals gradually move into preferred directions, in the process of which they receive a certain amount of permanent distortion in the form of lattice curvature, or as fragmentation into still smaller crystals. In addition, the orientation texture set up by the deformation process gives the material a marked anisotropy in its physical and mechanical properties.

The physical and mechanical properties, then, clearly depend on a number of factors. If for the moment we restrict ourselves to homogeneous single-phase material of prescribed composition, we shall avoid the complications caused by the presence and manner of distribution of a second constituent. Assuming the material to

* In this chapter, the terms "grain size" and "crystal size" have the same general meaning. A crystallite is a very small crystal.

have been freed from residual stresses by a suitable annealing process, the two most important factors which control the working properties are grain size and grain orientation. These two factors go hand in hand, but for the purpose of discussion it will be more convenient to treat them as quite separate entities.

As the grain size diminishes, there is a corresponding increase in tensile strength as exemplified by the work of Edwards and Pfeil [62] on pure iron. Their results are reproduced in Table XII.

TABLE XII

THE EFFECT OF GRAIN SIZE ON THE ULTIMATE TENSILE STRENGTH OF PURE IRON

Grain Size (Grains per sq. mm.)	Ultimate Tensile Strength (Tons per sq. inch)
Single crystal	10
0·15	11·70
0·4	13·66
6·3	15·03
15·3	16·33
35·6	17·05
48·8	17·10
51	17·37
75	18·73
92	17·97
130	18·56
194	18·69

We also obtain a parallel increase in the hardness of the metal, which the results of Ishigaki [63] given in Table XIII reveal. This parallelism is not surprising, for the tensile test and the standard methods of measuring hardness in terms of resistance to indentation refer to indefinable properties based on the work-hardening characteristics of the aggregate material.

TABLE XIII

THE EFFECT OF GRAIN SIZE ON THE BRINELL HARDNESS OF PURE IRON

Grain Size (Grains per sq. mm.)	Brinell Hardness
Single crystal	65
0·5	70
2·5	77
33	86
111	90
641	93
1,245	98
1,855	100

Grain size exerts a considerable influence upon the texture of cold-rolled steel during the earlier stages of the rolling treatment, for the smaller the initial crystals, the less cold work is required to

H

produce a "fibred" structure.   According to J. D. Jevons,[64] the deep
drawing and pressing properties of sheet in a given metal are determined primarily by crystal size.   An increase in grain size causes
an increase in ductility, a decrease in yield stress, hardness and rate of
work hardening, but it also causes an increase in the roughness of
the surface of the finished pressing.   The converse holds equally true.

Grain size is dependent on the composition and on the thermal
and mechanical histories of the metal.   In slowly cooled billets, the
individual grains may be so large as to be readily distinguished with
the naked eye, whereas in heat-treated steels, they may be so small
as to elude resolution by a powerful microscope.

The Measurement of Grain Size—Optical Methods.
Before we attempt to study X-ray methods of measuring crystal sizes,
it will be necessary as a basis of comparison to review some of the
more important standard metallurgical methods.   It has long been
known that excessive brittleness in a hardened piece of steel is accompanied by a fracture, which, to the naked eye, reveals the facets of
coarse crystals, while an equally hardened piece exhibiting great
toughness reveals a fracture which is fine and silky.   The microscopical methods of grain size measurement are more refined.   A
polished and etched specimen of the metal reveals, under the microscope, a boundary network outlining the crystal grains.   The pattern
is usually compared, under standard conditions, with a series of
graded standardized networks which may consist of typical photomicrographs or idealized patterns.   The microscope, in effect, sub-
stitutes a grain size based on grain cross-section for one expressive of
grain volume.

In a polished section we observe a plane taken at random through
an assemblage of solid crystals.   Such a plane will reveal a network
consisting of sections of grains ranging in size from zero up to the
maximum cross-sectional area of any grain in that plane.   We thus
obtain a *range* of areas even when all the grain volumes are, in reality,
substantially equal.   Unless great care is taken in the appraisal of
the apparent grain sizes seen in the plane of section, the tendency
will be to infer the presence of a larger proportion of smaller sizes
than is actually the case.   The actual grain size will, in general, be
much more uniform than the grain areas observed, a fact which has
been verified by disintegrating specimens of brass and stainless steel
by intercrystalline corrosion.

Grain size with reference to a plane section through the polycrystalline aggregate is reported in a number of ways, the more
common methods being

(a) Mean diameter of grain in millimetres by an intercept method.

(b) Number of grains per square millimetre.

(c) Average area of grains in square millimetres.

(d) J.K.M. "leading" grain size classification.

(e) Arbitrary numbers based upon an exponential formula adopted by the American Society for Testing Materials.

The mean grain diameter is a figure not easily arrived at and is in any case much less informative than a scheme based upon the number of grains per unit area, such as, for example, the A.S.T.M. standards. Its use is therefore to be discouraged.

Berglund, Hultgren and Phragmén [65] use a standard grain size series known in Sweden as the J.K.M. grain classification. This is defined on the basis of a grain section area, where the terms form a geometric series with common ratio 2, as shown below:

J.K.M. Grain Class No.	0	1	2	3	4	5	6	7	8
Grain Section area μ^2.		1	2	4	8	16	32	64	128	256
9	10	11	12	13...					
512	1024	2048	4096	8192...					

Using the J.K.M. classification as a basis, they then examine a given microsection and plot a statistical curve, the total of grains within a given class number as ordinate, plotted against the class number as abscissa. For ordinary structures such distribution curves have a distinct maximum at a certain J.K.M. grain size which is termed the "leading grain size". This is considered to be more characteristic of the structure than a simple average grain size, since it approximates more closely to the larger grains present, which are believed to be of greater importance for the usefulness of the material. Furthermore, the determination of the leading grain size of a structure is not subject to error from neglecting the smallest grains.

A series of standard J.K.M. grain-size charts has been established on the basis of an actual microstructure, each member of the series having a leading grain size conforming to one of the J.K.M. grain classes at a magnification of 100 ×. The microstructure of the specimen under examination is projected up to 100 × upon a screen, and compared directly with the various J.K.M. grain-size charts until a match is obtained with a chart bearing the required leading grain-size number.

The A.S.T.M. adopt a somewhat similar procedure based upon the formula

$$n = 2^{N-1}$$

where n is the number of grains per square *inch* when viewed at a magnification of 100 ×, and N is the grain-size number. A series of standard charts based upon a real structure at 100 × is compared directly with the microstructure, thereby yielding the A.S.T.M. grain-size index without the need for further calculation.

Practically all American specifications and reports of grain size are referred to the A.S.T.M. index numbers. Two sets of charts have been constructed. One set has been developed for use in conjunction with the McQuaid-Ehn test for determining the austenitic grain size of steel, a factor which exerts a considerable influence upon the mechanical properties of the metal. A second set of charts, giving the mean diameter of grains, has been constructed for use

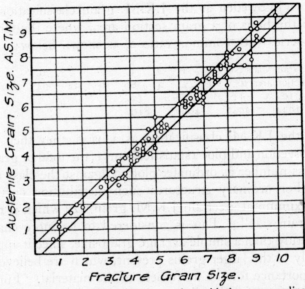

Fig. 141.—Comparison of A.S.T.M. grain-size numbers with the corresponding fracture rating for a range of austenitic grain size. Note close agreement in numbers.
(E. C. BAIN, *Journ. Iron and Steel Inst.*, 1938.)

mainly with non-ferrous materials. Both types of chart, reproduced from the American specifications, are given in Fig. 140 (*a*) and (*b*).*
It will be seen that the orientations of the grains in the charts are perfectly random, that is, the grains are "equiaxed". The microsections represent ideal types, and any marked deviations from them must be considered abnormal. Thus the elongation of grains produced by rolling or drawing is not covered by the charts, nor is the presence of abnormal clusters of small or large grains taken into consideration. These factors must be taken into account in appraising the mechanical properties of the material, for elongated grains will

* Figs 140 (*a*) and (*b*) will be found in the pocket inside the back cover of this book.

tend to make the metal anisotropic, while clusters of small grains may seriously reduce its ductility.

Fracture grain size can be estimated with a remarkably high degree of accuracy with the naked eye. A ten-step standard scale of fracture grain size has been adopted in Sweden by Jernkontoret, and a similar set of standards has been developed by Shepherd in America. McQuaid and Ehn found that the austenitic grain-size designations 1 to 8 inclusive were almost identical with the fracture numbers as applied to correspondingly quenched steels. The exactness of the correlation taken from a paper by Bain [66] is strikingly brought out in Fig. 141.

As it is valuable to have a numerical comparison of various methods of grain-size determination, Table XIV, originally obtained by Rutherford, Aborn and Bain,[67] is included. Its derivation requires some explanation. From theoretical considerations, supported by much experimental observation, the most probable shape of a grain

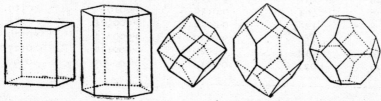

Fig. 142.—Parallelehedra of Von Fedorow. The six regular solids, repetition of which will fill all space. Cube, hexagonal prism, rhombic dodecahedron, elongated dodecahedron, tetrakaidekahedron.

in an equiaxed polycrystalline aggregate is the 14-faced solid figure, the tetrakaidekahedron. This figure is outlined by the forms $\{111\}$ and $\{100\}$ of a cube, and represents one of the five regular solids, any of which with mere duplication can completely fill space, the others being the 6-sided cube, the 8-sided hexagonal prism, the 12-sided rhombic dodecahedron and the 12-sided elongated dodecahedron, illustrated in Fig. 142.

The metal is supposed to be made up of tetrakaidekahedra, and all grain sectional areas, surface areas and grain volumes in Table XIV are computed upon this basis.

X-ray Determination of Grain Size in the Microscopic Range. Visual Estimation Method. In X-ray work of this nature, it is most convenient, though not absolutely essential, to work with filtered $K\alpha$ radiation emitted by a suitable target. This means that we have present a strong $K\alpha$ component superimposed upon a relatively weak background of white radiation. When such a beam falls upon a large stationary single crystal, the white radiation will give

IDEAL RELATION BETWEEN GRAIN SIZE AND AVERAGE NUMBER, DIAMETER, CROSS-
calculated on Basis of the 14-Faced

I	II	III	IV	V
		Mean Area of Cross-Section of a Grain.		Diameter of Cross-Section of Equivalent Spherical Grain, mm.
A.S.T.M. Grain-Size Number N	Mean Number of Grains per sq. in. as viewed at 100 × $n = 2^{N-1}$	As viewed at 100 × sq. in. $A' = 1/n$	True Size sq. mm. $A = 0 \cdot 0645 A'$	d
— 1	0·25	4	0·258	0·574
0	0·5	2	0·129	0·406
1	1	1	0·0645	0·287
2	2	0·5	0·0323	0·203
3	4	0·25	0·0161	0·144
4	8	0·125	0·00806	0·101
5	16	0·0625	0·00403	0·0718
6	32	0·0313	0·00202	0·0507
7	64	0·0156	0·00101	0·0359
8	128	0·0078	0·000504	0·0254
9	256	0·0039	0·000252	0·0179
10	512	0·0020	0·000126	0·0127
11	1,024	0·0010	0·000063	0·0090

Notes to

Column IV. In German usage, this area is expressed in terms of μ^2, where $\mu = 0 \cdot 001$ mm.; to transform to German units, the numbers given in this column have to be multiplied by 1,000,000.

Column V. $d = \sqrt{\dfrac{4A}{\pi}} = \sqrt{\dfrac{4}{\pi} \cdot \dfrac{0 \cdot 0645}{n}}$. This column is in terms of the units commonly used for non-ferrous metals.

rise to a pattern of Laue spots, but the monochromatic component will not be reflected unless the Bragg condition is satisfied by one or other sets of lattice planes within the crystal. If we now imagine the single crystal to be replaced by a cluster of much smaller randomly oriented crystals, each little crystal will give rise to its own Laue pattern, and according to the laws of probability a few will be oriented in a position to reflect the monochromatic component. We therefore obtain a set of broken, spotty Debye-Scherrer rings superimposed upon a confused background of discrete Laue spots. Finally, when the crystals become small enough, we reach a stage in which the background becomes continuous and the spots on the Debye-Scherrer circles merge into each other to produce perfectly smooth, continuous diffraction haloes. This stage is reached when the crystal size

XIV

SECTIONAL AREA OF GRAINS, AND TOTAL INTERFACIAL AREA (Columns VI–IX are Solid of Minimum Surface Area).

VI	VII	VIII	IX
Mean number of Grains per		Mean Total Interfacial Area	
cu. in. m'	cu. mm. m	sq. in. per cubic inch S'	sq. mm. per cubic mm. S
92,100	5·6	125	4·7
261,000	15·9	170	6·7
739,000	45·1	240	9·5
2,090,000	128	340	13·4
5,910,000	360	480	18·9
16,700,000	1,020	679	26·7
47,300,000	2,880	961	37·8
134,000,000	8,160	1,360	53·4
378,000,000	23,000	1,920	75·6
1,070,000,000	65,300	2,720	107
3,030,000,000	184,000	3,840	151
8,560,000,000	522,000	5,430	214
24,200,000,000	1,470,000	7,690	302

Table:

Column VI. $m' = \dfrac{1}{8\sqrt{2}\,l^3}$ where l is length in inches of edge of any of the 14 faces; the

volume of the solid is $8\sqrt{2}\,l^3$. Its maximum cross-section area is $7l^2$, or $\dfrac{1·7}{10,000n}$ when

expressed in sq. in.; its surface area is $l^2(6 + 12\sqrt{3})$.

becomes of the order of 10^{-4} cm. An excellent example of this progressive change is given by H. P. Rooksby [68] for powdered quartz, but precisely the same type of sequence will apply to metal in sheet or powder form (Fig. 143).

When an attempt is made to put the grain-size measurement upon an exact, quantitative basis, certain precautions must be observed if the results are to have any real meaning. In the first place, if sheet is being examined, it is necessary for the grains to be equiaxed and not preferentially oriented in a given direction, so that the discrete spots do not overlap in favoured portions of the Debye-Scherrer rings. Secondly, it is important to realize that if transmission photographs are taken, the section on which the X-ray sizes are to be referred is not necessarily the plane of the specimen. This is brought out in

Fig. 144, from which it is clear that any comparisons of grain size made by microscopic methods must be referred to the section AB, and not to the section CD.

With these points in mind, it is possible to build up a picture gallery of transmission and back reflexion photographs from a series of carefully annealed standard specimens graded according to the A.S.T.M. or J.K.M. charts and these may be used for direct visual comparison with the test samples photographed under *identical* conditions of camera and specimen geometry and of exposure period. Once this set of standards has been established, it is a relatively simple matter to establish the grain size index of the test piece. Care must be taken to have a sufficiently large pinhole system

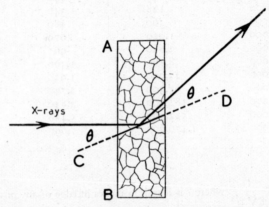

FIG. 144.—Distinction between plane of section *AB* viewed under the microscope and plane of X-ray reflexion *CD* to which X-ray grain-size measurement must be referred.

in the camera to enable an adequate number of grains to be irradiated.

One of the advantages of the X-ray method lies in not having to prepare a highly polished surface of the specimen. The microscope will detect only the grain boundary envelopes of the individual grains. Unlike the X-ray method, it will reveal nothing about the internal stresses which may still be present in the crystal lattice, nor will it reveal any fragmentation of the individual crystal grains into still smaller crystallites. In the latter case, the grain size observed by the microscope would be several times larger than the true value portrayed by the X-ray method.

Method Employing the Measurement of Spot Dimensions. Instead of taking the appearance of the diffraction pattern as a basis of visual comparison, we may note that as the crystal grains get larger, the sizes and the intensities of the individual spots also increase.

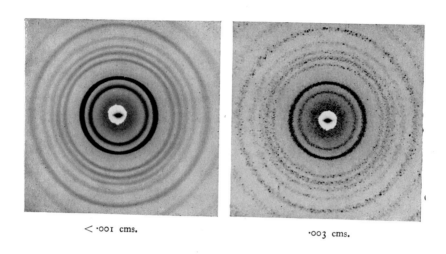

$< \cdot 001$ cms. $\cdot 003$ cms.

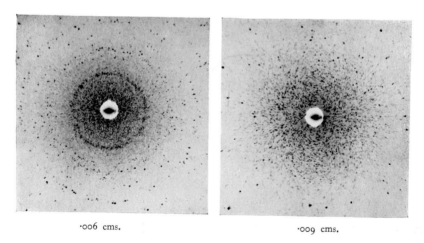

$\cdot 006$ cms. $\cdot 009$ cms.

FIG. 143.—X-ray patterns of powdered quartz crystals of different ultimate particle sizes.
(H. P. ROOKSBY, *Cantor Lectures*, Royal Society of Arts.)

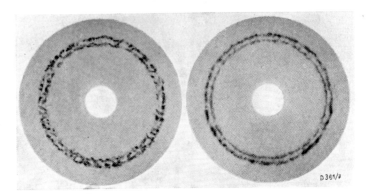

FIG. 146.—(*a*) Back reflexion.

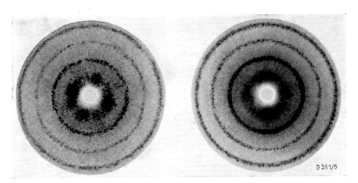

FIG. 146.—(*b*) Transmission patterns from two steels with different rolling and heat treatments. Note the similarity between the back reflexion patterns while the transmission patterns reveal differences of texture in the interior.

(*Courtesy, Philips Industrial.*)

Each crystal acts like a little mirror which reflects the X-ray beam diverging from the target on to the photographic film. The shape and size of the recorded spots will be a function of the dimensions of the reflecting crystal, the divergence of the X-ray beam and the angle at which the reflected beam strikes the film. The researches of Bass [69] have revealed a strictly linear relation between the microscopically measured diameters of grains in the 10–100μ range with the vertical diameters of the X-ray reflexions measured by the aid of a scale under a magnification of 10 ×. The work has been con

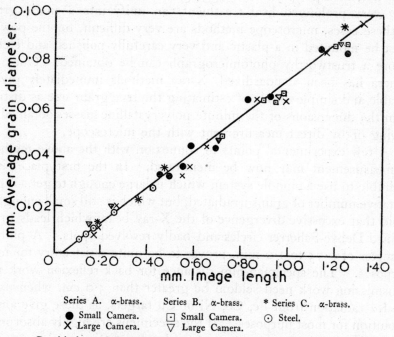

Series A. α-brass.   Series B. α-brass.   * Series C. α-brass.
● Small Camera.   ⊡ Small Camera.   ⊙ Steel.
X Large Camera.   ▽ Large Camera.

FIG. 145.—Graphical correlation between image lengths of X-ray diffraction interferences and average grain diameters in microscopic range.

(After CLARK and ZIMMER.)

siderably extended by Clark and Zimmer [70] using brass samples from which the standard A.S.T.M. non-ferrous photomicrographs were prepared. They obtained the straight-line plot of Fig. 145. The relationship must be universal, for they found that the results of two other series of brass samples, steel, carborundum, silica, etc., all lay on the same curve. It will be noted that it is immaterial whether a large or a small camera is used, provided that each is properly calibrated with a set of A.S.T.M. standards.

Although Clark and Zimmer have used the "mean grain diameter" as a standard of reference, the results could have been expressed equally well in terms of leading grain size or in terms of A.S.T.M. index number.

The method of measuring the sizes of the spots is admirably suited to the investigation of powder compacts for it does not depend upon the packing density of the material, a factor which must be taken into account in any method based on visual appraisal of the pattern as a whole.   It is particularly useful in this instance, for the individual fragments of a powdered metal consist, more frequently than not, of a polycrystalline aggregate of still smaller grains which only very prolonged heat treatment can unify into a single grain. In these cases, microscope methods are very difficult, for the powder must be mounted in a plastic and very carefully polished and etched before a trustworthy photomicrograph can be obtained.   Once the camera has been standardized, X-ray methods immediately give a reliable and simple means of estimating the true grain size as distinct from the dimensions of the minute polycrystalline masses obtained by sieving or by direct measurement with the microscope.

A few experimental points in connexion with the above methods of measurement may now be mentioned.   In the first place, it is desirable to use a pinhole system which is large enough to get a representative number of grains irradiated, but which is still small enough to avoid that excessive divergence of the X-ray beam which leads to ill-defined Debye-Scherrer circles and badly resolved spots.   A pinhole diameter of 0·75 to 1·0 mm. proves to be quite satisfactory for most purposes.   The specimen-film distance for back-reflexion work and transmission work need seldom be greater than 5·0 cm. when using the Kα radiation from Fe, Co, Ni or Cu targets, as these give ample resolution for most purposes.   If the specimens are highly absorptive, it may be necessary to go over to a hard radiation such as Ag or Mo Kα for transmission work on sheet in order to bring the exposure time down to reasonable limits.   To offset the much smaller angles of diffraction in the lower orders which results from the use of Ag or Mo radiation, the film-specimen distance may be increased to 10 cm. or more without unduly increasing the exposure time.

When examining a specimen, it is most important to use transmission methods conjointly with the back-reflexion technique, for the former yields information concerning the internal state of the metal, while the latter only gives the condition of the irradiated surface to a depth of a few thousand atoms.   As an example, we illustrate two samples of steel examined by transmission and back-reflexion methods, in Fig. 146.   While the condition of the surfaces of both samples are substantially the same, the interiors exhibit marked differences in texture initiated by different methods of preparation.

If the specimen is in the form of a block, the transmission technique is of course quite impracticable. Resort must then be made to etching away successive layers of the surface or to facing it up on a lathe, taking back-reflexion photographs at convenient stages. The use of a diamond cutting tool to take off the bulk of the surface layers before finally etching is recommended, as it cleaves through the material without appreciably distorting the layers of metal below. Care must be taken to avoid undue heating, as this may have profound effects upon the texture of the metal.

Methods Dependent on Counting Reflexion Spots. In a specimen consisting of a large number of randomly oriented crystals

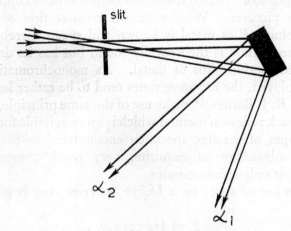

FIG. 147.—Illustrating how excessive divergence of incident beam produces two reflexions from one small crystal. Not to scale.

irradiated by a fine pencil of monochromatic X-rays, there will always be a definite fraction oriented to give a particular hkl reflexion in accordance with the Bragg Law. In general, each crystal will give rise to one spot upon the film, either from an α_1 or an α_2 reflexion. It is possible to record the α-doublet simultaneously from one grain if the divergence of the primary beam is large enough, as shown in Fig. 147. By using a small sharp focus in the tube and small pinholes in a long slit system, the divergence can be cut down and the difficulty overcome. Diffracted beams incident at large angles to flat film record *two* spots out of alignment, since both sides of the film are coated with emulsion and due allowance must be made for this effect.

By counting the number of spots upon a Debye-Scherrer ring, we determine the number of grains oriented in a position to give the

particular *hkl* reflexion.   Following the lines of Chapter VI, we find
that if there are v crystals in the beam, the total number of spots
recorded in the halo must be equal to $\Upsilon = \frac{1}{2}vp \cos\theta\,d\theta$ where p is
the number of planes with the form $\{hkl\}$ and $\frac{1}{2}\cos\theta.d\theta$ is the probability that a particular crystal will reflect, $d\theta$ being the divergence
of the beam calculated from the dimensions of the slit system and its
distance from the specimen.   Since p, $\cos\theta$ and $d\theta$ are all known, it
should be possible, in principle at least, to calculate back from the
number of observed spots Υ, and obtain the total number of crystals
in an irradiated volume of metal V, and hence the volume v of a single
grain.   In practice it is not as simple as this, for various difficulties
arise owing to the finite size of tube focus and the dimensions of the
slit system.

H. S. Schdanow [71] used specimens of thin slips of copper and took
transmission pictures.   With a known cross-section of beam, the
irradiated volume V of metal is known and v can thereby be determined.   The method is theoretically sound but has its drawbacks in
being limited to thin slips of metal.   As monochromatic radiation
must be employed, the exposure times tend to be rather long.   R. A.
Stephen and R. J. Barnes [72] make use of the same principle, employing
instead the back reflexion method which is more suitable for examining
the usual types of massive specimen encountered in practice, with
the added advantage of requiring very much shorter exposure
periods lasting only a few minutes.

The number of spots on a Debye-Scherrer ring is given by the
expression

$$\Upsilon = \tfrac{1}{2}vp \cos\theta.d\theta$$

and since the volume v of 1 grain will be $\dfrac{V}{v}$, it follows that

$$v = \frac{Vp \cos\theta}{2\Upsilon}d\theta.$$

Assuming that the grains are roughly cubic in shape, the mean length
of the grain edge G is given by

$$G = \sqrt[3]{\frac{Vp \cos\theta.d\theta}{2\Upsilon}}.$$

The irradiated volume V cannot be known directly as it depends on
the maximum depth d to which the X-ray beam can penetrate and
then re-emerge from the surface to produce a visible record on the
film.   Stephen and Barnes overcome this difficulty in a most in-
genious way by taking *two* exposures, the first one being so short
that only the surface crystals with the strongest reflexions produce

spots of medium blackening B. The photograph is then repeated with a much longer exposure time which enables crystals in the interior of the specimen to record their reflexions. The two photographs are then compared and the number of spots having an intensity greater than B in the second photograph is counted. This number bears a definite relation to the exposure periods, and to the effective depth of penetration, d, from which the irradiated volume, V, and hence the mean grain size, G, is derived.

As an alternative to the double exposure method, Stephen and Barnes employ an empirical relationship between the numbers of spots on photographs taken under standard conditions and the grain sizes for a given series of standard specimens. They express this relationship in the form of a graph from which the grain size of an unknown specimen can be read after observing the number of spots on a photograph taken under these standard conditions. Graphs relating the total number of observable spots to grain size for a series of aluminium specimens are given in Fig. 148. The 331 reflexion given by Co Kα radiation emitted by a sharp focus Philips Metalix tube was observed. Curve (1) shows the number of spots plotted against crystal size determined by the microscope while in curve (2) it is plotted against the crystal size determined by X-rays. The method is not very sensitive for grain sizes much larger than $5 \cdot 10^{-3}$ cm. but in the useful region down to 10^{-3} cm. results to within 10 per cent. are claimed.

It will again be noticed that the results are given in terms of crystal diameter. It would have been preferable to have given them in terms of crystals per square millimetre or as A.S.T.M. ratings. Nevertheless the above methods show great promise and the technique, though still in its early stages of development, is capable of yielding results with an acceptable degree of accuracy.

Effect of Twinning. When a metal is strained, slip processes may take place in the lattice and produce a slight reshuffle of the atoms (Chapter X). What were formerly single crystals now become two (or more) with quite different orientations, the lattice of one having a definite symmetry orientation with respect to the other. Such "twins" must be regarded as separate grains as far as X-ray investigation is concerned, for in taking a Debye-Scherrer photograph each twin will record its reflexion spot in an entirely different region of the diffraction ring. In other words, a metal which is heavily twinned behaves, radiographically, as if it were composed of much smaller grains.

An examination of the A.S.T.M. charts for non-ferrous materials (brass) reveals black streaks running across the individual grains.

Each streak is the trace of a twin whose presence in the original grain is exposed by its different etching characteristics on the plane of section. In the A.S.T.M. specifications, the twins are *not considered as separate entities*, but are counted as part of the original grain from which they are generated. This is quite wrong from a strictly crystallographic point of view and the application of an X-ray method based on

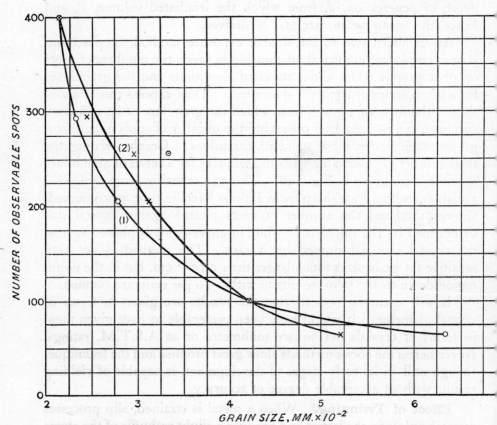

FIG. 148.—Chart relating number of observable diffraction spots with grain size.

(R. A. STEPHEN and R. J. BARNES, *Journ. Inst. of Metals*, **60**, 285, 1937.)

counting the number of X-ray reflexions will inevitably give a grain size much smaller than the standard A.S.T.M. rating. Due emphasis must be laid on this fact when correlating grain-size measurements with mechanical properties.

Grain Sizes in the Region of 10^{-4} cm. When the individual unstrained crystals become smaller than 10^{-3} cm. in cross-section, so many of them are now irradiated by the X-ray beam that the Debye-Scherrer rings produced by a stationary specimen cease to show perfectly isolated clear-cut reflexion spots. By calibrating for known grain sizes, it can be shown that the coalescence of the spots into perfectly sharp, continuous rings actually requires the dimensions to be of the order of 10^{-4} cm. The *continuity* of the diffraction circles is therefore an indication that the crystal size is of the order of 10^{-4} cm.

Clark [73] has shown that it is essential for the crystal grains to be uniform in size since the presence of large crystals will produce individual sharp interferences superimposed on the smooth diffraction circles arising from the smaller grains. The bigger the crystals, the more prominent will be their reflexion spots, for, as we have shown in Chapter VI, the *intensity* of reflexion is proportional to the volume of the reflecting unit. There is a marked tendency for the observer to lay undue emphasis on the prominent reflexion spots from the large crystals, and unless great care is taken, the mistake will be made of assigning too large a grain size to the polycrystalline aggregate.

The Measurement of Grain Size below 10^{-4} cm. When the crystal grains, or "crystallites", are less than 10^{-4} cm. in size, the lines of the powder photograph begin to grow diffuse. This is an effect identical to the imperfect resolution of the spectral lines by an optical grating which has an insufficient number of rulings. From the breadth of the lines, we can form a good estimate of the average thickness of each crystal grain. The breadth of a line may be conveniently defined as the *angular width in radians* at a point where the intensity has fallen to half its maximum value, as illustrated in Fig. 149 (a). A much better method, which takes into account the width at the base of the line, is to obtain the Laue integral breadth by dividing the area under the peak by the maximum height of the line and converting the result into radian measure.

With crystals larger than 10^{-4} cm. the lines are perfectly sharp and each will have an individual half-peak width b which will depend only on the geometry of the experimental arrangements, the size of the focal spot, the absorption by the specimen, and the angle at which the reflexion occurs. Let us consider a line from a cylindrical specimen in a cylindrical Debye-Scherrer camera, which has increased in half-peak width from b corresponding to "particles of infinite size", i.e. larger than 10^{-4} cm. to a new value B when the crystallite size has fallen below 10^{-4} cm. P. Scherrer [74] has shown that if β is the extent of the angular broadening which we derive from B and b, the crystal dimension ε normal to the reflecting planes is given by an expression of the form

$$\beta = \frac{K\lambda}{\varepsilon \cos \theta} . \qquad . \qquad . \qquad . \qquad . \qquad (1)$$

where θ is the Bragg angle, λ the wavelength of the radiation employed

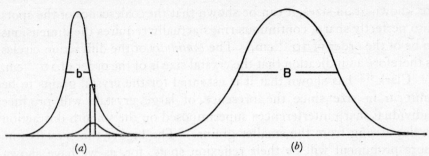

FIG. 149.—Scherrer half-maximum breadths of (a) sharp line from grains larger than 10^{-4} cm. (b) Broadened line from particles smaller than 10^{-4} cm., drawn to same vertical scale.

and K is a constant. Laue [75] has extended this equation to cover crystals with non-cubic lattices having any arbitrary shape. Different methods of arriving at equation (1) lead to slightly different values of the constant K. This has been discussed by Jones,[76] and by Patterson, [77] who also considers the effect on K of crystallite shape. For most purposes it is sufficiently accurate to take $K = 1$ and to define the "apparent crystallite size" by the formula

$$\beta = \frac{1 \cdot 0\lambda}{\varepsilon \cos \theta}. \qquad . \qquad . \qquad . \qquad . \qquad (2)$$

Scherrer gives the following simple definition of the line broadening:

$$\beta = B - b \qquad . \qquad . \qquad . \qquad . \qquad (3)$$

This definition is much too simple. If we consider each element of the sharp line b to broaden out according to an exponential law as shown in Fig. 149 (a), the broadened elements build up the broadened reflexion with the new integral width B. B. E. Warren, and A. Taylor [78] have shown that the relation is really

$$\beta = \sqrt{B^2 - b^2} \qquad . \qquad . \qquad . \qquad . \qquad (4)$$

A still more satisfactory expression which makes some allowance for the crystallite size distribution is the geometric mean of the values in equations (3) and (4), namely

$$\beta = \{(B - b)\sqrt{B^2 - b^2}\}^{\frac{1}{2}} \qquad . \qquad . \qquad . \qquad (5)$$

but the experimental accuracy seldom exceeds 10 per cent. and leaves little to choose between expressions (4) and (5).

The determination of the crystal size from the broadened line proceeds in four steps:

(a) The evaluation of b which an unbroadened line would have if it were in the position of the maximum of the broadened reflexion.

(*b*) The direct measurement of *B*, the total integral half-peak width from the broadened reflexion.

(*c*) The calculation of the amount of line broadening *β* from *B* and *b* using equation (4) or (5) or a simplified modification of the Jones graphical method described below.

(*d*) The calculation of the apparent crystallite dimension from *β*.

Jones has adopted a mixture method which enables the particle size determination to be made by using standard cylindrical Debye-Scherrer cameras described in Chapter V. A suitable powder consisting of large particles, considered infinitely big, is mixed with the substance to be investigated. The Debye-Scherrer photograph then reveals the sharp lines from the large crystallites and the diffuse bands from the material under investigation. Both sets of lines have in this manner been taken under exactly the same conditions. From the set of sharp lines it is possible to interpolate the widths *b* of lines which would have been produced by infinitely large particles at the positions of the peaks of the diffuse lines.

A graph relating the ratio $\dfrac{\beta}{B}$ to $\dfrac{b}{B}$ is drawn. After *B* is found from the photometry, b/B is calculated and the graph used to evaluate $\dfrac{\beta}{B}$. The true diffraction broadening is then easily obtained as

$$\beta = \left(\frac{\beta}{B}\right) . B \qquad . \qquad . \qquad . \qquad (6)$$

Equations (3) and (4) may be re-written as the line

$$\frac{\beta}{B} + \frac{b}{B} = 1$$

and the circle

$$\left(\frac{\beta}{B}\right)^2 + \left(\frac{b}{B}\right)^2 = 1.$$

These are drawn in Fig. 150. The values of $\dfrac{\beta}{B}$ corresponding to equation (5) can then be obtained by taking the root mean of the ordinates of the circle and the line at the experimentally determined value of b/B, from which *β* can be found as in equation (6).

When *B* is large, we may, for purposes of rough comparison, neglect the value of *b* altogether and simply write *β* = *B*. Taylor has found that for crystallite sizes up to 30 Å the 9-cm. Debye-Scherrer camera with a ⅓-mm. diameter specimen is most satisfactory, while for larger grain sizes it is preferable to go over to the 19-cm. diameter camera.

Scherrer, Haley and Terry, and Jones [76] have studied the crystallite size of colloidal gold. The mean crystallite dimensions normal to the (111), (200), (220) and (311) planes for a particular sample were found by Jones to be 315, 212, 232 and 229 Å respectively. Westgren, Wever, Seljakow, and Clark have measured the grain size of martensite in steel. Their measurements lie in the range $1 - 20 \times 10^{-6}$ cm. Determination of the crystallite sizes of catalysts is also specially valuable. Clark and Aborn have shown that the activity of platinum catalysts does not continue to increase with diminishing crystal size, but reaches an optimum value.

Amorphous Materials. The atoms in a solid, such as glass, retain their neighbours at the correct interatomic distances but permit deviations from their correct angular relationships. Thus the regularity of pattern repetition is lost after proceeding only a few atomic distances in the lattice. Such a solid is essentially non-crystalline, or amorphous, being devoid of that anisotropy so characteristic of the individual crystal. Liquids too have much the same type of atomic packing as amorphous solids, although the linkages are so feeble that the thermal vibrations cause a considerable measure of atomic mobility.

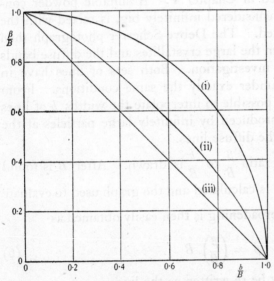

FIG. 150.—Jones' curve for the derivation of the amount of line broadening (β).

Curve (i) $\left(\dfrac{\beta_w}{B}\right)^2 + \left(\dfrac{b}{B}\right)^2 = 1$;

Curve (iii) $\left(\dfrac{\beta_s}{B}\right) + \left(\dfrac{b}{B}\right) = 1$;

Curve (ii) $\dfrac{\beta}{B} = \sqrt{\left(\dfrac{\beta_w}{B}\right) \cdot \left(\dfrac{\beta_s}{B}\right)}$.

(A. TAYLOR, *J. Scientific Instruments*, **18**, 91, 1941.)

Amorphous solids and liquids yield X-ray diffraction patterns consisting of one or two very broad diffraction bands similar in nature to those given by crystalline particles which are of the order of 10^{-7} cm. in size. It is possible to analyse these patterns by the methods of Fourier analysis and so determine the nature of the packing. Liquid metals and alloys have been studied by reflecting X-rays from the molten surface. The technique is not easy, and to date results are very meagre. A full account of the subject is given in *The Diffraction of X-rays and Electrons from amorphous Solids, Liquids and Gases*, by J. T. Randall (Chapman & Hall).

Size of Ordered Domains. Debye-Scherrer photographs illustrating the growth of ordered nuclei in Cu_3Au have already been shown in Fig. 116 of Chapter VIII. The main lattice lines remain perfectly sharp throughout the series, for the lattice *as a whole* in each individual grain is perfectly continuous. Superimposed upon the continuous three-dimensional pattern of the lattice is the segregation of copper and gold atoms into adjacent nuclei of complete order. Order within the lattice gives rise to the superlattice lines, and if the regions of order are on a small scale, the superlattice lines must broaden by a corresponding amount. Since the broad superlattice lines alternate regularly with the sharp main-lattice reflexions, it is very easy to interpolate the values of b for the positions of the maxima of the broadened lines, without the necessity of mixing a calibration material with the alloy. In this case it is unnecessary to use powder specimens and wire may be used instead, provided the grain is fine enough to yield sharp continuous rings for the main lattice reflexions when the specimen is rotated.

Resolution of α–Doublet as an Index of Crystallite Size. As the crystallite size diminishes below 10^{-4} cm. the first stages of line broadening are to be observed in the sensitive high-order reflexions where the Bragg angle approaches $90°$. The resolution of the α-doublet provides a very useful criterion of the average size of the crystallites. We may treat the problem in a manner analogous to resolution by a simple diffraction grating. The two lines forming the α-doublet will be resolved if

$$nN > \frac{\lambda}{\Delta\lambda}$$

where n is the order of the reflexion, N the number of crystal planes, λ and $\lambda + \Delta\lambda$ the wavelengths of the doublet.

When θ approaches $90°$, we may write

$$2d \approx n\lambda$$

and obtain the criterion for resolution

$$nN = \frac{2Nd}{\lambda} = \frac{2\varepsilon}{\lambda} > \frac{\lambda}{\Delta\lambda}.$$

With cobalt K radiation $\lambda(\alpha_2) = 1\cdot78919$ Å, $\lambda(\alpha_1) = 1\cdot78529$ Å which gives

$$\frac{2\varepsilon}{1\cdot787} = \frac{1\cdot787}{0\cdot0041}.$$

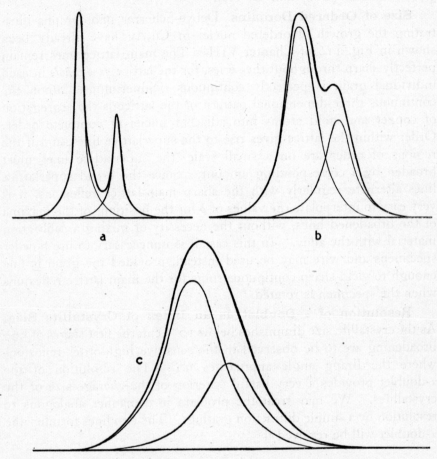

FIG. 151.—Influence of grain size on resolution of α-doublet.

(a) Grains larger than 8×10^{-5} cm.
(b) $8\cdot0 \times 10^{-6}$ cm.   Partial resolution.
(c) $4\cdot0 \times 10^{-6}$ cm.   No resolution.

Calculated for CoKα radiation and $\theta = 85°$.

In other words, ε must be somewhat larger than 390 Å in order to resolve the α-doublet.   The effect of crystallite size on an α-doublet at $\theta = 85°$ is illustrated in Fig. 151 (a), (b) and (c), the extent of line broadening being calculated from the Scherrer formula.

The Effects of Crystal Deformation.   The question of crystal deformation is very important, for it has a pronounced influence on the physical and mechanical properties of a metal. From the X-ray investigator's point of view it is also important because effects similar to those produced by small grain size are recorded on the X-ray photographs. Under the influence of internal strains, the crystal grains may be extended, compressed or sheared, and so the lattice planes become curved and twisted. Variations in interplanar and interatomic distances are set up which differ appreciably from the normal values of the stress-free material. Each strained crystal will reflect X-rays over a range of angle owing to the local departures from the normal spacings and hence gives rise to broadened lines.

A considerable amount of investigation has been carried out on the nature of crystal deformation at the National Physical Laboratory by Shearer, Wood, and their collaborators. One of the interesting discoveries they made was the development of a temperature coefficient of resistance in constantan wire when reduced in diameter by cold drawing, which, of course, ruined the wire for making standard resistances. It was naturally expected to find the cause to lie in a preferential orienting of the crystals, but X-ray investigation proved otherwise. The growth of a temperature coefficient with successive reductions in diameter could be correlated quantitatively with an increase in the state of internal strain of the crystals, measured by the width of the powder lines as illustrated in Fig. 152.

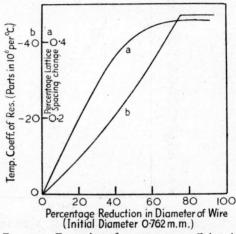

FIG. 152.—Formation of temperature coefficient in drawn Constantan Wire by lattice distortions.

(After W. A. Wood, *Proc. Phys. Soc.*, **44**, 67, 1932.)

We have already seen how very important is the effect of internal strain in giving permanent magnet alloys of the Fe_2NiAl type their high coercivity. Internal strain is a prerequisite of a good permanent magnet. Tungsten magnet steels heat treated in the region of 900° C. are spoilt, losing their high retentivity. A good steel shows only the lines of body-centred cubic α-iron phase, the other constituents apparently being held in solid-solution. Spoiling of the steel is accompanied by the appearance of a new pattern of lines identified as belonging to Fe_4W_2C and WC.   These carbides again disappear when the properties of the steel are recovered by a suitable heat treatment.   Furthermore, a good tungsten magnet steel yields diffuse powder lines, probably due to strains set up in the crystals on taking up the carbon and tungsten from the carbides into solution.   A spoilt steel gives a photograph of sharp lines showing that the crystals are perfect.

A state of high coercivity can be produced in an alloy containing equal atomic proportions of iron and platinum.   H. Lipson, D. S. Schoenberg and G. V. Stupart [79] have found that the structure is ordered face-centred tetragonal like AuCu, although the authors

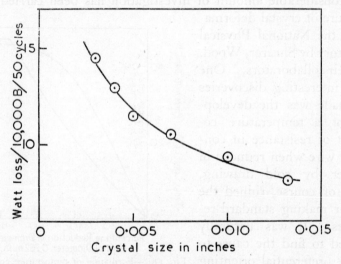

FIG. 153.—Relationship between magnetic loss values and crystal size in a 4 per cent. silicon transformer steel.

(A. H. JAY, *J. of Scientific Instruments*, **18**, 81, 1941.)

believe it to be face-centred cubic at a temperature considerably higher than 1,250° C.   The microstructure corresponding to the state of high coercivity reveals twinning bands due to the breakdown from the high temperature cubic form.   Very large strains are set up in the lattice and it is concluded that they are the cause of the very high coercivity.

While internal strains are beneficial in preventing the loss of magnetism in a permanent magnet alloy, quite opposite conditions are required for the magnetically soft permalloy and silicon steels used in transformer cores.   Where a low hysteresis loss is required, the crystals must be as large and as perfect as possible, typical results for a 4 per cent. silicon transformer steel being illustrated in Fig. 153.

Such alloys are very coarse-grained and give rise to spotty X-ray photographs. It is found that the magnetic losses are smaller the sharper the reflexions given by the X-rays. Further benefits can be conferred upon the magnetic properties by rolling the sheet so as to give a preferred orientation of the crystals in the plane of rolling.

Crystal Recovery, Recrystallization and Grain Growth. Severe cold-working of a metal may introduce grain fragmentation and grain orientation in addition to the permanent lattice distortions set up when the material has been strained beyond its elastic limit. This deformation is accompanied by an increase in the strength properties, namely hardness, yield point and tensile strength, while, on the other hand, a decrease in ductility is to be observed.

When a cold-worked metal is annealed, three mutually distinguishable processes occur. These are crystal recovery, recrystallization and grain growth. By crystal recovery, we mean the relief of lattice strain which allows a reversion of the physical and mechanical properties towards

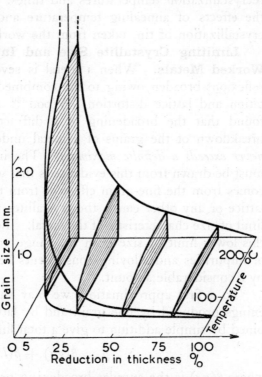

Fig. 154.—Recrystallization diagram of cold-worked tin according to Czochralski. The same type of diagram is shown by nearly all metals.

the original values occasioned by low temperature annealing, without any detectable change taking place in the microstructure or crystal size of the cold-worked metal. Recrystallization occurs at higher temperatures than crystal recovery and is a process of formation and growth of new unstrained grains which eventually supplant the original grains in the cold-worked structure. Grain growth takes place in the completely recrystallized metal and is merely a continued growth of the newly constituted recrystallized grains.

The rates of crystal recovery, recrystallization and grain growth depend upon the nature of the metal or alloy, the annealing temperature and on the amount of cold work applied at the outset. Recrystallization occurs at a higher temperature the smaller the amount of cold deformation, while increasing the time of annealing displaces recrystallization to a lower temperature. If grain growth is allowed to continue, the final grain size is larger, the smaller the degree of deformation. It is also found that the larger the original grain size the greater is the amount of cold deformation to yield equivalent recrystallization temperatures and times. In Fig. 154 we illustrate the effects of annealing temperature and cold work upon the recrystallization of tin, taken from the work of Czochralski.

Limiting Crystallite Size and Internal Strains in Cold-Worked Metals. When a metal is severely deformed, the X-ray reflexions broaden owing to the combined effects of grain fragmentation and lattice distortion. Wood [80] and his collaborators have found that the broadening of a diffraction line produced by the breakdown of the grains of a metal under progressive deformation *never exceeds a definite maximum.* The important conclusion which must be drawn from this evidence is that whether the line-broadening comes from the fine-grain effect or from the distortion of the crystal lattice or any other cause, the crystallites must reach a definite lower limit of size characteristic of the metal. For most pure ductile metals, this lower limit of size is in the range 10^{-4} to 10^{-5} cm., the effect of impurities and alloying constituents being to reduce these values by a considerable amount.

To a first approximation, we may suppose that the line broadenings produced by fine grain and by lattice distortion can be combined by simple addition to give a total line broadening *

$$\beta = \beta(g.s) + \beta(l.d)$$

where $\beta(g.s)$ is the angular broadening produced by grain size alone and $\beta(l.d)$ is the angular broadening produced by lattice distortion. If the deformed mass of metal is given just sufficient annealing to effect crystal recovery without promoting recrystallization, the lattice distortion will disappear and we shall be left with $\beta(g.s)$ from which the true crystallite size ε may be determined with the aid of the Scherrer formula:

$$\beta(g.s.) = \frac{1 \cdot 0 \lambda}{\varepsilon \cos \theta}$$

* This relation is the one used by W. A. Wood. If the line broadening is regarded as in Fig. 149, we should really add the *squares* of the angular broadenings.

The Experiments of W. A. Wood on Cu, Ag, Ni, Al, Mo and Fe of High Purity. In his experiments, Wood used specimens of exceedingly high purity machined to approximately 3 cm. long and rectangular cross-section 0·5 × 0·3 cm. They were then annealed *in vacuo* until the grains were about 10^{-1} to 10^{-2} cm. in size and gave quite sharp reflexion spots. After etching, the specimens were cold-rolled into strip and X-rayed after every 1 per cent. reduction up to 10 per cent. (reckoned on the original thickness) and then after every 5 per cent. approximately up to 99 per cent.

The specimens were examined in a back-reflexion camera which recorded the sensitive high-angle reflexions as full circles concentric with the X-ray beam, upon a flat film. Photographs were taken with the specimen stationary, its surface perpendicular to the beam, and also when oscillating $\pm$ 10° about that position.

To determine the value b for an unbroadened spectrum line, fully annealed specimens were employed, the specimens being oscillated to give the continuous line necessary for the microphotometer measurements. A check was applied by photographing specimens of ZnO and ZnS under the same conditions. It was then possible to use the value of b to determine the line-broadening for fine grained and deformed specimens.

Typical photographs of copper after various stages of reduction are illustrated in Fig. 155. The following effects are to be observed:

(1) *Expansion of the Lattice.* Fig. 155 (1) of the annealed specimen shows the separate sharp reflexion spots of the initially large perfect grains. Fig. 155 (2) taken after 4 per cent. reduction shows the transition to continuous arcs and the beginnings of radial diffusion, indicating the onset of crystallite formation. The inner ring is the 400 α-doublet occurring at a Bragg angle 83·2° which is very much more sensitive to changes than is the outer ring from the 331 β-reflexion at only 77·7°, unfiltered cobalt K radiation being used.

Fig. 155 (3), after 80 per cent. reduction, shows the diffraction rings in an abnormally diffuse condition. The inner 400 ring has increased considerably more in diameter than the less sensitive 331 reflexion. The bodily shift of the 400 ring demonstrates that the internal strain or distortion which can be imposed upon the lattice is of the nature of an expansion, for the ring is made up of reflexions from three mutually perpendicular (400), (040) and (004) planes, and all these directions must have increased.

The expansion of the lattice with its attendant fall in density under the distorting influences is not surprising, for it is a well-known fact that any effort to increase the density of lead by hammering produces quite the contrary result. The same sort of effect occurs when a bag of sand which has been well shaken down is compressed. The grains are disturbed from their equilibrium positions and the net effect is to increase the volume they occupy and so reduce the density. Thus the decrease in density of a cold-worked metal may be compared with the effect of "dilatancy" in sand.

(2) *Recovery Effect.* Fig. 155 (4) shows the diffraction rings after the same specimen of copper has been reduced further in thickness to 85 per cent. The photograph shows directly that the diameter of the 400 reflexion has contracted and at the same time the radial diffusion of the rings has *decreased*. The further deformation has *removed* the previous expansion of the distorted lattice, thus producing recovery without recrystallization. The abnormal diffusion associated with the expansion effect is attributed to irregularities in the expansion which influences the lattice spacings and not to any appreciable further breakdown of the crystallites. Otherwise, on recovery it would be difficult to explain why the crystallites should again increase in size to the arbitrary value corresponding to the line breadth of the recovered state.

The lattice expansion followed by crystal recovery was found to be a periodic phenomenon. After initial changes accompanying breakdown, the diffusion and expansion effect reached a maximum after about 8 per cent. reduction. This was followed by crystal recovery at 10 per cent. and the whole cycle of diffusion and lattice expansion, followed in turn by crystal recovery, was continually repeated as the deformation of the specimen continued. During each recovery, the line breadth decreased to the same value. From this observation we may conclude that the residual broadening is entirely due to the fine-grain effect and therefore affords a measure of the lower limiting grain size.

For comparison between the lattice spacing of the initial unstressed material and the recovered state, enlarged photographs of each are shown side by side in Fig. 155 (5a) and (5b). The unstressed material was oscillated in order that smooth lines would be obtained for measurement of the true diffraction angle. The relative movement of the diffused α-doublet in the recovered state is quite apparent, and, contrary to the findings for material under internal stress, it is in the direction corresponding to a *contraction* in the lattice.

Similar results were to be found for silver, nickel, molybdenum and iron, but not for pure aluminium. This is because aluminium is spontaneously self-recovering during cold-working at room temperature. Nevertheless, it is found that coarse-grained aluminium

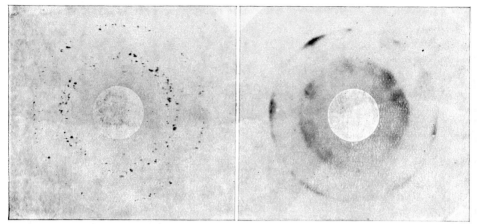

(1) Cu, annealed.   (2) Cu, 4 per cent. reduction.

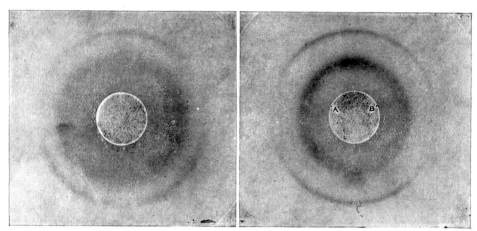

(3) Cu, 80 per cent. reduction.   (4) Cu, 85 per cent. reduction.

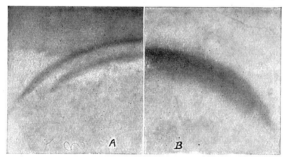

(5 *a*) Initial State.   (5 *b*) Recovered State.

Copper : (3) shows the expansion of the inner ring towards the outer ring due to lattice expansion effect ; (4) the contraction on recovery caused by further cold working ; (5 *a*) and (5 *b*) show a difference between the recovered and initial state.

FIG. 155.—Back-reflexion patterns from Cu after various stages of cold working. Cobalt *K* ($\alpha + \beta$) radiation. Inner ring, 400 doublet. Outer ring, 311 β.

(W. A. WOOD, *Proc. Roy. Soc.*, (A) **172**, 231, 1939.)

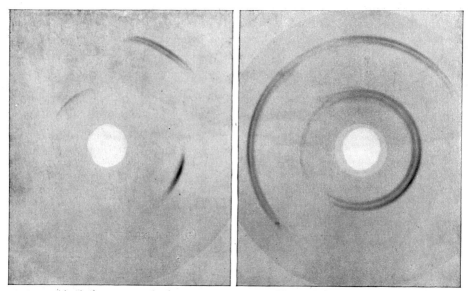

(a) Al, 6 per cent. reduction (b) Al, 98·6 per cent. reduction.

(a) and (b) show that a complete ring is not produced even after heavy cold working of pure aluminium.

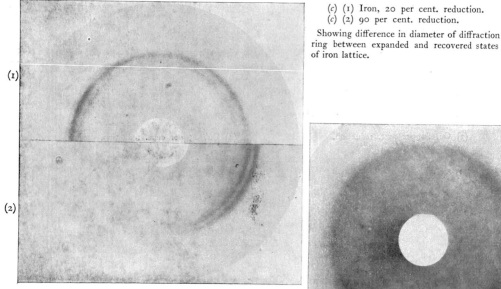

(c) (1) Iron, 20 per cent. reduction.
(c) (2) 90 per cent. reduction.

Showing difference in diameter of diffraction ring between expanded and recovered states of iron lattice.

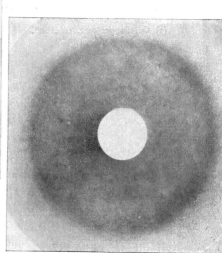

(d) shows the much greater line-broadening effect in a carbon steel compared with that in pure iron above.

FIG. 156.—(a) and (b) Back-reflexion patterns from Al.
(c) and (d) Back-reflexion patterns from pure Fe and 0·1 per cent. carbon steel.
(W. A. WOOD, *Proc. Roy. Soc.*, **172**, 231, 1939.)

can be fragmented by cold-work to give partial arcs of perfectly resolved α-doublets. In the absence of any line broadening, it would appear that the lower limit of crystallite size is very definitely in the region of 10^{-4} cm. With the very pure aluminium used by Wood, it was found impossible to obtain full circles for the diffraction haloes (Fig. 156). The arcs showed a point of maximum intensity indicating that the majority of crystallites do not depart widely in orientation from the parent grain. This is not due to preferred orientation of the crystallites in the specimen as a whole, since the arcs are differently placed when a photograph is taken from another point on the specimen.

Table XV contains a summary of the lattice changes while in the recovered and distorted states.

TABLE XV

LATTICE EXPANSIONS, CONTRACTIONS AND LOWER LIMITING CRYSTALLITE SIZES FOR VARIOUS METALS (W. A. Wood, *Proc. Roy. Soc.*, **172**, 231, 1939).

Metal	Purity	Lattice Parameter of Annealed Metal	Maximum Contraction in Recovered State	Maximum Expansion from Contracted State	Lower Limiting Crystallite Size
	%	Å	%	%	cm.
Copper . . .	99·999	3·6086	0·06	0·27	0·7.10^{-5}
Nickel . . .	99·97	3·5170	0·07	0·13	1·2.10^{-5}
Silver . . .	99·999	4·0779	0·03	0·45	0·8.10^{-5}
Aluminium . .	99·99	4·0413	0·00	0·00	≈10^{-4}
Molybdenum .	99·95	3·1403	0·05	0·10	2·2.10^{-5}
Iron	99·96	2·8610	0·05	0·10	3·2.10^{-5}

Impurities and alloying constituents have an enormous influence on the results of deformation. In Fig. 156 are compared the X-ray photographs taken for deformed pure iron and for a deformed 0·1 per cent. carbon steel reduced by about 40 per cent. to produce the maximum degree of line broadening. By lowering the permissible limit of crystallite size, the effect of carbon on the iron lattice is greatly to extend the potential range of structure-sensitive properties.

Grain Distortion in Electrodeposited Metals. By comparing the line breadths from nickel-plated specimens with those of cold-rolled pure nickel and cold-rolled nickel-plated copper specimens, Wood was able to demonstrate that the fine-grained structure of nickel deposits may be accompanied by lattice distortion.[81] The contribution of lattice distortion to the line breadth may be a very appreciable proportion of the whole, and, if the lines in the X-ray spectrum have a breadth greater than the value corresponding to maximum lattice distortion, then it may be safely concluded that the broadening is in some degree due to a fine-grained structure.

With chromium plate, the line breadths are very large in comparison with the value at the lattice distortion limit, and in this particular instance the lattice distortion effect may be safely neglected in computing the grain size. In other cases, the possibility of lattice distortion should be taken into account.

The Stress–Strain Curve for the Atomic Lattice. F. Wever and B. Pfarr [82] in their X-ray studies on grain size and recrystallization of rolled steel sheet made the interesting discovery that when a test piece from the sheet was held in tension a marked contraction of the lattice was to be observed, but if the sample were stretched beyond the yield point and then unloaded, the lattice parameter not only increased to its original stress-free value, but actually rose to a much higher figure. Thus the deformed material was left with a permanent lattice expansion. Much more detailed work of a similar character has been carried out by S. L. Smith and W. A. Wood [83] on the lattice changes when aluminium, iron and steel are subjected to static loading as in a tensile test. As all these materials gave results differing only in detail, their work on normalized mild steel (0·1 per cent. C.) will be described.

As in the previous section, the back-reflexion method utilizing cobalt K radiation was employed, thus recording the sensitive 310 high angle reflexion. The specimen was contained in a combined tensile testing machine and back-reflexion camera which enabled the X-ray photographs to be taken while the specimen was maintained under tensile stress. The changes in the external dimensions were obtained by means of an extensometer attachment.

The tensile stress-strain curve for a typical specimen and for the crystal lattice are given in Fig. 157 (a) and (b). It will be seen that at a stress coincident with the external yield point, the curve for the lattice exhibits a marked discontinuity. Below this stress, the lattice spacing contracts linearly with increasing load. At the critical stress, instead of a continued contraction, the spacing undergoes an abrupt expansion which remains fairly constant as the stress is further increased.

The expansion of spacing observed at the lattice yield point becomes permanently superimposed on the lattice dimensions. Specimens were taken through slow cycles of stress and photographed at the peak stress and at the zero stress between each cycle. A photograph was first taken at zero stress, then with a load of 1 ton per square inch and then again at zero stress when the load had been

removed.   Photographs were then taken at loads of 2, 0, 3, 0, · · ·
tons per square inch.   The results are shown in the lattice stress-
strain diagram in Fig. 157 (b).   It will be seen that on passing the yield
point, further increments of permanent expansion can be effected by
increasing the previous maximum load.   Under stress, the actual

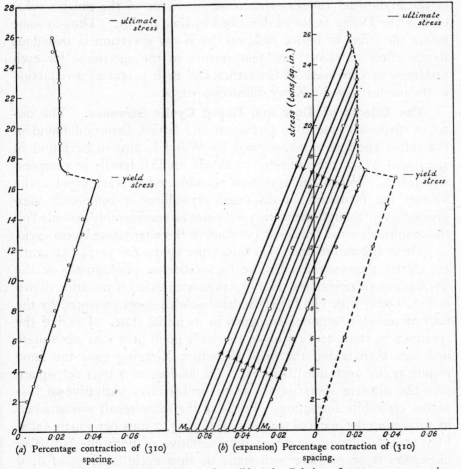

(a) Percentage contraction of (310)
spacing.

(b) (expansion) Percentage contraction of (310)
spacing.

FIG. 157.—(a) Lattice stress-strain curve for mild steel.   Relation of percentage contraction
of (310) planes, practically perpendicular to stress direction, to applied stress.
(b) Changes in (310) spacing on loading and unloading of tensile specimens.
(S. L. SMITH and W. A. WOOD, *Proc. Roy. Soc.*, **179**, 450, 1942.)

change exhibited by the lattice is the resultant of the permanent
expansion and the ordinary reversible elastic contraction.   The higher
the applied stress, the greater becomes the permanent expansion
effect, but the resultant contraction never exceeds a definite limiting
value.

One of the effects of the permanent lattice deformation is to produce a sharp drop in the intensity of the 310 reflexion. At the yield point the drop in intensity is of the order of 50 per cent. as shown in Fig. 158.

When the temperature of a specimen is raised, two things happen. The first is that the lattice spacing increases, and secondly the intensities of the high-order reflexions decrease by virtue of the greater value of B in the Debye factor as described in Chapter VI. Thus to some extent the effect of lattice yield on the X-ray spectrum is analogous to the effect of raising the temperature of the specimen, for each produces an expansion of the lattice and each produces a reduction in the intensity of the X-ray diffraction rings.

The Effects of Slow and Rapid Cyclic Stresses. The on-set of dispersed crystallite formation and lattice distortion found in the rolled specimens investigated by Wood is also to be found in specimens which are subjected to slowly applied tensile or compres-sive forces. When the specimen is subjected to very rapid cyclic stresses the formation of dispersed crystallites is completely sup-pressed even though the static yield point be considerably exceeded on the compressive and tensional portions of the alternating stress cycle.

These effects for brass (Cu 69·43 per cent., Zn 30·54 per cent.) are clearly demonstrated by the back-reflexion photographs of the 331 high-angle reflexion α-doublet, taken with nickel K radiation shown in Fig. 159. Fig. 159 (1) shows the isolated spots produced by the fully annealed, unstrained specimen in its initial state. Loading the specimen in static tension up to the yield point at 5 tons per square inch and then taking the load off before X-raying gave the same results as the unstrained material. On loading to 7 tons per square inch the discrete spots gave way to broken arcs indicative of dis-persed crystallite formation. Precisely the same result was attained by subjecting the material to a slow cycle of $\pm$ 7 tons per square inch, Fig. 159 (2a) being shown as representative of both effects. The dispersion is progressive with static or slow cycle loadings of 8, 9 and 10 tons per square inch, the last named being represented in Fig. 159 (3a).

The X-ray photographs of similar specimens subjected to reversed stresses in a standard form of electromagnetic fatigue-testing machine operating at 2,200 cycles per minute do not show anything more than a very slight diffusion of spots. The large angular dispersion of the crystallites which physically marks the primitive yield point has therefore been suppressed or removed although the maximum stress of the cycle in one case was practically double the initial yield stress under static tension. This is well brought out in Fig. 159 (2b)

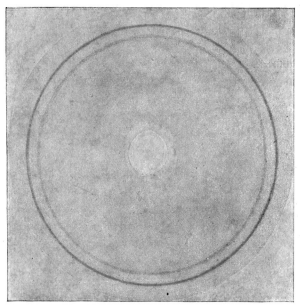

(*a*) Before yield.

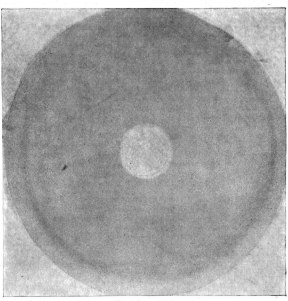

(*b*) After yield.

FIG. 158.—(*a*) and (*b*), obtained under identical conditions, illustrate the drop in intensity of X-ray reflexion which occurs when the tensile specimen passes through the yield point.

(W. A. Wood and S. L. Smith, *Proc. Roy. Soc.*, **179**, 450, 1942.)

[*Facing page* 238.

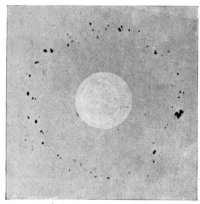

(1) Initial state.

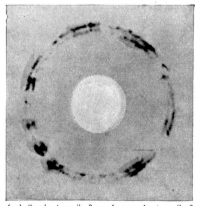 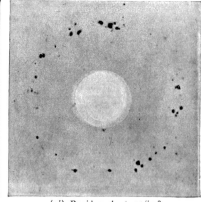

(2a) Static $+ 7t/$in.^{2} or slow cycle $\pm 7t/$in.^{2} (2b) Rapid cycle $\pm 7t/$in.^{2}

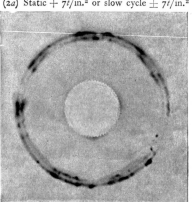 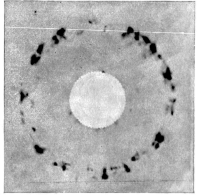

(3a) Static $+ 10t/$in.^{2} or slow cycle $\pm 10t/$in.^{2} (3b) Rapid cycle $\pm 10t/$in.^{2} (fractured).

(4) Static load $+ 8t/$in.^{2} after prior cycles at $8t/$in.^{2} (yield just beginning). This shows inhibition of breakdown of grains under rapid cyclic stressing to persist (up to maximum stress of prior cycle) when specimen is subsequently stressed statically. Note Laue spots in the background.

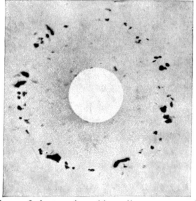

Fig. 159.—Effects of slow and rapid cyclic stresses on brass.

(Cu, 69·43 per cent. Zn, 30·54 per cent.)

(W. A. Wood and P. L. Thorpe, *Proc. Roy. Soc.*, (A) **174**, 310, 1940.)

for $\pm$ 7 tons per square inch, and Fig. 159 (3*b*) for $\pm$ 10 tons per square inch in rapid cycle. If the crystallites are formed at all, they must retain to within a degree or so the crystallographic orientation of the parent grains, and, as far as the X-rays are concerned, do not behave independently of the initial grains.

After the rapid cyclic stressing has ceased, subsequent static loading fails to produce any permanent set until the maximum loading attained in the cyclic stressing has been applied. In other words, the primitive yield point has been raised. The effect is shown

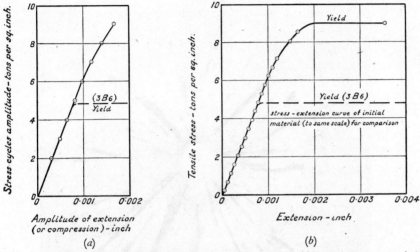

FIG. 160.—Difference between extension produced by : (*a*) Rapid stress ($\pm$ 9 tons/sq. in.). Specimen 4B2. Extension under alternating stress (after 30,000 cycles at 9 tons/sq. in.). (*b*) Slow static tensile stress. Specimen 4B2. Subsequent static test (showing permanent rise of yield point).

(W. A. Wood and P. L. Thorpe, *Proc. Roy. Soc.*, **174**, 310, 1940.)

in Fig. 160 (*a*) and (*b*), where no marked yield is visible for specimen 4B2 subjected to a rapid alternating stress of $\pm$ 9 tons per square inch and where the static yield point for the same specimen, after 30,000 reversals, is now permanently raised from 5 to 9 tons per square inch.

Although dispersed crystallite formation is inhibited by the application of rapid cyclic stresses, a slight diffusion of the spots does occur accompanied by a marked increase in lattice volume. The magnitude of lattice expansion expressed in terms of a percentage change in the side of the original unit cell, after carrying numbers of cycles for a load of $\pm$8 tons per square inch, was as follows:

No. of cycles	0	50,000	90,000	150,000	300,000	636,000*
Lattice change %—		0.02_0	0.02_4	0.02_4	0.02_9	0.03_5

* Fracture stage.

Taking the lattice expansion together with the slight broadening of the spots, the evidence is indicative of internal strain produced by the cyclic stressing, and it is this factor which must be responsible for the abnormally high primitive yield point in subsequent static loading.

Asterism.   When a Laue photograph is taken of a stress-free polycrystalline metal, the pattern consists of a multitude of sharp reflexion spots.   Distorting the metal introduces curvature of the lattice, or fragmentation, into a mosaic of submicroscopic crystallites, the orientations of which are independent of their neighbours.   Lattice

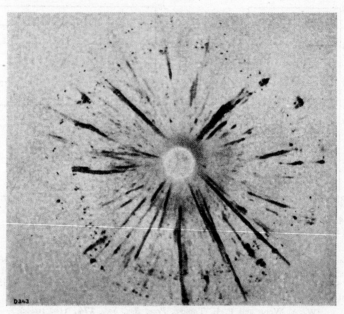

FIG. 161.—"Asterism".   The formation of radial streaks by distorted crystals.   Photograph of recrystallized sheet in which a few large crystals are subjected to strong internal tensions.
(Courtesy, Philips Industrial.)

distortion, or fragmentation, is revealed in the Laue photograph by the drawing out of the reflexion spots into diffuse bands whose radial lengths are much greater than their widths.   This phenomenon, to which the name "asterism" is applied, can be seen in the photographs of a polycrystalline metal in which a few individual crystals are strained, as shown in Fig. 161.

In the annealed specimen, each crystal acts as a little plane mirror which reflects a narrow pencil of radiation on to the film whatever its inclination to the X-ray beam, for in the Laue technique there will always be an appropriate wavelength in the range of available "white" radiation to satisfy the Bragg reflexion condition.   We may now treat a distorted crystal plane as if different portions of it were tilted at random through small angles with respect to the normal of the average direction. Referring now to Fig. 162, let us suppose that a mirror is reflecting a fine pencil of light at a small glancing angle θ and that we tilt it slightly at random to make its normal move about within a cone of semi-vertical angle α. The area traversed by the reflected beam will be a very elongated ellipse. Considering the major axis of the ellipse, the angular length of it must be twice the

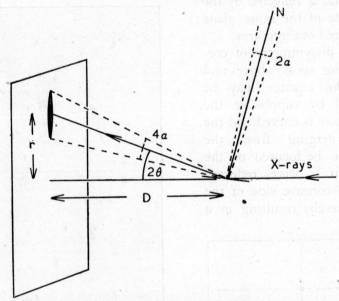

FIG. 162.—"Asterism" in Laue reflexion from distorted lattice plane.

angle through which the mirror is rocked about an axis normal to the plane of the paper, that is, to 4α, and so the length of the major axis of the ellipse will be $4\alpha D$ approximately. Rocking the mirror at right angles to the plane of incidence gives a horizontal angular movement of only 2α to the reflected ray, so that for small values of θ the minor axis of the ellipse which such a movement traces will be $2\theta D.2\alpha$ or $2\alpha r$. The axial ratio will thus be $4D\alpha/2r\alpha$ which is $1/\theta$. If θ is $3°$ or 0.052 radians, the major axis will be twenty times as long as the minor axis.

A Method of Distinguishing between Lattice Curvature and Fragmentation. The asterism described above may be due to large distorted crystals or to fragments which are oriented more or less in the same direction. Orowan and Pascoe [84] have recently shown how in special circumstances we may use X-rays as a criterion

for distinguishing between lattice curvature and lattice fragmentation.
Rotation photographs taken with copper Kα radiation in a camera of
radius 3·0 cm. of a moderately extended cadmium single crystal showed
reflexion spots which were unusually sharp, sharper even than the
spots obtained before distortion.   Whenever a spot 1 (Fig. 163) is
unusually sharp, the corresponding spot 2 on the same side of the
equator reflected by the same lattice plane after the crystal rotates
through 90° (or 270°) is equally sharp.   The two corresponding
spots 3 and 4 reflected by the
other side of the same plane
are smeared out into arcs.

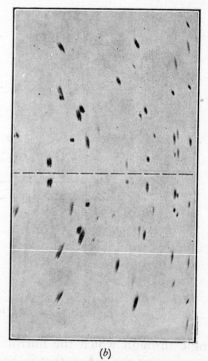

The dissymmetry of cor-
responding spots above and
below the equator may be
explained by supposing the
lattice plane is curved and the
beam emerging from the
pinhole to be focused on the
film as if it were reflected
from the concave side of the
plane, thereby resulting in a

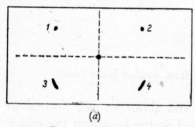

(a)   (b)

FIG. 163.—(a) Sharpened and elongated spots showing lattice curvature.
(b) Part of a rotation photograph, enlarged 1·62 times. Cd. crystal, about 1 mm. thick;
extension about 2 per cent. The dotted line is the equator. CuKα radiation. Camera
radius, 3·0 cm.

(E. OROWAN and K. J. PASCOE, *Nature*, **148**, 467, 1941.)

particularly sharp spot.   On the other hand, beams incident on the
convex side of the plane are reflected with a strong divergence and
produce elongated traces on the film.

For cadmium, the dissymmetry effect was greatest for basal plane
reflexions and for planes lying at a small angle to it.   This is attributed
to the *disintegration* of the bent crystal into glide lamellæ as shown in
Fig. 164, for otherwise bending would produce extremely high tensile
stresses on the convex side and extremely high compressive stresses

on the concave side of a thick block (cf. section on flexural glide in Chapter X). Planes running perpendicular to these bent planes show no dissymmetry of X-ray reflexion since they remain approximately plane in elastic bending.

With polycrystalline metals a very complex system of stresses is set up among the neighbouring crystals which give rise to particularly sharp curvatures and thin lamellæ. The dissymmetry effect can no longer be observed if the focal length of the curved lattice "mirror" becomes too small compared with the radius of the X-ray camera, but the X-ray reflexions will now show the *diffusion into Debye-Scherrer circles and broadening* usually attributed to random fragmentation.

With increasing deformation, the elastic energy of the bent lamellæ and their mutual surface energy become high enough for recrystallization to occur. As we have already seen, for a given amount of cold-work the temperature at which this takes place is characteristic of the metal. Andrade and Chow found that the tails on the Laue photographs of distorted iron crystals broke into distinct spots at sufficiently high temperatures. This also happened at room temperature

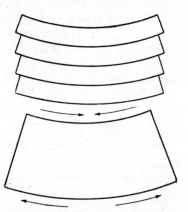

FIG. 164.—Disintegration of bent crystal into lamellæ. Cf. flexural glide in Chapter X.
(E. OROWAN and K. J. PASCOE, *Nature*, **148**, 467, 1941.)

with deformed sodium and potassium, but at very low temperatures only continuous tails were observed. All metals may recrystallize at room temperature if the distortion is severe enough. At a given temperature, therefore, local curvature of the lattice and its splitting up into lamellæ, with the accompanying diffusion of X-ray reflexions, increases only up to a critical distortion at which recrystallization begins.

Application of X-rays to Depth of Cold-Working. In the course of machining an article, the influence of the cutting tool penetrates for quite a distance below the surface of the metal. The considerable distortion and fragmentation of crystal grains in the surface layers can be readily observed by means of the line broadening found in diffraction patterns. By etching away successive layers of the worked surface, X-ray photographs corresponding to the condition of the material at various depths can be obtained. When the undistorted basis material is reached, no further changes are to be observed in the diffraction pattern. The effect of machining on the surface of steel is illustrated in Fig. 165, the penetration in this instance being of the order of 0·003 inch.

The effect of cold-work is of particular importance in specimens prepared for fatigue-testing and precautions are always taken to minimize the cold-work in the machining operations. A typical set of figures given by Barrett which may be taken as representative for the depth of penetration is given in Table XVI below.

TABLE XVI

DEPTH OF COLD-WORK FROM SPECIMEN PREPARATION

Material	Depth of Cold-Work in.	Method of Preparation
0·42% C. Steel Hot Rolled	0·002 ± 0·001	Lathe cut of 0·015 in., repeated, then cut of 0·002 to 0·001 in. filed and polished to remove an additional 0·001 in.
0·19% C. Steel Annealed	0·005 ± 0·001	Ditto
Copper, Annealed	0·008 ± 0·002	Ditto
Aluminium, Annealed	0·008 ± 0·002	Final operations were shallow lathe cuts, polished with No. 218 Aloxite cloth, then with 00 paper, then buffed.

The Beilby Layer. A highly polished metal surface is usually obtained by buffing. Under the influence of the polishing material, the ductile surface of the metal flows, losing thereby its crystalline regularity to a depth of about 20 to 50 Å. The " amorphous " surface is often referred to as a Beilby-layer. There is far too little of it to be revealed by X-ray diffraction methods and recourse must be had to the electron diffraction technique which is more suited to the study of surface phenomena. Methods of electrolytic polishing have been developed for removing the " amorphous " surface, notably by Jacquet.

Application of X-ray Methods to the Measurement of Stress. The important changes in the diffraction patterns observed when a metal is subjected to slow or rapid cyclic stresses have already been described. In laboratory experiments, the investigator is particularly fortunate in that he can choose the specimens to be examined and has perfect control over the magnitude and directions of the applied stresses. In practice, observations may be required on massive cylinders or shafting which cannot be manipulated as simple laboratory specimens. The problem then becomes one of bringing the

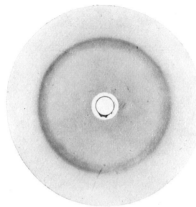

(a) Surface as turned. Diffuse doublet from distorted crystal fragments.

(b) After removing 0·001 in. with acid.

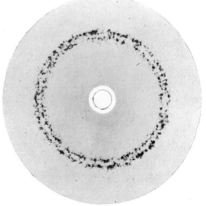

(c) After removing 0·002 in. Most of stressed surface removed.

(d) After removing 0·008 in. Sharp spots reveal unstressed crystals of interior.

Fig. 165.—Effect of lathe tool on the surface texture of an annealed 0·10% C. steel bar.

Co K radiation. 310 a — doublet. Film-specimen distance, 10·0 c.m. Beam diameter, 1·0 mm. Exposure time, 2 hrs. at 35 k V, 10 milliamps. Victor XRD unit and back-reflexion camera. (A. Taylor and H. Sinclair.)

(*Reproduced half size.*)

[*Facing page* 244.

X-ray equipment to the object of investigation. Portability and manœuvrability must be essential features of the X-ray apparatus and it will be necessary for the camera to swivel as a unit with the X-ray head into a position adjacent the specimen.[85] For this type of work, a sealed-off tube is most suitable (cf. Fig. 47).

Reflexions at high angles are employed. If the crystal grains are similarly stressed, the diffracted rays will produce sharp reflexion spots displaced from the normal positions corresponding to un-strained material. It is usually impracticable to rotate or oscillate the specimen through an angular range in order to smooth out the spotty reflexions for accurate spacing measurements. Recourse must be had to rotating the film in its own plane about the incident beam as axis, to produce the same effect. Some workers apply aluminium paint or gold leaf to the surface of the metal in order to obtain cali-brating spectra which do not change in position no matter how the basis material may be subsequently stressed.[85] In principle, this is the mixture method sometimes employed in powder photography. Others prefer to impress fiducial marks upon the film by means of accurate jigs. From changes in spacing from the normal values and a know-ledge of the elastic moduli of the material, it is possible to calculate the exact magnitude of the internal stresses. In effect, then, we are using the high angle X-ray reflexions as a simple extensometer.

Let us suppose we are observing the change in diameter of a Debye-Scherrer ring taken with the back-reflexion technique from a specimen SS. The changes in the interplanar spacing d to which the measurements refer are measured in the direction XQ, the normal to the reflecting planes which bisects the angle PQR (Fig. 166).

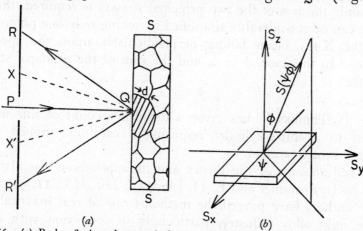

FIG. 166.—(a) Back-reflexion photograph from surface of specimen stressed in direction SS. (b) Measurement of lattice stress $S(\psi\phi)$, normal to the crystallographic plane (hkl). S_x, S_y, S_z are the principal stresses referred to the surface of the specimen.

If θ approaches $90°$, we may, without introducing any serious error, consider the changes to occur normal to the plane of the specimen which is stressed in the direction SS.

Under the action of the stress, the interplanar distance d_0 changes to a new value d, and so the strain normal to the reflecting crystallographic plane will be

$$\varepsilon = \frac{d - d_0}{d_0} \qquad . \qquad . \qquad . \qquad . \qquad (1)$$

Let S_x and S_y be the directions of the principal stresses in the plane of the surface (Fig. 166b), then the strain ε in any direction ϕ, ψ will be given by

$$\varepsilon E = \{ S_x \sin^2 \phi \cos^2 \psi - v S_x (\sin^2 \phi \sin^2 \psi + \cos^2 \phi) $$
$$+ S_y \sin^2 \phi \sin^2 \psi - v S_y (\sin^2 \phi \cos^2 \psi + \cos^2 \phi) \}. \qquad (2)$$

where E = Young's modulus
and v = Poisson's ratio.

To obtain the strains S_x and S_y, it is necessary to take X-ray photographs at two different angles to the surface. We then get reflexions from crystallographic planes with the same indices hkl, but which have different inclinations to the surface of the metal and therefore have different values for the strain ε. If we take photographs with a constant angle ϕ and for values of $\psi = 0°$ and $90°$, equation (2) takes the forms

$$S_x + S_y = (\varepsilon_{\psi=0} + \varepsilon_{\psi=90°}) E / [(1 + v) \sin^2 \phi - 2v] \qquad . \quad (3)$$
$$S_x - S_y = (\varepsilon_{\psi=0} - \varepsilon_{\psi=90°}) E / (1 + v) \sin^2 \phi \qquad . \qquad . \quad (4)$$

The sum and difference of equations (3) and (4) immediately give S_x and S_y in terms of known or measurable quantities.

If only the *sum* of the two principal stresses is required, the procedure can be considerably simplified by taking only one photograph with the X-ray beam falling perpendicularly upon the specimen surface. In this case, $\phi = 0$, and the sum of the principal stresses becomes

$$S_x + S_y = - \varepsilon E / v \qquad . \qquad . \qquad . \qquad (5)$$

D. E. Thomas [85] has given a detailed account of this method applied to a ship's-cylinder requiring a carefully applied stress-relieving heat treatment.

A full account of the theory and its applications has also been given by L. Frommer and E. H. Lloyd (*J. Inst. Met.*, **11**, 91, 1944). These authors have proved the method to be of real practical value to the light alloy industry, particularly in connexion with design and heat treatment and allied problems in components where optimum mechanical and physical properties are essential.

CHAPTER X

GRAIN ORIENTATION

The Stereographic Projection. The relationships between crystallographic axes, planes and angles can be comprehensively represented by methods of projective geometry. The stereographic projection described below is one used very frequently.

Let us suppose that we have a crystal of negligibly small dimensions situated at the centre of a sphere, commonly referred to as the *polar sphere*, or *reference sphere*, illustrated in Fig. 167 (*a*). The plane *A* may be represented on the surface of the sphere by the point of intersection, or *pole*, of its normal at *N*. Alternatively the

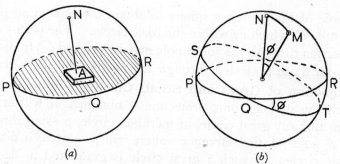

Fig. 167.—(*a*) Representation of a plane by a pole *N*, or great circle *PQR*, upon the Reference Sphere.

(*b*) Angle ϕ between two planes measured along arc of great circle *MN*, or by the intersection of the great circles *PQR*, *SQT*.

plane may be imagined to extend until it cuts the sphere in the great circle *PQR*, which also may be used to represent the plane. The angle between two crystallographic planes *A*, *B*, may be measured in degrees along the arc of the great circle between the poles *N*, *M* of the normals to *A* and *B* respectively. Alternatively, if the planes of the crystal are projected on to the surface of the sphere as great circles, then the great circles will intersect each other at the same angle as do the planes in the crystal.

In the stereographic projection, the array of poles on the reference sphere belonging to the planes in the crystal are projected upon the equatorial plane, which is commonly referred to as the *basic circle* or *reference circle*. The stereographic projection *Q*, in the equatorial plane, of the pole *P* in the northern hemisphere, is obtained by joining *P* to *S* as shown in Fig. 168. If a pole, such as *R*, lies in the southern or negative hemisphere, its stereographic projection T will lie *outside* the basic circle on the extended equatorial plane. It is often convenient to project such poles as R in the southern hemisphere through

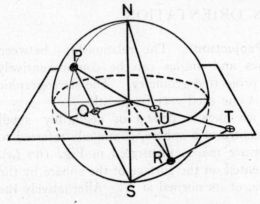

FIG. 168.—Stereographic projection through N and S Poles of reference sphere upon the equatorial plane.

the N pole of the reference sphere to obtain corresponding points, as for example U, which lie within the basic circle. The points obtained by projection through the south pole may be marked $\otimes$ to distinguish them from those projected through the north pole, marked $\odot$

Projection of Great and Small Circles. From the manner in which the stereographic projection is obtained, it will at once be apparent that any great circle, or meridian circle, passing through the N and S poles of the reference sphere will project as a diameter of the basic circle. If such a great circle is graduated in degrees, its projection EE will be a scale of stereographically projected degree points and will be useful in reading off angular distances in the projection. It is shown with $5°$ graduations in Fig. 169 (b).

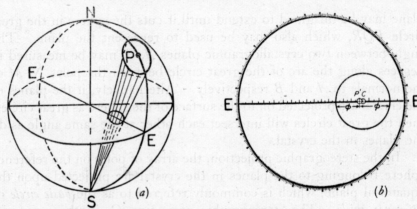

FIG. 169.—Stereographic projection of a small circle. Projection of great circle through NS is EE. The projection of the small circle with centre P is a circle having a centre C displaced from the projected centre P',

Latitude circles which lie parallel to the equatorial plane will, of course, project as small circles concentric with the basic circle.   Any circle inscribed on the surface of the reference sphere about a point such as P will also project on to the equatorial plane as a true circle. The centre P will project to the point P' which is *not* the geometric centre of the projected circle, which is at C. P' will lie on the line EE at a point distant an equal number of stereographically projected degrees from all points of the projected circle.

If the radius of the small circle with centre P is increased, it finally becomes a great circle.   The stereographic projection of this circle will not be a straight line since the great circle will not be a meridian circle passing through the N–S poles.   The projection will be a circle with a large radius, with its centre on EE, extended if necessary.   It will cut the basic circle at two diametrically opposite points and it will cut the line EE at the point $\phi = 90°$ from P'.   Thus its position and radius will be uniquely determined.   Just as it is customary to project poles in the southern hemisphere through the N pole of the reference sphere in order to make the projected points lie within the basic circle, the same practice is observed in the projection of circles, or those portions of them, which lie in the southern hemisphere.

Measurement of Angle between Poles—Stereographic Nets. The angle between two poles on the surface of the reference sphere is the number of degrees separating them on the great circle passing through them.   A ruled globe marked out with meridian circles and latitude circles in precisely the same manner as globes used for geography is commonly employed in crystallographic work.   If we imagine two poles P_1 and P_2 marked out on a transparent celluloid cap free to slide over the surface of the globe, we could move it about until P_1 and P_2 lay on the same meridian circle passing through the N-S poles.   The angle between P_1 and P_2 would then be read off by counting the number of degrees of latitude between them (Fig. 170).

In the stereographic representation of poles, we make use of a stereographic net to carry out the same operation in the plane of the reference circle as is carried out by means of the transparent cap on the surface of the sphere.   The stereographic net, often referred to as a Hutchinson's or Wulff's net, is illustrated in Fig. 171.   It is very similar in appearance to a globe with its rulings of latitude and meridian circles.   It is obtained by projecting the meridian and latitude circles through a pole taken *in the equator* of the globe upon the plane bounded by a great circle through the N-S poles.   The radius through the

I*

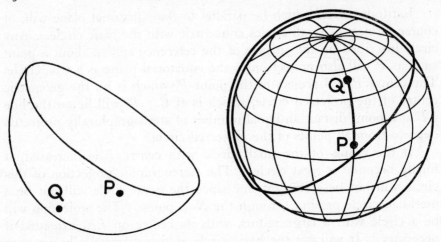

FIG. 170.—Use of ruled globe and transparent cap. The cap is moved over the sphere until
P and Q lie on the same meridian circle. The angle between P and Q is then measured
as the difference in latitude.

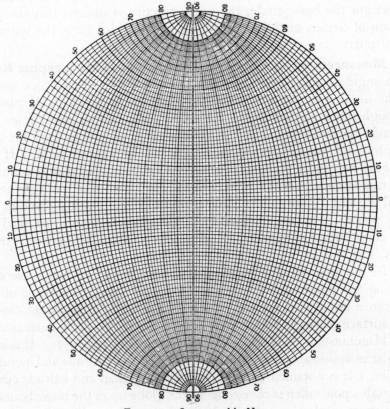

FIG. 171.—Stereographic Net.

pole of projection is normal to the plane on which the projection is made. The meridians in the projections extend from top to bottom and the latitude lines from side to side. The net shown is graduated in intervals of 2°, but much larger nets can be obtained up to 50 cm. in diameter, accurately graduated in 1° intervals.

The manipulation of the stereographic net is analogous to the movement of the transparent cap over the ruled globe. The reference circle with the projected points is drawn on tracing paper to the same scale as the net. The tracing is then placed centrally over the net and held through its centre by means of a pin which leaves it free only to rotate. To measure the angular distance between any two points P, Q in the projection, the tracing paper is turned round the centre pin, until P and Q both lie upon the same meridian circle, which corresponds to one of the great circles on the sphere. The angle between P and Q is then measured as the difference in latitude.

Spherical and Stereographic Projection of a Crystal— Standard Forms. A spherical projection of a cubic crystal is illustrated in Fig. 172 (*a*). The fourfold axes which are the lattice directions [001] intersect the sphere in the points marked □, while the intersections of the twofold [110] and the threefold [111] axes

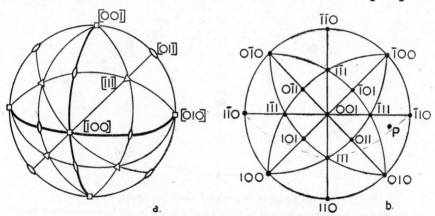

FIG. 172.—(a) Spherical projection of a cubic crystal.
() △ □ Poles of 2-fold, 3-fold and 4-fold axes.
(b) Stereographic projection of a cubic crystal. The point *P* represents the stereographic projection of the axis of the wire upon the basic circle (001).

are indicated by the symbols () and △ respectively. The planes to which these lattice directions are the normals intersect the reference sphere in great circles as shown in the figure. The surface of the sphere is thus divided into 48 equivalent spherical triangles.

The stereographic projection upon the equatorial plane of the cubic crystal with [001] as the projection pole is shown in Fig. 172 (*b*).

The basic circle is divided into 24 curved triangles, since the projections from the North and South hemispheres coincide.   The triangles are angle-true but not area-true.   Such a stereographic projection of the poles of the most important planes of a crystal, the low index planes, is termed a standard projection.   Standard projections of cubic crystals may be had with (001), (110), (112), (130), and (111) as the projection plane.[86]   The projections are constructed by calculating the angles between the poles and crystallographic axes and

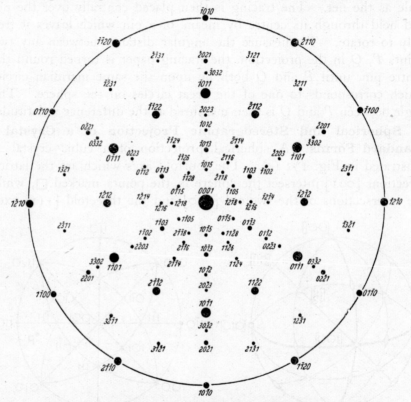

FIG. 173.—Pole figure of Mg-crystal about hexagonal axis [0001].

The indices are those of the normals to the planes.   The size of the spots corresponds to the intensities of the X-ray reflexions from the planes.

laying off these angles with the aid of a Wulff's net.   A table of angles for cubic crystals is given on page 270.   In the cubic system, and only in the cubic system, can a standard projection of poles of planes also serve as a standard projection of crystallographic directions of similar indices, for only in this system is the direction [hkl] perpendicular to the plane (hkl) for all values of the indices h, k and l. A standard projection for a hexagonal crystal upon the basal plane (0001) is given in Fig. 173.

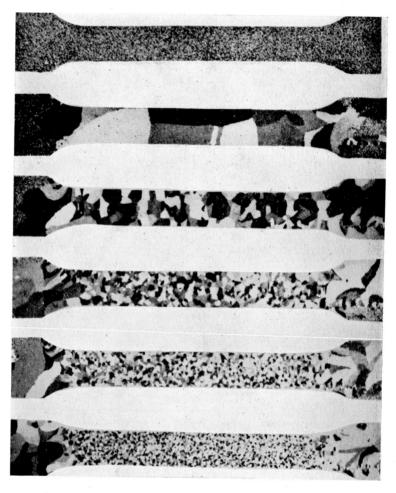

FIG. 174.—Recrystallization of Al rods after extensions of 0, 2, 4, 6, 8 and 10 per cent. (J. CZOCHRALSKI).

Representation of Orientation of Single Crystal Wire. A standard projection enables us to represent in a convenient manner the orientations of single crystal wires, rods or discs. The specimen axis is indicated on the projection as a point such as P in Fig. 172 (*b*) at the requisite angular distances from the axes of the crystal. It is not essential to draw the whole of the standard projection before plotting the axis P in it, as all the necessary information may be obtained by referring it to the three neighbouring poles [100], [110] and [111] which specify one of the 24 equivalent triangles in the projection. Generally, only one of these triangles or two adjacent triangles are drawn before drawing in the orientation of the specimen axis.

Single Crystals, their Growth and Properties. A full understanding of the physical and mechanical properties of poly-crystalline metals would demand complete knowledge of the single crystals of which they are composed. In spite of the considerable amount of work undertaken on this subject, our knowledge is still insufficient to offer a completely satisfactory explanation of the observed strength s of metals.

Single crystals of metal can be divided into two classes, *soft* or *ductile*, and *brittle*. Brittle crystals have very little tensile strength and snap clean through without any appreciable increase in length. In what follows we shall only consider ductile crystals which form the basis of the more important commercial metals, but which, when examined alone, exhibit astonishing differences from the polycrystalline aggregates of which they form a part.

Crystals of metals grow from nuclei in the cooling fused mass. A polycrystalline metal results from growth starting out from several nuclei. To obtain single crystals, the method of J. Czochralski [87] may be used. A thread of the crystal is drawn slowly upwards out of the fused mass at a speed corresponding to the rate of growth of one of its crystal faces. This speed is determined by trial and error. By means of a suitable grafting stick, circular crystals with a given orientation can be produced with a diameter of a few millimeters and a length of 20 cm. or more. A second method of producing single crystals developed by H. C. H. Carpenter and C. F. Elam [88] is founded upon the principle of *recrystallization after stretching*. The material is given a preliminary anneal to remove any initial strain. It is then stretched plastically by about 2 per cent., after which it is subjected to a final heat treatment lasting several hours. The precise amount of preliminary stretch and the time and temperature of the anneal must be found by trial-and-error methods. Typical results from aluminium are shown in Fig. 174. (See also Fig. 154 on page 231.)

Unlike polycrystalline aggregates or amorphous materials like glass, a single crystal is strongly directional in character. The anisotropy owes its origin to the marked variations in spacing between the rows and planes of atoms which differ according to the directions in which they are measured and which, in turn, influence the magnitude of the cohesive forces along these directions and planes. The symmetry of the lattice is thus displayed by the directional values of the elastic moduli in much the same way as it is revealed by the bounding faces of a perfectly developed crystal. In Fig. 175 are shown a number of such models for single crystals of cubic and hexagonal metals.

The Geometry of Simple Glide. Single crystals of ductile metals require only the most minute forces to exceed the elastic limit and enter the region where plastic (permanent) deformation begins. It is not uncommon to extend single crystals several hundred per cent. by the application of small tensional forces. The extension does not take place smoothly as the load is applied, but in a series of discontinuous small jumps each accompanied by a noise like the ticking of a clock.[89] The surface of the crystal, originally smooth, now becomes scaly.

The movement which takes place is a shearing of the crystal upon certain "glide planes" and is, in many ways, closely analogous to the behaviour of a pack of cards when subjected to shearing forces. The scaly appearance of the once smooth surface of the crystal is due to the formation of "glide ellipses" which are produced during the course of the extension. In face-centred cubic and hexagonal close-packed metals, the glide plane is the one with the greatest density of atoms, and the direction in which glide takes place is the one with the greatest line density of atoms. As glide proceeds, the resistance to extension increases. That is, the metal becomes *strain-hardened* by local deformation of the glide planes by an amount dependent on the rate of applying the load.

Conditions of glide are simplest for hexagonal close-packed crystals. Glide normally takes place on the basal planes (0001) in the direction of the Digonal Axis I [$1\bar{2}10$], [$11\bar{2}0$] or [$2\bar{1}10$] whichever is nearest to the direction in which load is applied. In face-centred cubic crystals, glide takes place on the octahedral planes (111), of which there are four sets, and in the direction [110] which is the row of closest packing. Conditions are rather more complex for body-centred cubic metals, for although the most closely packed rows [111] are always the directions of glide, the (110), (112) or (123) planes may function in turn as planes of slip according to the element and the temperature.[90]

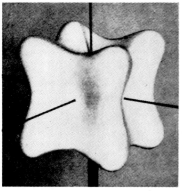

Elasticity Modulus Au.

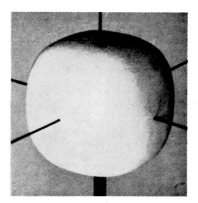

E-Modulus Al.

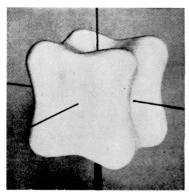

E-Modulus Fe.

Rigidity Modulus Fe.

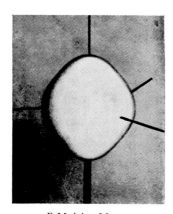

E-Modulus Mg.

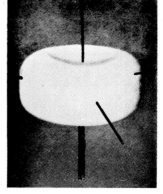

E-Modulus Zn.

FIG. 175.—Elasticity moduli for single crystals of various metals.
(E. SCHMID and W. BOAS, *Kristallplastizität*.)

[*Facing page* 254.

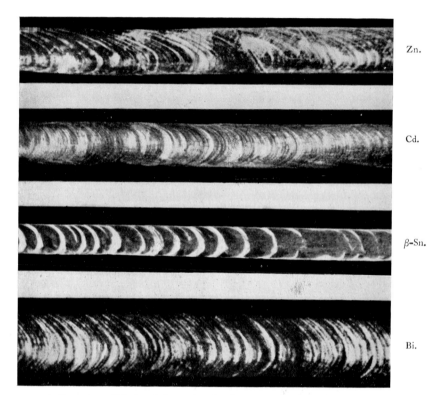

Zn.

Cd.

β-Sn.

Bi.

FIG. 177.—Slip-band formation in single-crystals of metal.

The gliding process is most easily studied in hexagonal close-packed crystals. In Fig. 176, due to M. Polanyi,[91] is shown a model of a cylindrical zinc wire, represented by a pile of wooden discs of equal thickness whose upper and lower faces are the (0001) planes of the single crystal. The crystallographic orientation is shown by the hexagon on the topmost face and the arrow through one of the apexes shows the position of a Digonal Axis I, which is a direction of greatest row density in the lattice. If the crystal is stretched, then in the model the wooden discs slide over one another in the glide direction, as shown in Fig. 176 (c), which is the direction of that Digonal Axis I for which shear stress is greatest.

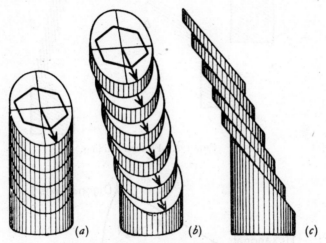

FIG. 176.—Polanyi's Model of Gliding in Zinc.

The crystal moves in "blocks" or "glide lamellæ", for although every lattice plane (0001) is a possible slip plane, not all of them function at once. Owing to lattice distortions which are ultimately produced as strain hardening sets in, there is a limiting thickness for the glide lamellæ which is of the order of 10^{-4} cm.[92] As a result of the gliding, the cross-section of the wire changes from a circular section to an ellipse, so that the wire becomes flattened in the course of the extension (Fig. 177). By taking X-ray photographs, it is possible to determine the orientation of the lattice with respect to the axis of the wire and thereby obtain the indices of the glide planes and the glide directions.

The glide elements of a number of metals are given below in Table XVII. Where glide elements are not crystallographically equivalent to each other, they are listed in order of the frequency with which they are found to occur.

Flexural Glide.   If, in subjecting the crystal to tensional forces, only simple gliding as described above took place, the final appearance of the crystal would be similar to that shown in Fig. 178 (*b*), where the change in length is accompanied by a change in the direction of the wire axis.   But since the ends of the crystal are held in line by the grips of the tensile machine, the glide planes are forced to change

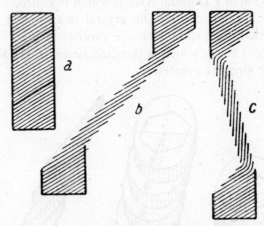

FIG. 178.—Flexural Gliding.

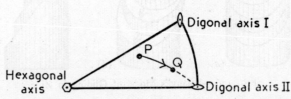

FIG. 179.—Stereographic projection showing glide in zinc crystal. The axis of the crystal moves from *P* to *Q* in the direction of the Digonal Axis II.
(C. F. ELAM, *Distortion of Metal Crystals*, Oxford University Press.)

their original angle of inclination.   This is accomplished by *flexural gliding* [93] whereby the lattice planes become curved in the region of the unstretched portion of the crystal as shown in Fig. 178 (*c*).   It is evident that the heavily distorted regions are the points of greatest lattice stress.   The movement of the normal of the slip plane relative to the axis of the wire for a zinc crystal is illustrated by the stereographic projection shown in Fig. 179.[94]

Critical Shear.   As a result of the researches of G. I. Taylor and C. F. Elam and of E. Schmid, it has been conclusively established that glide occurs whenever the tension in the wire generates in the glide plane and glide direction, a component of shearing stress which exceeds a certain critical value.

TABLE XVII

GLIDE ELEMENTS AND FRACTURE PLANES OF METAL CRYSTALS (after E. Schmid & W. Boas.—*Kristallplastizität*)

Metal	Lattice Type and Crystal Class	Glide Elements				Most Closely Packed		Fracture Plane
		at 20° C.		at elevated temperatures		Lattice Plane	Lattice Direction	
		Glide Plane G	Glide Direction g	Glide Plane G	Glide Direction g			
Aluminium, Copper, Silver, Gold, Lead	Cubic Face-Centred A1 O_h	(111)	[101̄]			1. (111), 2. (100), 3. (110)	1. [111], 2. [100], 3. [112]	∣ ∣ ∣
α-Iron, Tungsten	Cubic Body-Centred A2 O_h	—, (101̄), (112), (123), (123), (112)	[111̄], [111̄], [111̄], [111̄]	approximately 450° C. (100)	[011̄]	1. (101̄), 2. (100), 3. (111̄)	1. [111], 2. [100], 3. [110]	(001)
Magnesium, Zinc, Cadmium	Hexagonal Close-Packing A3 D_{6h}	(0001)	[112̄0]	approximately 225° C. (101̄1) or (101̄2)	[112̄0]	(0001)	[112̄0]	(0001), (101̄1), (0001), (101̄2), (101̄0)
β-Tin (White)	Tetragonal A5 D_{4h}	(110), (100), (101̄), (121̄)	[001], [001], [101̄]	approximately 150° C. (110)	[111̄]	1. (100), 2. (110), 3. (101̄)	1. [001], 2. [111], 3. [100], 4. [1̄01]	
Arsenic, Antimony, Bismuth	Rhombohedral A7 D_{3d}	(111), (111̄)	[1̄01] and [1̄01]			1. (1̄10), 2. (111̄)	1. [1̄01], 2. [1̄01]	(111), (110); (111), (110), (111̄); (111), (111̄), (110)
Tellurium	Hexagonal D_3	(101̄0)	[112̄0]?			(101̄1)		(101̄0)

Let T be the tensional stress per unit area in the wire acting on a cross-section q perpendicular to the axis as shown in Fig. 180 (*a*). Further, let χ be the angle between the axis and the glide plane G, and λ the angle between the axis and glide direction g. The component of force in the direction of glide is $T \cos \lambda$, and this acts over the area $q/\sin \chi$ over which gliding takes place. Thus the component of shearing force per unit area in the direction of glide is equal to

$$S = \frac{T \cos \lambda \sin \chi}{q} \quad . \quad . \quad . \quad . \quad (1)$$

When S exceeds a critical value dependent on the crystal and the temperature, glide commences upon the lattice plane. It follows from equation (1) that conditions for slip are least favourable when the glide plane is nearly parallel to the axis of the wire, when $\chi \approx 0$, and when the glide plane is nearly normal to the axis of the wire, $\lambda \approx 90°$. The most favourable positions for glide are those where the glide plane has a moderate slope. The maximum value of S occurs when $\lambda = \chi = 45°$. A more rigorous analysis of the problem takes into account the effect of internal friction. The value of χ then turns out to be slightly higher than $45°$, a result which agrees with experiment.

Multiple Glide. A face-centred cubic crystal such as aluminium has four pairs of parallel octahedral faces comprising the form $\{111\}$ and in each octahedral face there are three directions of greatest row density of the form $\langle 110 \rangle$. If we imagine a single crystal of aluminium to be subjected to a tensional force, gliding will take place along the glide plane and glide direction for which the resolved shearing force is greatest. If the extension is continued, the flexural

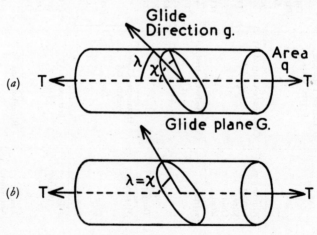

FIG. 180.—Glide Planes and Glide Directions in single crystals subjected to tensile stress.

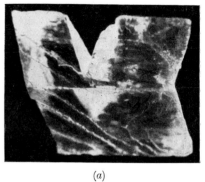

(a)

(b)

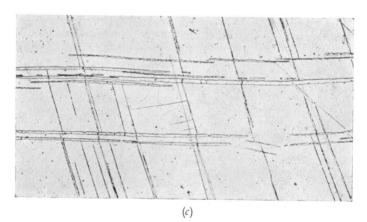

(c)

FIG. 181.—Formation of Twins.

(a) Twins in calcite produced by pressure of a knife-blade. (According to BAUMHAUER.)
(b) Twins in α-brass.
(c) Neumann bands in pure iron × 350. (PFEIL.)

glide will rotate this glide plane into a less favourable position, and, as the extension proceeds, another (111) plane and [110] direction will become just as favourably placed. The extension will then continue as a sequence of alternate slips, some on one set of glide planes and some on the other, a process referred to as *multiple glide*.

Twinning. A crystal is said to be twinned if it is made up of two portions which are symmetrically related to each other. The best-known example is to be found in calcite, in which twins may be formed by pressing a knife into a polar edge of a calcite rhomb as illustrated in Fig. 181 (*a*). The twin is generated by a glide of a *definite amount*, with the glide plane horizontal and the glide direction that of the rhombohedral edge. Such gliding, which takes place in one glide system only, is termed a "simple shift". Only a very definite amount of shift by one lattice plane on its neighbour is permissible, for conditions are stabilized once the twin has formed.

Twins may, in general, be produced in two distinct ways, namely those formed by deposition from the molten mass on cooling, and those produced by severe mechanical deformation or shock. In metals the traces of twins may be observed in the surface of an etched specimen due to the different etching characteristics of the planes exposed by each portion. Twins in α-brass are shown in Fig. 181 (*b*). The fine pattern of lines known as Neumann bands (Fig. 181*c*) which are produced in α-iron upon impact are the traces of twins with a very thin cross-section.

The two symmetrical portions forming a twin are related by definite laws. One half of the twin may be imagined to be derived geometrically from the other by rotation about an axis termed the *twinning axis*, or by reflexion across a plane.[120] In the latter case, rotation about any axis does not make the two parts alike, whereas rotation twins are also usually reflexion twins. The twinning axis in a rotation twin is not necessarily at right angles to the twinning plane, nor is the plane which separates the twin from the parent crystal necessarily the plane of twinning. Simple gliding will not produce twinning, for, in simple glide, the lamellæ move past each other in an arbitrary number of interatomic distances and the relative orientation of the lattice in the sheared portions remains unchanged. To produce twinning, the relative orientation of the *lattice* in the two portions of the twin *must be different*. This is accomplished by moving the atoms in *small local* shifts by an amount which is less than the interatomic distance measured in the direction of shear. The nature of the deformations produced by gliding and twinning are illustrated in Fig. 182.

Twinning is important for the following reason. When a crystal is subjected to tensile or compressive forces the crystal deforms under the resolved shearing stresses upon certain glide planes. As the

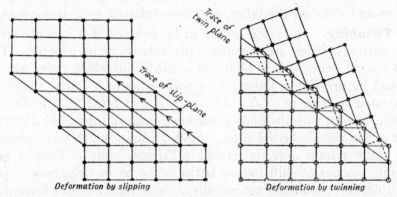

Deformation by slipping   Deformation by twinning

FIG. 182.—Deformation by slipping and twinning. In both cases the plane upon which movement takes place is the same. (C. F. ELAM.)

deformation continues, flexural glide sets in, which rotates the glide lamellæ into positions unfavourable for further deformation. If the stresses are severe enough, twinning occurs and produces new orientations which favour the continuance of deformation by gliding upon

TABLE XVIII

TWINNING PLANES AND TWINNING AXES FOR VARIOUS METALS

Metal	Crystal Type	Twinning Plane		Twinning Axis
		1	2	
Cu α-Brass	Cubic Face-Centred, A1	(111)		[111]
α-Fe	Cubic Body-Centred, A2	(112)	(11$\bar{2}$)	[111]
β-Sn	Tetragonal, A5	(331)	(111)	[331]
As Sb Bi	Rhombohedral, A7	(011)? (011) (011)	(100) (100) (100)	
Zn Be Mg Cd	Hexagonal, A3	(10$\bar{1}$2) (10$\bar{1}$2)	(10$\bar{1}$2)	[10$\bar{1}$2]

a fresh set of slip planes. A list of twinning planes for a number of metals is given above in Table XVIII.

Kinking. When long single crystals of hexagonal metals such as zinc or cadmium are grown with the glide plane (0001) nearly parallel to the wire axis, the orientation is unfavourable to the operation of the usual glide mechanism under the action of tensile or bending loads. If compressive loads are applied, the crystals suddenly collapse, forming kinks with sharp ridges and regular curvatures as shown in Fig. 183. The deformation cannot be ordinary glide or twinning on account of the regular curvatures and the non-crystallographic orientation of the planes determined by the ridges.

X-ray studies by E. Orowan[95] show that the kink has the structure of Fig. 183 (*c*). In addition to the curved regions where the lattice is subjected to flexural glide, the deformed crystals contain the planes *kk'* in which the glide lamellæ are so sharply bent that they appear broken. The plane of kinking, *k*, need not be a crystallographic plane. Since the *lattice* in the kink is not a mirror image of the undeformed lattice in the plane of kinking, the two portions are not the components of a twinned crystal.

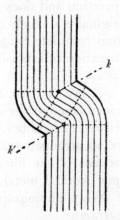

FIG. 183 (*c*.)—Structure of the kink in Fig. 183 (*a*).

Thin parallel lines, glide planes. Broken lines, boundary of the wedge-shaped regions of flexural glide. Dash-dotted lines, *k* and *k'*: planes of kinking.

When mild steel is subjected to stress, the test-piece is covered by stress marks known as Lüder's lines. These are related to kink bands, and it is suggested that the deformation producing the sharp yield point observed in mild steel may begin with kinking instead of glide or twinning.

Fibre Structures. In the production of an ideal Debye-Scherrer powder photograph, an important feature is the complete randomness of orientation possessed by the crystal grains which constitute the irradiated specimen. At any given setting of the powder specimen, only a very small fraction of these crystals are in a position to reflect. Thus, a stationary specimen tends to produce spotty, discontinuous haloes if insufficient grains are bathed in the incident radiation. In order to bring other crystals into a position where they too can make a contribution to the diffraction rings, the specimen is continuously rotated. In this way, the fullest use is made of all the crystals in the specimen and perfectly uniform, continuous haloes are thereby recorded.

If, now, instead of a powder, the specimen consists of a poly-crystalline cold-drawn wire or a narrow strip of cold-rolled sheet, we find that the Debye-Scherrer rings are no longer continuous and uniform, but exhibit regions of locally enhanced intensity, while adjacent portions of the haloes are considerably weakened (Fig. 184*b*). These discontinuities are a direct consequence of the *preferential orientations* of the crystals.   The action of drawing, rolling, extruding or forging results in breaking up the original large crystal grains and, by flexural gliding, rotates the fragments into a definite preferential orientation with respect to the direction in which the metal has been worked.   The final result is always the same for a given type of operation and does not depend on whether the starting material was originally a single crystal or a polycrystalline mass.   The departure from complete randomness of crystal orientation leads directly to the formation of intensified and weakened regions in the Debye-Scherrer haloes.

X-ray patterns from cold-drawn wire and sheet bear a striking resemblance to the diffraction patterns from cellulose, asbestos fibre, or stretched rubber.   In all these materials, the minute crystal grains are so arranged that a definite crystallographic axis lies parallel to the axis of the fibre.   By analogy, the orientation texture imposed upon worked metals is termed a *fibre structure* and the special types of X-ray photograph which they produce are referred to as *fibre diagrams*.

The effect seems to have been observed first of all by Nishikawa and Ono as long ago as 1913,[96] seven years later by N. Uspenskij and Konobejewski,[97] and, shortly afterwards, independently by K. Becker, R. O. Herzog, W. Jancke and M. Polanyi.[98]   This discovery of a fibre structure in cold-worked metals is of special importance, for the physical and mechanical anisotropy which such metals exhibit must be a direct consequence of the mechanism by which plastic deformation proceeds.   X-ray methods present a specially favourable means of studying this mechanism, particularly in fine-grained materials.

There are important points of difference between the fibre struc-tures of wires and the fibre textures imposed on sheet.   In a wire a definite crystallographic direction, or zone axis, tends to lie along the longitudinal direction of the wire, and with this limitation only, the crystals may have any angular orientation about the fibre axis, as shown in Fig. 185 (*a*).   Thus it follows that whatever the setting of the wire specimen, provided the X-ray beam is always at right angles to the axis of the wire, and therefore to the fibre axis, the X-ray

(a)   (b)

FIG. 183.—Deformation of Cd single crystals by "Kinking".
(E. OROWAN, *Nature*, **149**, 643, 1942.)

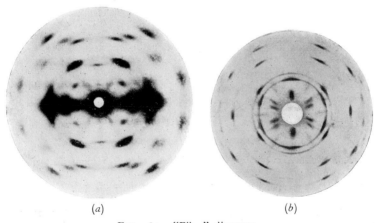

(a)   (b)

FIG. 184.—"Fibre" diagrams.

(a) Cellulose fibre. Fibre axis vertical (ASTBURY).
(b) Aluminium wire. Wire axis vertical. Mo.$K\alpha$ radiation (CLARK).

[*Facing page* 262.

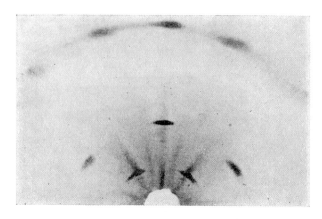

(a)

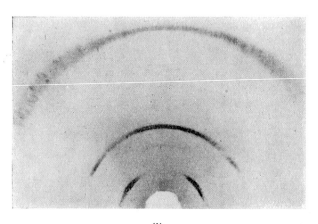

(b)

FIG. 186.—Orientation patterns from straight-rolled molybdenum sheet after 93 per cent cold reduction.

(a) X-ray beam perpendicular to rolling direction.
(b) X-ray beam parallel to rolling direction.

Cu Kα radiation. Cross-section of beam, 1 mm². Specimen bent in the form of a **U** with the X-ray beam at glancing angle to curved surface in order to avoid shadow effects as produced by a flat specimen, and thus obtain whole pattern. Etched surface.

(C. E. RANSLEY and H. P. ROOKSBY, *J. Inst. Met.*, **5** (1), 29, 1938.)

pattern will always be the same. In these circumstances it is quite unnecessary to rotate the wire in taking the Debye-Scherrer photograph, since no new orientations are thereby introduced.

With sheet, the situation is rather different. Here the texture is dependent upon several factors, namely whether the sheet is forged or rolled, the number of passes, the reduction per pass, the diameter of the rolls, the amount of friction between the rolls and the metal, and on many other factors which differ from alloy to alloy and from

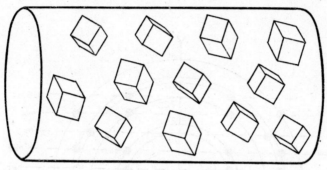

(a) Drawn Al wire. [111] fibre axis.

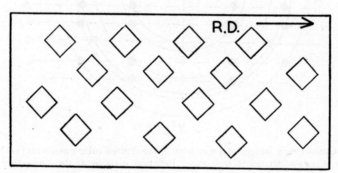

(b) Rolled Fe sheet [100] parallel to direction of rolling **R.D.** —→. (100) in plane of rolling.
[110]

FIG. 185.

operator to operator. As a general rule, a definite crystallographic plane lies parallel to the rolling plane, and a specific zone axis lies, or tends to lie, parallel to the rolling direction. For example, in rolled iron or molybdenum sheet which has undergone heavy reduction, all the individual crystallites lie with a cube face (100) parallel to the rolling plane and with a face diagonal [110] parallel to the rolling direction (Fig. 185b). The X-ray fibre pattern obtained from sheet is different according to whether the direction of the incident beam is parallel or perpendicular to the rolling plane, even though in each case it is incident normally to the rolling direction. The effect for rolled molybdenum sheet is illustrated in Fig. 186.

A cold-drawn aluminium wire has a texture imposed upon it such that a [111] direction in the crystal lattice of each grain is oriented in the direction of drawing, but apart from this restriction, the crystal grains may have any orientation whatever about the axis of the wire. With the X-ray beam normal to the axis of the wire, each crystallite gives the pattern of a single crystal rotated about the [111] zone

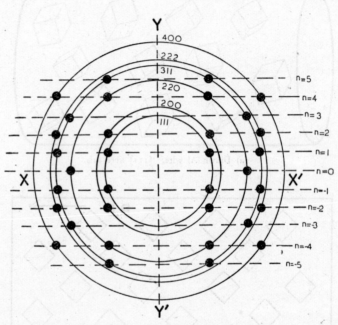

FIG. 187.—Characteristic pattern of a wire from a face-centred cubic metal with [111] crystallographic direction parallel to wire axis. Reflexion spots lie at the intersection of "layer lines" and Debye-Scherrer circles. Wire axis vertical.

axis, and since all the grains have a [111] direction parallel to the axis of the wire, the resulting photograph is merely an enhanced single crystal pattern. With a perfectly developed preferred orientation, the Debye-Scherrer haloes contract into strongly localized spots. These spots lie on the intersections of the Debye-Scherrer haloes and the layer lines of a single crystal with [111] as rotation axis. The effect is illustrated in Fig. 187.

In practice, the orientation of the crystals in wire and sheet is seldom perfect. We usually find a statistical distribution or "scatter" of the crystal axis and planes with regard to some average fibre direction. The effect of the scatter is the same as introducing a small amount of randomness into the orientations of the crystals, thereby increasing the circumferential lengths of the locally enhanced arcs, an effect customarily referred to as *peripheral widening* which must not be confused with the *radial broadening* resulting from small grain size. In a later section we shall develop methods of determining and expressing these departures from an ideal orientation.

The preparation of fibre diagrams may be carried out in a number of different ways. Transmission and back-reflexion Laue photographs utilizing white radiation, Debye-Scherrer photographs, or surface reflexion methods have all been successfully applied. Any standard cylindrical Debye-Scherrer camera, as described in Chapter V, will reveal preferred orientation. To make a full investigation of the orientation texture it is generally more convenient to record the diffraction haloes as full circles upon a flat film. It is seldom necessary to exceed 5 cm. for the specimen-film distance so that cameras of large radius are not required.

The orientation texture of wire or sheet can be deduced quite accurately from a study of the lowest orders of reflexion. If a hard radiation such as Mo Kα or Ag Kα is employed, the absorption by the specimen is low. Thus in a wire, the whole of the cross-section is irradiated and the fibre pattern is an average for the whole of the wire. On the other hand, a softer radiation such as Cu, Ni, Co or Fe Kα may fail to penetrate to the core of all but the very lightest of alloys, and so the fibre diagram is representative only of the outermost layers of the specimen. Further information for different depths below the surface may be obtained by etching away successive layers and taking photographs at each stage. Fibre diagrams for hard-drawn copper wire subjected to this manner of investigation are shown in Fig. 193.

To study the texture in sheet, transmission pictures are most commonly used, although surface-reflexion methods are also sometimes employed. In some cases, thin strips of metal are cut from the sheet in the rolling or cross direction and these are rotated in the X-ray beam in the same manner as a specimen of wire. Such specimens should be etched down to the final dimensions in order to remove the edges which sustain severe cold-work in cutting and filing the specimen to shape.

The Determination of the Fibre Axis in Drawn Wires. It is a straightforward matter to index the diffraction rings of the Debye-Scherrer haloes from randomly oriented crystals or the shorter enhanced arcs or spots from fibred hexagonal or cubic metals. If r

is the radius of a given halo and a is the distance between the flat film and the specimen (Fig. 188), the Bragg angle θ is easily obtained from the expression

$$\tan 2\theta = \frac{r}{a} \qquad . \qquad . \qquad . \qquad . \qquad (1)$$

The angles at which the haloes appear depend only upon the inter-planar distances and the wavelength of the radiation employed. For convenience, a few of the low order reflexions in cubic and hexagonal crystals in order of sequence from the centre spot are listed in Table XIX. With a little experience, the investigator will be able to index the cubic reflexions at a glance. This is not immediately possible with hexagonal crystals, for the sequence of the spectra depends on the axial ratio of the unit cell.

TABLE XIX

ORDER OF APPEARANCE OF DEBYE-SCHERRER HALOES FOR CUBIC AND CLOSE-PACKED HEXAGONAL METALS

Face-Centred Cubic		Body-Centred Cubic		Hexagonal Close-Packed Lattice	
Indices hkl	$h^2 + k^2 + l^2$	Indices hkl	$h^2 + k^2 + l^2$	$c/a = 1 \cdot 633$ Ideal Case. Mg $c/a = 1 \cdot 62$	$c/a = 1 \cdot 86$ (Zn)
111	3	110	2	$10\bar{1}0$	0002
200	4	200	4	0002	$10\bar{1}0$
220	8	211	6	$10\bar{1}1$	$10\bar{1}1$
311	11	220	8	$10\bar{1}2$	$10\bar{1}2$
222	12	310	10	$11\bar{2}0$	$10\bar{1}3$
400	16	222	12	$10\bar{1}3$	$11\bar{2}0$
331	19	321	14	$20\bar{2}0$	0004
420	20	400	16	$11\bar{2}2$	$11\bar{2}2$
$\sin^2 \theta = \left(\dfrac{\lambda}{2}\right)^2 \dfrac{h^2 + k^2 + l^2}{a^2}$				$\sin^2 \theta = \left(\dfrac{\lambda}{2}\right)^2 \left(\dfrac{4(h^2 + hk + k^2)}{3a^2} + \dfrac{l^2}{c^2}\right)$	

We must now attempt to correlate the positions of the enhanced portions of the Debye-Scherrer rings with the fibre texture of the specimen. Consider a crystallographic plane (hkl) whose normal ON makes an angle α with the axis of the wire OP, shown vertical in Fig. 188. Let us suppose the wire to be rotated about its own axis perpendicular to the incident X-ray beam so that the normal to the plane traces out the surface of a cone. At some stage in the rotation, the crystallographic plane will move into a position which satisfies the Bragg condition, and a reflexion will flash out to give a spot on the appropriate Debye-Scherrer ring, the azimuthal position δ at which it occurs being a function of α and the Bragg angle θ. In general, there will be four opportunities for a reflexion to occur

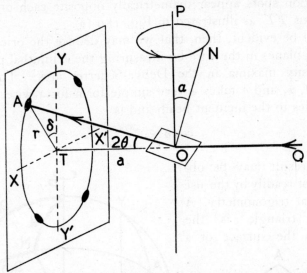

FIG. 188.—Formation of four-point fibre diagram with X-ray beam. *QO* perpendicular to wire axis *OP*.

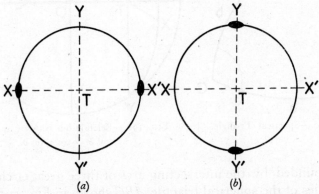

(a)   (b)

FIG. 189.—Two-point and two-point fibre diagrams with X-ray beam perpendicular to axis of wire.

from that particular plane in the course of a 360° rotation of the wire, and so four spots which are symmetrically disposed with regard to the vertical *YY'* and the horizontal *XX'* will appear on the Debye-Scherrer ring.

If α is 90°, the crystallographic plane lies parallel to the axis of rotation, in which case only two spots can appear on the horizontal axis XX' as shown in Fig. 189 (*a*). On the other hand, if ON coincides with the axis of the wire, the X-ray beam will lie in the crystallographic plane whatever the angle of rotation and the condition for a reflexion will never be attained. There is also the possibility that α will just equal the Bragg angle θ. In such a case, $\delta = 0$ and two reflexion spots appear diametrically opposite each other on the vertical axis YY' as illustrated in Fig. 189 (*b*).

It will be evident, then, that we may deduce the orientations of the lattice planes in the wire by measuring the azimuthal positions of the intensity maxima in the Debye-Scherrer arcs. The relation between θ, α, and δ takes a very simple form for a wire rotating at right angles to the incident beam and is

$$\cos \delta = \frac{\cos \alpha}{\cos \theta} \qquad . \qquad . \qquad . \qquad . \qquad (2)$$

This result may be ob-tained most readily by the use of spherical trigonometry. A spherical triangle is the region on the surface of a

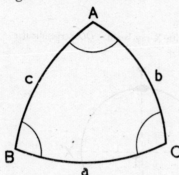

FIG. 190.—Spherical Triangle.

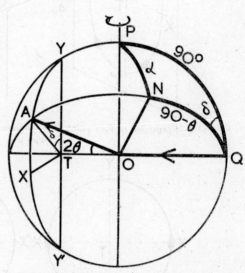

FIG. 191.—Relationship between α, δ and θ.
$\cos \delta = \cos \alpha / \cos \theta$.

sphere bounded by the intersecting arcs of three great circles. The curved sides of the spherical triangle ABC shown in Fig. 190 subtend angles a, b, c at the centre of the sphere. Useful relationships between the angles are

$$\frac{\sin a}{\sin A} = \frac{\sin b}{\sin B} = \frac{\sin c}{\sin C}$$

and
$$\cos a = \cos b . \cos c + \sin b . \sin c . \cos A$$
$$\cos b = \cos c . \cos a + \sin c . \sin a . \cos B$$
$$\cos c = \cos a . \cos b + \sin a . \sin b . \cos C$$

Let us describe a reference sphere about the reflecting plane at O as centre (Fig. 191). The incident ray QO, the normal ON to the reflecting plane, and the reflected ray OA must all lie in the same plane $ANQOT$ which traces a great circle ANQ on the reference sphere. The axis of the wire cuts the sphere in the pole P. The Debye-Scherrer ring containing the reflexion spot A is represented by the latitude circle $YAXY'$. The angle Q equals δ, the angle YTA, while the arc of the great circle through P and N subtends the angle α. Since the normal ON to the reflecting plane must make an angle of $90 - \theta°$ with the incident ray OQ, it follows that arc $NQ = 90 - \theta°$. The spherical triangle PQN immediately gives

$$\cos \alpha = \cos (90 - \theta) \cos 90 + \sin (90 - \theta) \sin 90 \cos \delta$$

and therefore

$$\cos \delta = \frac{\cos \alpha}{\cos \theta}$$

which is the relation required. With a hard radiation such as Mo or Ag $K\alpha$, the reflexion angles θ for the low orders of most metals are small. Hence, we may write $\delta = \alpha$ since in such cases $\cos \theta$ is approximately equal to unity.

By measuring the fibre diagram, we obtain a list of reflexion haloes and appropriate values of δ for the positions of the intensity maxima in the intensified arcs. To determine from the δ's which crystallographic axis $[uvw]$ lies parallel to the axis of the wire, we require to know the angle α between the normal to the lattice plane (hkl) and the zone axis $[uvw]$. For a cubic lattice, this angle is given by the relation

$$\cos \alpha = \frac{hu + kv + lw}{\sqrt{u^2 + v^2 + w^2}\sqrt{h^2 + k^2 + l^2}} . \quad . \quad (3)$$

Values of α from a paper by Bozorth [99] are tabulated below in Table XX.

In Fig. 187 is shown an idealized fibre diagram of aluminium wire taken with silver $K\alpha$ radiation. Since the angles θ are necessarily small, we may take $\delta = \alpha$. The innermost halo is the 111 reflexion. There are four points on it, the angle δ being 71°. Hence $\alpha = 71°$. Looking in Table XX for an angle of 71° related to the *plane* (111), we find it against the zone axis [111]. Hence [111] is probably the fibre axis. Now the 111 reflexion may arise from any of the octahedral planes (111), ($\bar{1}$11), (1$\bar{1}$1) and (11$\bar{1}$), and the other four parallel to these. Using equation (3), we find that for [111], $\alpha = 0$, which corresponds to $\alpha = 0$ in the table, while for the remainder, $\alpha = 70° 32'$. If [111] really is the fibre axis, the X-ray beam which is normal to it lies in the ($\bar{1}$11) plane so that a reflexion from (111) is impossible. Only a four-point pattern with $\delta = 70° 32'$ can appear by reflexion from the remaining planes.

The third ring 220 is the second order reflexion from the (110) planes. We obtain δ values from the diagram as follows:

$$(110) \quad (101) \quad (011) \qquad \delta = 35°$$
$$(\bar{1}10) \quad (\bar{1}01) \quad (0\bar{1}1) \qquad \delta = 90°$$

TABLE XX

ANGLES BETWEEN CRYSTALLOGRAPHIC PLANES IN CRYSTALS OF THE CUBIC SYSTEM

(R. M. Bozorth, *Phys. Rev.*, **26**, 390, 1925)

Values of α, the angle between (HKL) and (hkl) or zone axis $[uvw]$ and $[hkl]$.

(HKL) $[uvw]$	(hkl) $[hkl]$							
100	100	0°	90°					
	110	45°	90°					
	111	54° 44'						
	210	26° 34'	63° 26'	90°				
	211	35° 16'	65° 54'					
	221	48° 11'	70° 32'					
	310	18° 26'	71° 34'	90°				
	311	25° 14'	72° 27'					
	320	33° 41'	56° 19'	90°				
	321	36° 43'	57° 42'	74° 30'				
110	110	0°	60°	90°				
	111	35° 16'	90°					
	210	18° 26'	50° 46'	71° 34'				
	211	30°	54° 44'	73° 13'	90°			
	221	19° 28'	45°	76° 22'	90°			
	310	26° 34'	47° 52'	63° 26'	77° 5'			
	311	31° 29'	64° 46'	90°				
	320	11° 19'	53° 58'	66° 54'	78° 41'			
	321	19° 6'	40° 54'	55° 28'	67° 48'	79° 6'		
111	111	0°	70° 32'					
	210	39° 14'	75° 2'					
	211	19° 28'	61° 52'	90°				
	221	15° 48'	54° 44'	78° 54'				
	310	43° 5'	68° 35'					
	311	29° 30'	58° 31'	79° 58'				
	320	61° 17'	71° 19'					
	321	22° 12'	51° 53'	72° 1'	90°			
210	210	0°	36° 52'	53° 8'	66° 25'	78° 28'	90°	
	211	24° 6'	43° 5'	56° 47'	79° 29'	90°		
	221	26° 34'	41° 49'	53° 24'	63° 26'	72° 39'	90°	
	310	8° 8'	58° 3'	45°	64° 54'	73° 34'		
	311	19° 17'	47° 36'	66° 8'	82° 15'			
	320	7° 7'	29° 45'	41° 55'	60° 15'	68° 9'	75° 38'	82° 53'
	321	17° 1'	33° 13'	53° 18'	61° 26'	70° 13'	83° 8'	90°

TABLE XX (continued)

Values of α, the angle between (HKL) and (hkl) or zone axis [uvw] and [hkl].

(HKL) (hkl) [uvw] [hkl]							
211	211	0°	33° 33'	48° 11'	60°	70° 32'	80° 24'
	221	17° 43'	35° 16'	47° 7'	65° 54'	74° 12'	82° 12'
	310	25° 21'	49° 48'	58° 55'	75° 2'	82° 35'	
	311	19° 8'	42° 24'	60° 30'	75° 45'	90°	
	320	25° 9'	37° 37'	55° 33'	63° 5'	83° 30'	
	321	10° 54'	29° 12'	40° 12'	49° 6'	56° 56'	
		70° 54'	77° 24'	83° 44'	90°		
221	221	0°	27° 16'	38° 57'	63° 37'	83° 37'	90°
	310	32° 31'	42° 27'	58° 12'	65° 4'	83° 57'	
	311	25° 14'	45° 17'	59° 50'	72° 27'	84° 14'	
	320	22° 24'	42° 18'	49° 40'	68° 18'	79° 21'	84° 42'
	321	11° 29'	27° 1'	36° 42'	57° 41'	63° 33'	74° 30'
		79° 44'	84° 53'				
310	310	0°	25° 51'	36° 52'	53° 8'	72° 33'	84° 16'
	311	17° 33'	40° 17'	55° 6'	67° 35'	79° 1'	90°
	320	15° 15'	37° 52'	52° 8'	74° 45'	84° 58'	
	321	21° 37'	32° 19'	40° 29'	47° 28'	53° 44'	59° 32'
		65°	75° 19'	85° 9'	90°		
311	311	0°	35° 6'	50° 29'	62° 58'	84° 47'	
	320	23° 6'	41° 11'	54° 10'	65° 17'	75° 28'	85° 12'
	321	14° 46'	36° 19'	49° 52'	61° 5'	71° 12'	80° 44'
320	320	0°	22° 37'	46° 11'	62° 31'	67° 23'	72° 5'	90°
	321	15° 30'	27° 11'	35° 23'	48° 9'	53° 37'	58° 45'	63° 36'
		72° 45'	77° 9'	85° 45'	90°		
321	321	0°	21° 47'	31°	38° 13'	44° 25'	50°	60°
		64° 37'	69° 4'	73° 24'	81° 47'	85° 54'	

From equation (3) or from the table, we again find that only the [111] fibre axis will give these values, namely 35° 16' and 90°. This confirms that a [111] lattice direction lies in the axis of the wire. For rings outside 220, it is no longer permissible to use the approximation δ = α and the more exact relation given in equation (2) must be employed. These outer rings again confirm [111] as the fibre axis.

Departure from a Perfect Fibre Structure. With a perfectly developed fibre structure in aluminium wire, a [111] zone axis in every crystal grain lies in the direction of the axis of the specimen. Thus, if the incident beam is perpendicular to the wire, it must also lie in the (111) plane and, for the innermost halo, only the (1̄11), (11̄1), etc., planes move into a reflecting position as the wire rotates about its axis, producing, as we have already seen, a typical four-point diagram. Now, in general, the orientation will seldom be perfect and there will be a statistical deviation or angular scatter of the [111] lattice directions of the respective crystals about a mean position, namely the axis of the wire. Since for small angles θ, $\delta = \alpha$, any change in α must be accompanied by an equal change in δ, and so the strongly localized spots become drawn out into the circular arcs of a Debye-Scherrer halo. The angle subtended by such an arc at the centre spot is therefore equal to the angular deviation of the normals of the reflecting planes of the crystals between two extreme positions, and is, consequently, double the maximum angular deviation of a lattice direction from the axis of the wire.

The scatter may become so pronounced that some of the planes in the group originally containing the incident beam now incline at an angle in which they too satisfy the Bragg condition. They are thus able to reflect the incident beam to give two diametrically opposite arcs on the YY' axis in addition to the drawn-out four-point pattern as illustrated in Fig. 192, thereby converting the four-point pattern into an asymmetric six-point array.

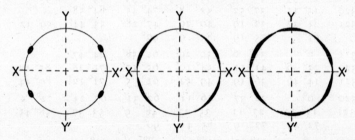

FIG. 192.—Effect of "Scatter" on 111 reflexion from a face-centred cubic wire. [111] vertical.

In Fig. 184 (*b*) (Al wire—Clark), it will be observed that radial streaks extend outwards from the centre towards each reflexion arc on the Debye-Scherrer circles. These are produced by the continuous, or white radiation, which is reflected mirror-like from the preferentially oriented lattice planes. The effect of varying wavelength is to change all the dimensions of the figure which otherwise retains the same symmetry. The white radiation has its peak value at 0·4Å. It therefore produces a streak pointing towards each spot formed by the Mo Kα line with a wavelength of 0·71 Å. Under certain conditions it is possible to determine the orientation texture of wire or sheet from these Laue patterns alone, without the need of employing filtered Kα radiation.

In metal specimens, all the gradations of preferred orientation are to be found ranging from the continuous rings of randomly arranged crystals to the sharp spots corresponding to a highly perfect fibre structure. The precise texture is dependent not only on the

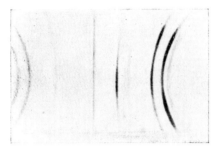

(a) 1·75 mm. diameter.

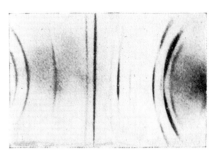

(b) Etched down to 1·3 mm.

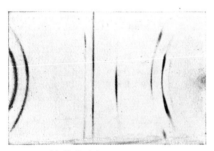

(c) Etched down to 1·0 mm.

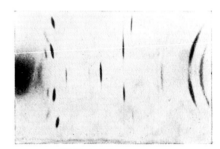

(d) Etched down to 0·4 mm.

FIG. 193.—Zonal texture of hard-drawn copper wire revealed by diffraction patterns from etched specimens.

(E. SCHMID and G. WASSERMANN.)

Facing page 273.]

nature of the cold-work applied and the heat treatment, but also, to a large extent, on the composition of the specimen.

Zonal Texture of Wires. Wires drawn through dies exhibit zonal structures in which the grains become more perfectly oriented as the centre of the wire is approached. This is strikingly displayed by the X-ray patterns of hard-drawn copper wire, taken after etching away successive layers from the surface (Fig. 193). In the outer-most skin of the wire, the effect of the die has been to keep the grains with a [111] axis nearly parallel to the direction of drawing. Slightly below this the flow is distinctly conical, while the innermost portion again has a perfect fibre structure with [111] accurately in line with the axis of the wire. Table XXI expresses the findings of Schmid and Wassermann on the zonal texture of copper wire.

TABLE XXI

ZONAL TEXTURE OF HARD-DRAWN COPPER WIRE

Distance of Layer from centre, in millimetres	Inclination Angle α degrees
1·75	2
1·6	9
1·3	6
0·9	4
0·4	0

It was also found that the tensile strength of the centre portion was greater than that of the wire as a whole. Results for two specimens of copper wire were as follows:

		Tensile strength Kg/mm.²
1. Original diameter . .	4·85 mm.	38·3
Etched to . . .	3·20 mm.	41·3
Drawn to . . .	3·20 mm.	45·2
2. Original diameter . .	1·75 mm.	46·1
Etched to . . .	1·00 mm.	52·8
Drawn to . . .	1·00 mm.	51·0

The enhanced tensile strength of the centre of the wire may be explained in the following manner. The shear stresses set up by the tensile forces tend to make the planes of highest atomic density slide over one another. In copper, these are the (111) planes. Since the greatest resolved shear stresses are at 45° to the axis of the wire, deformation by slip will be easiest for all (111) planes inclined

K

at this angle, while resistance to shear will be a maximum for all (III)
planes lying perpendicular to the direction of pull.   Since in copper
wire the central portion has a [III] crystallographic direction in the
axis of the wire, the (III) plane belonging to it must lie at right
angles to the direction of pull and so the resistance to deformation
attains a maximum value.   (See also Chapter IX.)

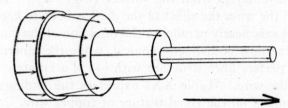

FIG. 194.—Schematic representation of the zonal texture of hard-drawn Cu wire (*cf.* Fig. 192).
The directions of the fibre axes and the degree of preferred orientation are represented
by the directions and lengths of the arrows.

(E. SCHMID and G. WASSERMANN.)

Because of the conical zonal structure to be found in the wire
(Fig. 194) the drawing and counter-drawing directions are not
equivalent, and therefore a plane lying perpendicular to the axis of
the wire is not a symmetry plane as far as the orientation texture is
concerned.

Multiple Fibre Structures.   When the wire possesses a simple
fibre structure, only one zone axis lies parallel to the axis of the wire.
The fibre structure may be much more complex in a manner which
depends entirely on the metal and the precise drawing technique
employed in manufacture.   We may, as a result of a modified technique, induce two discrete groups of crystal grains, each having a
definite, though different, crystallographic direction parallel to the
axis of the wire.   Such a dual texture is spoken of as a double, or
multiple, fibre structure.

E. Schmid and G. Wassermann [100] have studied the texture of
the face-centred cubic metals Al, Cu, Au and Ag and find that both
[III] and [100] directions may lie parallel to the wire axis, the precise
distribution of the orientations being dependent on the metal.   This
is brought out in Table XXII, where, in addition, the scattering round
the [100] preferred orientation will be seen to be twice as great as
the scatter round [III].

Hexagonal metals also exhibit a lack of homogeneity in their
drawing textures.   Zinc, for example, reveals a double conical or
"spiral" fibre texture, beneath an outer skin which possesses a simple
conical fibre structure.

TABLE XXII

DOUBLE FIBRE TEXTURE IN FACE-CENTRED CUBIC METALS

Metal Wire	Percentage of Crystals with		Half-length of Arcs on 200 reflexion	
	[100]	[111]	100	111
	parallel to direction of drawing			
Aluminium	0	100		3° 30'
Copper	40	60	7°	3°
Gold	50	50	8° 30'	4° 30'
Silver	70	25	7° 30'	3°

All the face-centred cubic metals have a [111] direction parallel to the wire axis with a second possible orientation [100]. Body-centred cubic metals such as α-iron are characterized by a [110] lattice direction lying parallel to the axis of the wire. As we have shown, the fibring tends to be most perfect at the core and the outermost skin of the wire. The general principle holds that a set of most densely packed crystallographic planes so orients itself as to offer a maximum resistance to shear and therefore to oppose any further

TABLE XXIII

FIBRE TEXTURES OF DRAWN WIRE

Metal	Parallel to axis of wire	
	1	2
Al	[111]	
Cu		
Au		
Ni	[111]	[100]
Pd		
Ag	[100]	[111]
α-Fe		
W	[110]	
Mo		
Mg. Drawn . . .	(0001)	
Extruded . . .	[10$\bar{1}$0]	
Zn	(0001)	

drawing of the wire. It is probably for this reason that extension in a tensile testing machine and drawing through a die each lead to the same orientation texture. The drawing textures of the more important metals are summarized in Table XXIII.

Polanyi's Method of Diatropic Planes. It is not always possible or desirable to impinge the incident X-ray beam at right angles to the fibre axis. In Polanyi's method, the specimen is placed at an oblique angle with respect to the incident radiation as shown in Fig. 195. The Debye-Scherrer rings remain positioned exactly as before, but now the upper and lower intensified arcs move relative to the vertical YY'. Thus instead of a single angle δ which we

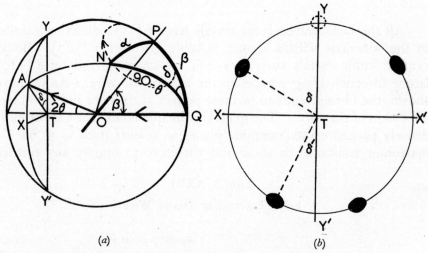

(a)   (b)

FIG. 195.—(a) Determination of fibre axis by method of oblique incidence.
(b) Asymmetric four-point diagram. A reflexion appears at Y when $\beta = 90 - \theta°$.

normally measure on a simple four-point diagram, we now have the two angles δ and δ' which are given by the formulæ:

$$\cos \delta = \frac{\cos \alpha - \cos \beta \sin \theta}{\sin \beta \cos \theta}$$

and

$$\cos \delta' = \frac{\cos \alpha - \cos (180 - \beta) \sin \theta}{\sin (180 - \beta) \cos \theta}$$

where α is the angle between the normal to the planes (hkl), and the zone axis $[uvw]$ which is parallel to the axis of rotation of the specimen.

We may use the method of oblique incidence to determine directly the indices of the fibre axis. A series of X-ray photographs are taken with different values of the angle β. Now if in any one of the series, the X-ray beam should strike the lattice planes normal to the fibre axis (the diatropic planes of Polanyi), at the Bragg angle, then β will be equal to $90 - \theta°$ and *two intensity maxima* will appear diametrically opposite each other on the vertical YY' of the Debye-Scherrer ring (hkl). In the cubic system, the normals to the planes (hkl) are also the crystallographic directions [hkl], and so the diatropic plane method yields the indices of the fibre axis immediately.

The Texture of Rolled Sheet. When metal is rolled into sheet, we find the major dimensional changes to be a diminution in thickness and an increase in length in the rolling direction. The width of the sheet remains substantially the same. This means that in addition to the compressive action of the rolls, certain frictional forces are operative between the surfaces of the sheet and the rolls, of sufficient magnitude to prevent sideways spreading. Under the influence of the combined forces, a fibre texture is produced in the sheet which gives it a marked anisotropy in mechanical properties. Not only do the tensile strength and ductility measured in the rolling direction differ appreciably from those measured transversely to the rolling direction, but the surface texture with regard to grain size and orientation will also be appreciably different from that in the interior.

The anisotropy may be controlled by modifying the rolling and heat treatment techniques, thereby reducing many of the harmful effects which flow as a natural consequence from a marked direction-ality in the material. For example, in straight-rolled magnesium sheet, the tensile strength in the direction of rolling is approximately 9 tons per square inch, while the value measured in the transverse direction is as high as $16\frac{1}{2}$ tons per square inch.[101] If the sheet is turned through 90° after each pass, i.e., if it is cross-rolled, the mechanical properties become uniform and the tensile strength in all directions attains a mean value of 10·5 tons per square inch. By way of contrast, low carbon steel sheet for deep drawing purposes exhibits a tensile strength which is 12 per cent. higher in the direction of rolling than in the transverse direction. Here, then, the anisotropy is opposite to that in straight-rolled magnesium, and the underlying causes may be ascribed to crystallographic differences which influence the rate of strain-hardening in different lattice directions when the material is subjected to tensile forces.

In deep-drawing or pressing operations, the anisotropy in tensile strength and ductility often reveals itself by the formation of wavy "ears" on the top edges of cups. The ears in themselves are of minor consequence for they can be cut off, but what is more objectionable and serious is the diminution in wall thickness in regions where the metal has flowed preferentially in the direction of greater ductility. This ear formation is not due to faulty manipulation in the drawing process but is definitely due to directionality in the material. To prove this, two cups in 80/20 cupro-nickel sheet made on the same machine under exactly the same conditions are shown in Fig. 196 (a). The only differences lie in the methods of rolling and annealing, which proves conclusively that the cause of ear formation is to be sought in the directional properties which an unsuitable rolling and annealing technique has produced. Debye-Scherrer photographs of similar cupro-nickel sheet taken by H. P. Rooksby are shown for comparison in Fig. 196b.

Even more remarkable than the formation of ears on cups is the extraordinary brittleness shown by cross-rolled molybdenum sheet. Fig. 197 shows a typical specimen prepared by H. P. Rooksby and C. E. Ransley[102] which gave a sudden brittle fracture along perfectly straight lines directed at 45° to the rolling directions after bending the quite pliable sheet backwards and forwards a few times.

Limited Fibre Structure. The anisotropy in physical and mechanical properties is obviously a direct consequence of the preferred orientation to be found in the crystals composing the sheet. In wire, a definite crystallographic direction, such as $[111]$ in a face-centred cubic metal, lies parallel to the wire axis. Apart from this restriction, the crystals may have any orientation around this direction. With rolled sheet the state of affairs is rather different, for the orientation may be restricted in two ways. Firstly, a definite crystallographic axis tends to lie with a specific orientation with regard to the rolling direction, and secondly, a well-defined lattice plane lies in the plane of the sheet. On account of the extra restriction imposed upon the texture of rolled sheet, and to distinguish it from the normal type of fibre structure found in drawn wire, the term "limited fibre structure" is applied.

The orientation texture in rolled sheet is seldom perfect. In rolled magnesium, the tendency is for the planes of closest packing (0001) to lie in the plane of the sheet, which means that the $[0001]$ crystallographic direction should be normal to the plane of the sheet. This is not quite the case, however, for deviations of $\pm 25°$ in the rolling direction and $\pm 15°$ in the transverse direction have been noted by D. E. Thomas[103] and others, which probably accounts for the directionality in mechanical properties. The texture in rolled sheet of a number of metals is given in Table XXIV.

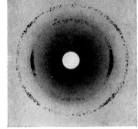

FIG. 196 (*b*).—X-ray photographs of suitable and unsuitable cupro-nickel sheet.

(H. P. Rooksby, *Journ. Sci. Inst.*, **18**, 84, 1941.)

(Similar results for copper and brass sheet have been obtained by M. Cook and T. Ll. Richards.
J. Inst. Met., **69**, 201, 1943; **69**, 351, 1943.)

FIG. 196 (*a*).—Formation of "ears" in deep-drawn cupro-nickel cups.

(J. D. Jevons, *Metallurgy of Deep Drawing*. Chapman & Hall.)

FIG. 197.—Sample of Cross-rolled Molybdenum Sheet showing
45° brittleness (natural size).
(C. E. RANSLEY and H. P. ROOKSBY, J. Inst. Met., 62, 205, 1938.)

TABLE XXIV
Textures of Rolled Metal

Metal	Parallel to Rolling	
	Direction	Plane
Al Ag α-brass (Pt)	[112]	[110]
Cu Ni (Au)	1. [112] 2. [111]	1. [110] 2. [112]
α-Fe Mo	[110]	(001)
Mg Zn Cd	— [11$\bar{2}$0] —	(0001) (0001) (0001)

To give an adequate representation of the fibre texture of rolled sheet, special contour graphs known as "pole figures" were developed by F. Wever,[104] which reveal at a glance the nature of the orientation texture. Pole figures offer a most convenient method of expressing the texture of worked metals generally, whether produced by rolling, drawing, forging, extruding or by simple extension or compression. They are much more satisfactory and informative than making a statement regarding the degree of "scatter", a practice which has been severely criticized by Wever. The method of representation by pole figures is also very useful for determining the orientations of grains in cast metals, in the study of recrystallization structures and in the relative orientations of crystals which precipitate from solid solutions upon definite lattice planes of the parent solid solution. For these reasons the pole figure method of presentation is now almost universally employed to represent orientation textures.

The Derivation of Pole Figures

The Plotting of Pole Figures. In specimens with randomly oriented grains, the normals to the crystal planes of given form {hkl} are similarly oriented at random. If, then, we describe a reference sphere about the specimen as centre, the normals will intersect the sphere in poles which are uniformly distributed over its surface. If the number of grains is sufficiently large, they will give rise to Debye-Scherrer circles which will be perfectly uniform and continuous.   The normals to those planes which are in a position to reflect, trace out the surface of a cone of semi-vertical angle $90 - \theta°$ which intersects the reference sphere in the "circle of reflexion" (Fig. 51, page 85).   If, however, the specimen possesses a definite orientation texture, then the poles of the crystallographic planes crowd into localized positions on the reference sphere. Those poles which still lie on the circle of reflexion now become densely crowded in some regions and sparsely distributed in others, and consequently, the Debye-Scherrer ring degenerates into localized intensified arcs, thus revealing the existence of the fibre texture.

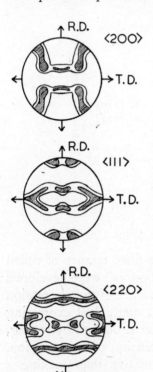

FIG. 198.—Pole figures for rolled aluminium sheet.

The plane of the sheet is also the plane of the reference circle. R.D. = rolling direction, T.D. = transverse direction. A separate figure is drawn for the normals to the 200, 111 and 220 planes of the face-centred cubic Al lattice.

The stereographic projections of all poles of given indices $\langle hkl \rangle$ of the grains in the sample form a pole figure.   To plot such a figure, it is necessary to amass sufficient data by taking a whole series of Debye-Scherrer photographs, with the specimen tilted at successively smaller angles with respect to the X-ray beam.   A sufficiently accurate representation of the orientation texture is obtained by plotting pole figures limited to a given set of planes with low indices.   With cubic crystals these are generally of the forms {100}, {110} or {111}, while for hexagonal metals a single pole figure for the basal plane (0001) is usually quite adequate.   The reference circle on which the projection is made is generally taken to lie in the surface of a sheet specimen, while for wires it is the plane normal to the axis of the wire.

It is customary to represent the areas most densely populated with poles by heavy shading in the projection.   Four degrees of shading usually suffice to display the texture.   An alternative representation can be effected by the use of contours drawn through points of constant frequency, in the same way as contours are drawn in ordinary map making.   The requisite intensity of the shading is deduced from the intensities of localized portions of the Debye-Scherrer arcs, and may be obtained either by visual estimation or by means of a microphotometer. Due allowance must be made for absorption of the X-ray beam within the specimen. This can be reduced to a negligible amount by using a hard radiation such as Ag or Mo Kα. Typical pole figures of rolled aluminium and zinc are illustrated in Figs. 198 and 199.

In Fig. 200, an X-ray beam QO is incident normally, ($\alpha = 90°$) upon the surface of a sheet specimen, giving rise to the intensified arcs of a Debye-Scherrer circle of indices hkl and centre T. The normal to the lattice planes giving rise to the centroid of the arc at A intersects the circle of reflexion at the pole P, which is inclined at an angle of $90 - \theta°$ to the incident ray. The pole P projects stereographically through the pole of projection, E, on the equator to give the point M in the plane of the reference circle, which contains the surface of the specimen.

We can readily fix the point M in the stereographic projection, for if R is the radius of the reference sphere, then

$$OM = OE \tan OEM = R.\tan \tfrac{1}{2}(90 - \theta).$$

Also, since E, A, M, P and Q must all lie in the same plane, the azimuthal angle δ of the point M must be the same as that of A which we measure directly on the X-ray photograph. If we take a series of X-ray photographs at successively smaller values of the angle α, the angle between the surface of the specimen and the incident beam, by turning the sheet in steps about the axis NOS, the pole P will trace out a small latitude circle on the sphere. The stereographically projected point, M, moves across the plane of the reference circle along one of the circles of latitude in the projection through the same number of degrees of longitude as the point P on the polar sphere. (This has been shown for the point D corresponding to $\phi = 90°$, or $\delta = 0$.)

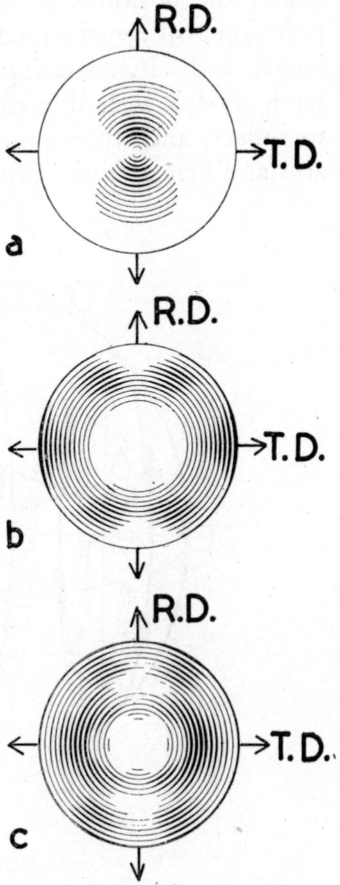

FIG. 199.—Pole figures depicting fibre texture of rolled zinc.

(a) Pole figure for the (0001) basal planes.
(b) Pole figure for the (10$\bar{1}$0) planes.
(c) Pole figure for the (10$\bar{1}$1) planes.
R.D. = Rolling direction.
T.D. = Transverse direction.

(E. Schmid and G. Wassermann, *Metallwirtschaft*, **9**, 698, 1920.)

K*

Only when the normal to the lattice planes again intersects the circle of reflexion will a fresh reflexion spot be produced. Although the plane of the specimen has been tilted with respect to the incident beam, the positions of the Debye-Scherrer circle and the circle of reflexion will remain unchanged for they depend only on the wave-length and lattice spacing. But in the new setting of the specimen, fresh crystals with different orientation will have moved into a position to reflect, and, therefore, the azimuthal positions of the intensified arcs and hence those of their poles will be modified accordingly.

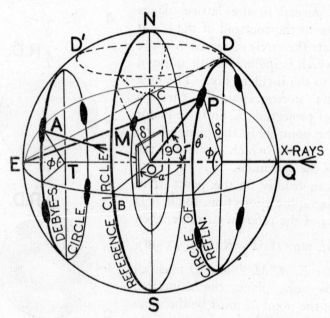

FIG. 200.—Stereographic Projection of Circle of Reflexion.

With $\alpha < 90°$, the plane of the specimen no longer lies in the plane of the basic circle. In order to refer the stereographic projection of the new pole positions to the plane of the specimen, we first of all draw the stereographic projection of the poles in the basic circle in the usual straightforward manner, and, by means of a "rotation", we refer the projection back to the specimen surface. This is done by moving the new pole position along its latitude circle on the sphere, through the same number of degrees of longitude as the angle through which the specimen was turned. Its stereographic projection therefore moves the same number of projected degrees along the corresponding projection of the latitude circle.

As an example, the plotting of data of C. S. Barrett from rolled steel will be given.[105] Using the characteristic Kα radiation of molybdenum, the diffraction from the (110) planes occurs at $\theta = 10°$, and the circle of reflexion thus lies at $90 - \theta = 80°$ from the centre of the pole figure. If the Debye-Scherrer photograph is taken with the beam normal to the surface of the specimen, i.e., with $\alpha = 90°$, the surface will appear on the projection as the basic circle, and the projection of the circle of reflexion will lie concentric with it. We now rotate the specimen through 30° and take a photograph in the new position. We first plot the new data with regard to the original

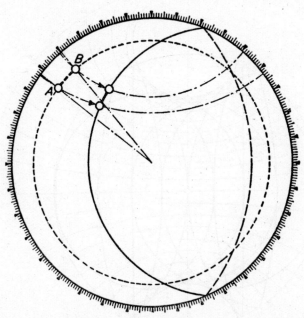

FIG. 201.—Plotting of Pole Figure - - - reflexion circle with beam normal to projection plane
———— and —— — reflexion circle with plane of specimen as projection plane.
(C. S. BARRETT, *Trans. Am. Inst. Min. and Met. Eng., Inst. Met. Div.*, **124**, 29, 1937.)

basic circle, and so the circle of reflexion again projects concentric, as shown by the dashed circle in Fig. 201. The azimuthal extent of the intensity maximum in the reflexion halo is indicated by the limits A and B. We now lay the reference circle upon a stereographic net and move A and B along their respective latitude lines a distance of 30° of longitude. This corresponds to a rotation of the poles round the reference sphere through 30° of longitude when the specimen is turned through the same angle. The movement is illustrated in the figure, where the circle of reflexion with the intensity maximum on it is plotted after rotation as a full line. Part of the reflexion circle on the right-hand side passes into the negative hemisphere. To avoid projecting it outside the basic circle, the negative portion is projected through the opposite pole Q, and thus takes the position shown by the dotted line.   The process is now repeated with different settings of the specimen and corresponding rotations of the data, until the areas on the pole figure are sufficiently well-defined.

In order to simplify the procedure outlined above, F. Wever has constructed a number of reference charts.   Each chart gives a series of projected circles of reflexion shown in the positions they would

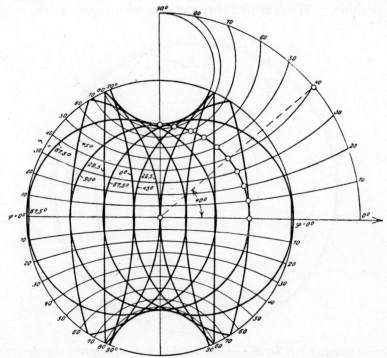

Fig. 202.—Chart for working out diffraction pattern of Aluminium with Copper radiation for the cube face (001).   The basic circle defines the plane of the specimen.   The poles of the projected circles of reflexion move along the equator according to the degree of rotation.

occupy after a rotation back to the setting which makes the plane of the specimen coincide with the plane of the basic circle.   A fresh chart must be constructed for every different value of the Bragg angle θ, and therefore for each wavelength, and for each set of reflecting planes of the metal to be investigated.   Figs. 202, 203 and 204 illustrate Wever's charts for copper $K\alpha$ radiation reflected from (001) and (111) planes of aluminium, and for iron $K\alpha$ radiation reflected from (110) of iron.   They have been constructed for $22 \cdot 5°$ increments in α.

To see how the charts have been obtained, the one in Fig. 202

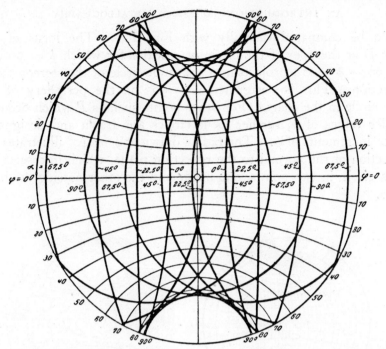

FIG. 203.—Chart for working out diffraction pattern of Aluminium with Copper radiation for the Octahedral Plane (111).

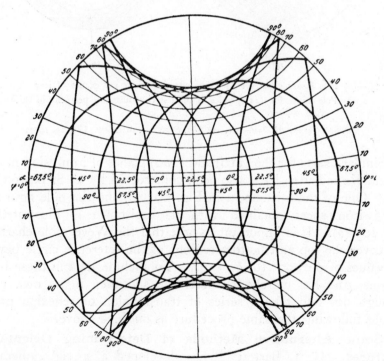

FIG. 204.—Chart for working out diffraction pattern of Iron with Iron radiation for the Dodecahedral Plane (011).

285

should be compared carefully with Fig. 200. The locus of the
point D at the apex of the circle of reflexion for which $\phi = 90°$, or
$\delta = 90 - \phi = 0°$, projects into a latitude circle of the stereographic
projection. This is designated $\phi = 90°$ on the periphery of the
basic circle in the chart. For other points such as P which occur at
smaller values of ϕ, further locus circles are drawn and designated
in $10°$ increments of ϕ. The radius drawn at $\phi = 40°$ illustrates the
projection of the normal to the reflecting plane, which intersects the
locus circle in two points, one inside and the other outside the basic
circle.

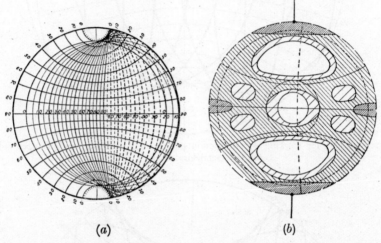

(a)   (b)

FIG. 205.—(a) Pole figure chart for Mo Kα reflecting from 110 planes of iron, $\theta = 10°$.
   (b) Pole figure for {110} poles of mild steel reduced 85 per cent. in thickness by
       cold rolling.

(C. S. BARRETT, *Am. Inst. Min. and Met. Eng., Inst. Met. Div.*, **124**, 29, 1937.)

Similar charts for the (110) and (200) planes of iron using molybdenum Kα radiation have also been constructed by C. S. Barrett (*loc.
cit.*). One of these is shown in Fig. 205 (a) and the pole figure for
rolled iron sheet obtained with its assistance is illustrated in
Fig. 205 (b). It is important to note that the Wever pole charts do
not cover the top and bottom regions of the reference circle beyond
the values of $\phi = 90°$ (or $\delta = 0°$). To include data in these blank
regions, one has merely to rotate the specimen in its own plane
through 90° and take a series of transmission or reflexion photographs following the same procedure as outlined above.

**Some Alternative Methods of Determining Orientation
Textures.** C. S. Barrett [106] has developed a special camera for
the purpose of determining pole figures. Instead of taking a different

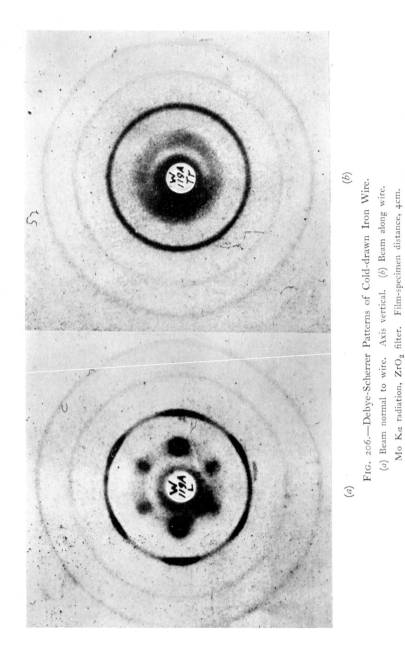

(a)   (b)

Fig. 206.—Debye-Scherrer Patterns of Cold-drawn Iron Wire.

(*a*) Beam normal to wire. Axis vertical. (*b*) Beam along wire.

Mo Kα radiation, ZrO$_2$ filter. Film-specimen distance, 4cm.

(J. T. Norton and R. E. Hiller, *Am. Inst. Min. and Met. Eng., Inst. Met. Div.*, **99**, 190, 1932.)

X-ray photograph for each position of the specimen with respect to the incident radiation, the film is made to oscillate together with the specimen through a small range of angles. Each Debye-Scherrer ring is thereby replaced by a band of considerable width and thus permits a considerable number of spots to be registered without over-crowding. In effect, it is a method whereby a series of diffraction rings are laid side by side, each being taken at a slightly different position of the specimen. The data from the bands of diffraction rings are then plotted on a stereographic projection to form a pole figure. Actually the film itself may be looked upon as a distorted pole figure and reveals the spreading of spots in all directions. Special charts have been constructed for obtaining the pole figures directly from the photographs, details of which are given in the paper by Barrett. A method suitable for the study of the orientation of crystals in electrodeposited metals has been devised by R. M. Bozorth.[99] Here the specimen is irradiated at oblique incidence in much the same manner as a wire in Polanyi's method of diatropic planes. Reference is then made to a chart constructed for that particular camera and angle of incidence, and to a table relating the angles between crystallographic planes having the same or different indices. From this, the crystallographic plane (hkl) which coincides with the plane of the electrodeposited metal is, in general, uniquely determined.

In suitable specimens, crystal orientation may be determined by the method of etch pits. This is a purely optical method and involves the measurement of the angles between the etch-pit faces by a gonio-meter. C. S. Barrett and L. H. Levenson [107] claim that it is equal to X-ray methods in many cases, having an accuracy of $\frac{1}{2}$ to $1°$. The difficulties lie in finding a suitable etching reagent which will give satisfactory etch pits. If the grain size is too small, the optical method is unsuitable, and the X-ray approach is the only one available.

The Texture of Tubing. The crystallographic orientations in steel tubing have been studied by J. T. Norton and R. E. Hiller.[108] They show how interesting analogies may be drawn between the texture of tube and those of drawn wire and rolled sheet. In steel wire, the crystallites are so arranged that each have a [110] direction parallel to the axis of the wire, but the orientation about this axis is perfectly random (Fig. 206). During the drawing of the wire, the tension and elongation are in the direction of the wire axis, while the cross-section is reduced uniformly in all directions.

With sheet, the orientation texture is one in which the cube faces (100) lie parallel to the rolling plane and with a face diagonal [110] parallel to the rolling direction (Fig. 185*b*, page 263).   In the rolling process, the sheet has been reduced in thickness, extended in length and kept at constant width by the frictional action of the rolls.   From a dimensional point of view, a tube is analogous to a sheet without edges.   The circumference of the tube corresponds to the width, and the wall thickness to the thickness of the sheet.   The most general conditions encountered in tube-drawing practice are those which involve a simultaneous reduction in wall thickness and circumference, but it is also possible to create conditions which keep the circumference constant while reducing the wall thickness, or which keep the wall thickness constant while reducing the circumference.   The ultimate type of fibre structure in tubing depends upon which of these three conditions is observed.

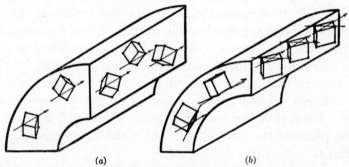

(a)   (b)

FIG. 207.—Orientation of Cubic Crystallites in Tubing.

(a) Equal reduction in wall and circumference.

(b) Reduction principally in wall thickness.

(J. T. NORTON and R. E. HILLER, *Trans. Am. Inst. Min. and Met. Eng.*, *Inst. Met. Div.*, 190, **99**, 1932.)

The results of Norton and Hiller on the texture of cold-drawn steel tubing may be summarized as follows.   As the length is increased, the crystal grains are broken down and so aligned as to make a [110] axis of each crystal lie in the general direction of the tube axis. This is the same as the fibre texture found in steel wire.   At the same time, if the wall thickness is reduced more rapidly than the circumference, the crystals are also aligned so that another [110] axis in each crystal, at right angles to the first, becomes parallel to a tangent to the tube wall, i.e., the structure is the same as in sheet. The orientation of cubic crystallites for the two kinds of reduction are illustrated in Fig. 207.   Tubing reduced so that the dimensional changes are between these shows an intermediate structure.   It was found that as long as the ratio of reduction in wall thickness to reduction in circumference was less than 2, the wire structure was to be found.   The sheet structure was definite when the ratio exceeded

2·5.   Preferred orientation first became evident at about 20 per cent. total reduction of area and increased with further reduction.   The structure obtained was independent of the method of reduction, and was a function only of the dimensional changes which took place during the reducing process.

Crystal Orientation in Deep–Drawn Brass Cups. For the most part, crystal orientation studies of cold-worked metals have been confined to the relatively simple operations of rolling, forging, drawing through dies, or elongating in tension. These processes involve deformations which are confined to one or two principal directions.

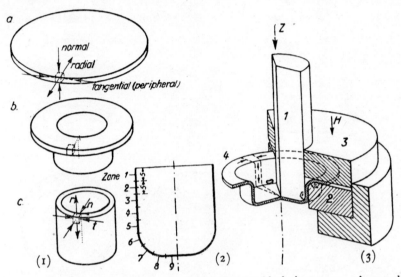

FIG. 208.—(1). a, b, c. Stages in drawing a circular brass blank into a cup.   Arrows show direction of forces.

    (2). Zones of drawn cup selected for examination.

    (3). Section through deep drawing apparatus.

        (1) Punch, operated under a pressure Z of 1975 Kg.
        (2) Die.
        (3) Pressure plate held with a total force H of 600 Kg.
        (4) Partly drawn blank.

Perhaps the first studies which involved forces acting in three principal directions were undertaken by L. Hermann and G. Sachs [109] who encountered this complex problem in the deep-drawing of brass cups. They examined the pressing at various selected points and compared the pole figures they obtained with the type of mechanical work which had been sustained by the regions in question.

The material used was sheet brass (Ms 63) which had been annealed in the hard condition at 550° C. for half an hour. The blanks were round discs, 64 mm. in diameter and 0·5 mm. thick and showed no sign of preferred orientation. The press is shown schematically in Fig. 208 (3), while stages in the fabrication of the cup and the direction of the acting forces are shown in Fig. 208 (1) *a*, *b* and *c*. Fig. 208 (2) shows the zones examined by X-ray diffraction methods. For this purpose small platelets, 5 × 5 mm. square, were

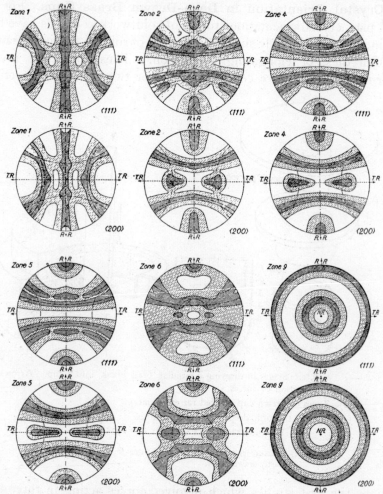

FIG. 209.—Pole figures for various zones of deep-drawn brass cup investigated by X-rays.

RR = Radial direction
TR = Tangential direction} (*cf.* with *a*, *b*, *c* in Fig. 208).

cut out and were etched in nitric acid to remove 0·02 mm. from the surface. Between 12 and 16 X-ray diffraction patterns were taken at various angles to a given platelet from which pole figures for the (111) and (200) reflecting planes were constructed.

Pole figures for various zones are shown in Fig. 209, and for comparison purposes pole figures from the same material deformed by simple tension and by rolling are given in Fig. 210. Ideal pole figures for elongation and forging are also shown. The types of pole figures obtained at the various portions of the deep pressing confirmed

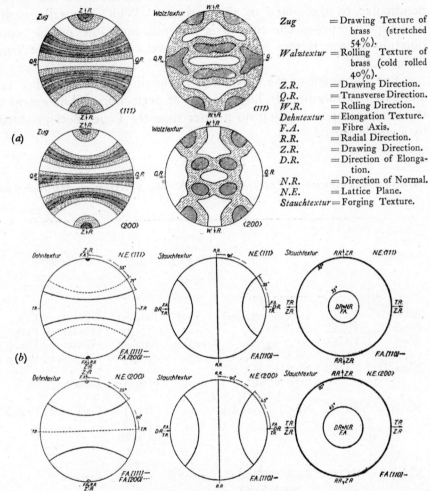

FIG. 210.—(a) Pole figures for brass used for making cups obtained by subjecting material to tensile tests and rolling treatment.

(b) Ideal pole figures of drawing and forging textures.

the theoretical calculations on the forces acting during the various stages of the forming process.

Preferred Orientation in Electrodeposited Metals. A considerable amount of investigation has been carried out on the structure of electrodeposited metals. The precise texture obtained is a function of many variables, the principal ones being the current density, concentration of the electrolyte, temperature, stirring, pH, buffer addition, base electrode and the thickness of the plated coating. If a fibre texture is set up, it is always one in which the fibre axis points in the direction of the flow of current, that is, the fibre axis is perpendicular to the plane of the cathode. Which crystallographic direction comprises the fibre axis depends upon the precise combination of the factors enumerated above. This is evident from Table XXV.

The alignment of the crystallites in the direction of the fibre axis attains an extraordinarily high degree of perfection. The extent of the reflexion spots is often no greater than the Laue spots produced by a single crystal.

TABLE XXV

ORIENTATION TEXTURES OF ELECTRODEPOSITED METALS (R. Glocker, *Materialprüfung mit Röntgenstrahlen*)

Element	Lattice	Solution	Current Density Amperes per sq. cm.	Fibre Axis	Observer
Silver .	F.C.C.	Cyanide (alkaline)	0·007	Random	Glocker and Kaupp
Silver .	F.C.C.	0·1 N AgNO$_3$	0·010	[111], [001]	Glocker and Kaupp
Silver .	F.C.C.	0·1 N AgNO$_3$	0·022	Random	Glocker and Kaupp
Copper .	F.C.C.	1·0 N CuSO$_4$	0·03	[011]	Glocker and Kaupp
Nickel .	F.C.C.	Ni(NH$_4$)$_4$SO$_4$ or 0·1 N NiCl$_2$ + 0·9 N NiSO$_4$	0·005	[001]	Bozorth
Nickel .	F.C.C.	NiSO$_4$+Boric Acid	0·10	[001] [011] (on underlying copper)	Clark and Frölich
Nickel .	F.C.C.	0·9 N NiCl$_2$ + 0·1 N NiSO$_4$	0·005	[211]	Bozorth
Lead .	F.C.C.	Pb(ClO$_4$)$_2$ or fluorosilicate	1·0	[211]	Clark, Frölich and Aborn
Chromium	B.C.C.	Grube's method	—	[111]	Glocker and Kaupp
Iron .	B.C.C.	10% N Fe(NH$_4$)$_4$SO$_4$	0·001	[111]	Glocker and Kaupp
Iron .	B.C.C.	10% N Fe(NH$_4$)$_4$SO$_4$	0·015	Random	Glocker and Kaupp
Iron .	B.C.C.	50% FeCl$_2$	0·001	[111]	Glocker and Kaupp
Iron .	B.C.C.	50% FeCl$_2$ at 100° C.	0·1	Random	Glocker and Kaupp
Iron .	B.C.C.	Same + CaCl$_2$	0·1	[112]	Glocker and Kaupp
Tin . .	B.C.Tetr.			[111]	

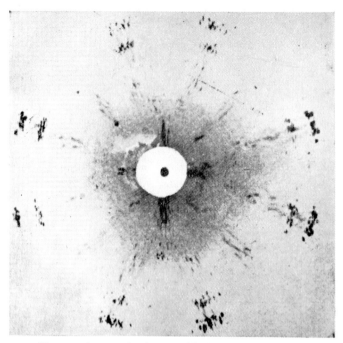

FIG. 211.—Texture photograph of recrystallized copper sheet, showing preferred orientation of recrystallized grains.

(VON GÖLER and G. SACHS, *Zeits. Physik*, **41**, 873, 889, 1927; **56**, 477, 485, 1929.)

FIG. 212.—A Typical Widmannstätten Structure.   Section of Casas Grandes Meteorite × 0·75.

Analysis: Fe, 95·13 per cent.; Ni, 4·38; Co, 0·27; P, 0·24.   Polished and etched with nitric acid.

Facing page 293.]

Recrystallization Textures. It is difficult to make any generalizations concerning the recrystallization textures produced by the annealing of cold-worked metals, for so much depends upon past history, the degree of purity, and the method of annealing the specimen. Any one of the following three possibilities may occur. The newly constituted grains may be oriented completely at random. They may be preferentially oriented at the beginning of the recrystallization only to lose this perfection of alignment by further annealing at yet higher temperatures. Finally the orientation texture may persist even at the highest temperatures. Copper sheet has been found to behave in the last-named fashion and an X-ray photograph illustrating the high degree of perfection attained in the fibre structure is shown in Fig. 211. The hexagonal metals not only recrystallize and maintain a preferred orientation at the highest temperatures, but also have an orientation texture identical with that of the original rolled sheet.

Table XXVI summarizes the recrystallization textures of rolled sheet. Pole figure analysis carried out on the X-ray photographs of rolled iron sheet revealed three distinct types of orientation texture, two of which were equally prominent while the third seldom appeared.

TABLE XXVI

RECRYSTALLIZATION TEXTURES OF ROLLED SHEET

(E. Schmid and W. Boas, *Kristallplastizität*)

Metal	Parallel to Rolling	
	Direction	Plane
Ag . . . . . . α-brass . . . . . Bronze (5% Sn) . .	$[112]$	$(\bar{3}11)$
Al . . . . . . Cu . . . . . . Ni . . . . . . Au	$[100]$	(001)
α-Fe (Ferrite) . . .	$[110]$ $[112]$ $[110]$	(001) $(11\bar{1})$ $(1\bar{1}2)$

Annealing a cold-drawn wire at low temperatures frequently produces a recrystallization texture which is identical with the original fibre texture and which is rarely completely eliminated even by a high temperature anneal. Annealing pure aluminium seems to enhance the existing fibre texture. On the other hand, copper wire when given a high-temperature anneal develops a fibre texture which is quite different from that originally possessed. After annealing, a [112] crystallographic axis lies parallel to the axis of the wire, an orientation formerly possessed by [111] and to a lesser degree by [100] as shown above in Table XXII, page 275.

The Widmannstätten Structure. We have already seen how an alloy which is a stable single phase at higher temperatures, may, upon cooling, precipitate a new phase out of solid solution. This new phase may appear in such a manner that its lattice bears a definite crystallographic relation to the lattice of the parent solid solution. When this happens, the microstructure of the alloy takes on a characteristic appearance as shown in Figs. 212 and 215 (d). The structure was first discovered in meteoritic irons by Alois de Widmannstätten in 1808, but it is to be found, with modifications, in a large number of non-ferrous alloys and even in non-metallic systems such as complexes of hematite and magnetite.

In steels and meteorites, the Widmannstätten figures owe their origin to a plate-like structure which appears as a network where the traces of the plates intersect each other on the surface of polish. In other alloys the precipitated phase may take the form of needles or laths. To obtain a Widmannstätten structure with a high degree of perfection, the rate of cooling must be just right, for if cooling is too slow, agglomeration or spheroidization of the deposited plates may occur, whereas if the rate of cooling is too rapid, too little time will have been given to allow the plates to develop and a fine-grained structure will result.

Widmannstätten figures have been made the subject of a vast amount of microscopic and X-ray study in order to ascertain their mode of formation and the crystallographic orientations of the precipitated constituent. Pole figures and the stereographic projection have played a large part in the most recent researches.[110]

The meteoritic irons, which give rise to perfectly developed Widmannstätten figures are essentially iron-rich nickel-iron alloys whose equilibrium diagram is illustrated in Fig. 117, page 185. The body-centred cubic phase referred to as kamacite, which forms the well-defined lamellæ in meteorites, has been shown by Young to lie parallel to the octahedral (111) planes of the face-centred cubic tænite, which may be regarded as the undecomposed residue of the high-temperature phase. The (110) planes in kamacite and the (111) planes of tænite are the most densely packed planes in their respective lattices. The (111) plane in the face-centred cubic phase becomes the (110) plane in the body-centred cubic phase by a slight shift or re-arrangement in atomic position, for measurement shows that the interatomic distances in the two planes differ by only 2 per cent. and the atomic composition by only 4 per cent. There is thus a definite relation in orientation between the lattice of the precipitate and the lattice of the parent solid solution. This is a general rule which applies to a large number of alloy systems; the lattice of the precipitated phase always orients itself to give a best fit on the parent lattice. The crystallographic planes which meet in the surface of separation need not necessarily be the planes of closest atomic packing of either lattice.[111]

Age Hardening. Closely connected with the formation of the Widmannstätten structure in alloy systems is the phenomenon known variously as "precipitation hardening", "dispersion hardening", or simply "age hardening". Almost any solid solution which is super-saturated will, in time, and with the correct heat treatment, attain equilibrium by rejecting the solute atoms as a separate phase, in the course of which considerable improvements in the mechanical pro-perties may be effected. As a typical example, the important system copper-aluminium will be discussed.

According to the equilibrium diagram illustrated in Fig. 213, aluminium will retain as much as 5 per cent. of copper in solid solution at 500° C., but, with lowering temperature, this value diminishes to 0·5 per cent. Alloys containing between 2 and 5 per cent. of copper may be improved by annealing at 500° C. until a homogeneous solid solution has been attained, and then quenched to retain the structure, which, at room temperature, is supersaturated with copper. By ageing at room temperature for several days, or by heating at a tem-perature not exceeding 200° C. for as little as a day or two, the tensile strength of the alloy may be raised from 12 to well over 20 tons per square inch while still retaining a reasonable degree of ductility.

The changes which take place in the lattice leading to the enhance-ment of mechanical properties are very complex, and numerous theories have been put forward to explain the facts. The ultimate composition of the phase precipitated out of solid solution is $CuAl_2$, but in room temperature ageing, no trace of this phase can be observed in the microscope when the hardening attains its maximum. Debye-Scherrer photographs do not reveal any pattern of lines belonging to the precipitate and no changes in lattice parameter are to be observed until the alloy has been "over-aged" by heat treatment. These facts were interpreted by P. D. Merica [112] to mean the formation of lattice "knots", that is, regions in the lattice where the local concentration of copper was increased by diffusion until it was more or less equal to that required for the formation of a CuAl$_2$ lattice (Fig. 214). These knots in the aluminium lattice were sufficiently distorted and "rough" in atomic structure to resist slip and deformation fairly efficiently.

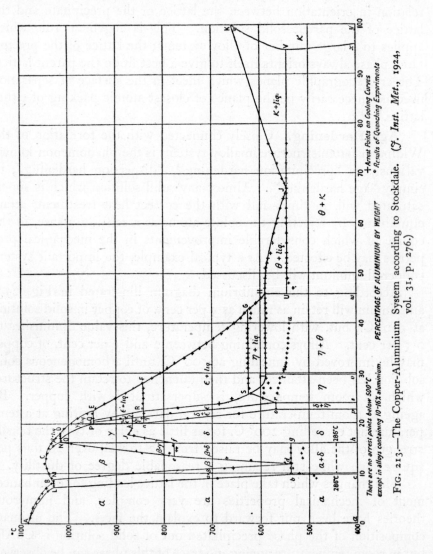

FIG. 213.—The Copper-Aluminium System according to Stockdale. (J. Inst. Met., 1924, vol. 31, p. 276.)

They were considered to act in substantially the same manner as hard crystalline particles of CuAl$_2$ would act could they be formed.

Whereas Debye-Scherrer photographs prove singularly uninformative during the hardening period, room temperature ageing will produce remarkable changes in the Laue diffraction pattern produced by a single crystal of the alloy.   G. D. Preston [113] has shown that certain well-marked streaks make their appearance on the photographs which are faint and diffuse in the early stages but which become progressively stronger and sharper as ageing proceeds (Fig. 215).   Such

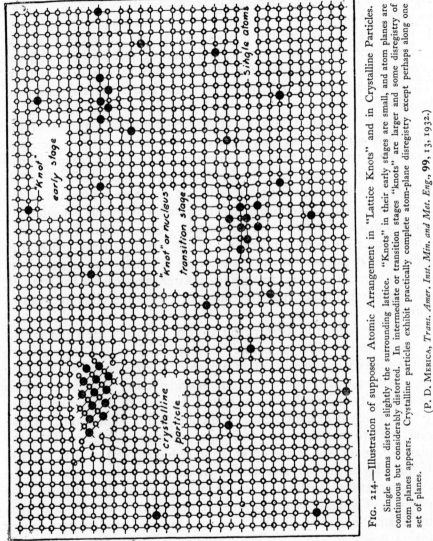

FIG. 214.—Illustration of supposed Atomic Arrangement in "Lattice Knots" and in Crystalline Particles.

Single atoms distort slightly the surrounding lattice. "Knots" in their early stages are small, and atom planes are continuous but considerably distorted. In intermediate or transition stages "knots" are larger and some disregistry of atom planes appears. Crystalline particles exhibit practically complete atom-plane disregistry except perhaps along one set of planes.

(P. D. MERICA, *Trans. Amer. Inst. Min. and Met. Eng.*, **99**, 13, 1932.)

a Laue pattern of an aluminium-copper alloy containing 4 per cent. by weight of copper, quenched at 500° C. and aged at room temperature for three days, is shown in Fig. 215 (*b*).   The reaction proceeds no further at room temperature and the hardness remains substantially constant over a period of months.

The streaks are interpreted to mean that the copper atoms are segregating on (100) planes of the crystal, and that in these copper-rich regions the spacing is a little less than elsewhere, since a local enrichment of the alloy with copper would be expected to produce a diminution of the spacing in the same way as the parameter of aluminium is reduced by copper in solution. It is possible to make an estimate of the size and distribution of the copper-rich patches. It turns out that their size is about 10 atomic distances or 40 Å. across, some 2 or 3 atoms thick, and they are scattered through the crystal at an average distance of about 200 Å from one another. These patches correspond somewhat to the lattice "knots" proposed by Merica.

Heat treatment at 200° C. at first reduces the hardness of the alloy fully aged at room temperature, and at the same time, the Laue streaks become much weaker, indicating a dispersal or "evaporation" of the copper atoms from the knots of high concentration. With further heat treatment for 5 hours at 200° C. there is a return of the Laue streaks and an increase in hardness which ultimately considerably exceeds that attained by room temperature ageing. The Laue streaks which recur on high temperature ageing are invariably sharp, and indicate that the area of the plates is greater than that of the plates formed in room temperature ageing. After the hardness has attained its maximum, further heat treatment over-ages the alloy and causes softening.

The prolonged heat treatment at 200° C. causes the Laue streaks to break up into discrete spots (Fig. 215c) indicating further growth of the plates which consist of an unstable intermediate phase with the composition $CuAl_2$ and a calcium fluoride (cubic) structure. This structure fits on the aluminium matrix, the side of the unit cell being 5·7 Å. which is exactly 2 times the cube side of aluminium. However, the two structures do not fit in a direction at right angles to the plane of union which sets up an appreciable amount of lattice strain. If the alloy is kept at 200° C. for 50 days, or 1 day at 300° C., the cubic structure transforms to the stable tetragonal form of $CuAl_2$, the particles of which have grown so large that sharp Laue spots are given by them. Fig. 215 (d) illustrates the same alloy after over-ageing for 1½ hours at 350° C. The precipitated $CuAl_2$ forms a perfectly developed Widmannstätten structure on the microscale. The plane of section of the aluminium grain in the photograph is (100) and the thin plates of precipitate are parallel to (010) and (001). The larger patches are plates of precipitate which lie nearly parallel to the plane of section. At this stage, when the precipitate becomes visible under

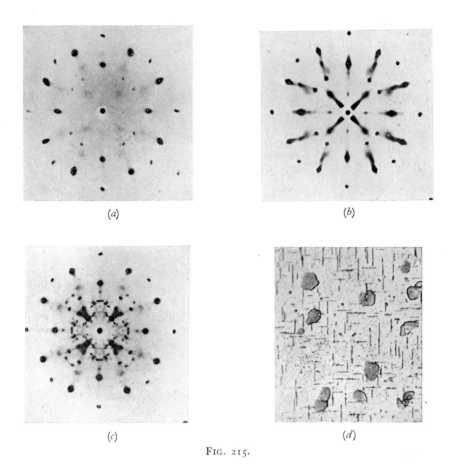

(a) (b)

(c) (d)

Fɪɢ. 215.

(a) Laue photograph of pure aluminium crystal.   X-rays parallel to [001]; [1̄10] vertical.   Ag Kα + β radiation.   The faint diffuse spots are due to the thermal vibrations of the lattice.

(b) Laue photograph of Al — 4 per cent Cu.   Aged 3 days at room temperature.

(c) Laue photograph of the same crystal annealed for 50 days at 200° C., 1 day at 300° C., and 1 day at 350° C.

(G. D. Pʀᴇꜱᴛᴏɴ, *J. Scientific Instruments*, **18**, 155, 1941.)

(d) Photomicrograph of Al — 4 per cent Cu.   Aged 1½ hrs. at 350° C.   Magnification 2500 reveals Widmannstätten structure on very fine scale.   The plane of section is (100) and the three groups of separating plates parallel to (100), (010), (001) are visible.

(M. Gᴀʏʟᴇʀ and Pᴀʀᴋʜᴏᴜꜱᴇ, *J. Inst. Met.*, **66**, 27, 1940.)

[*Facing page* 298.

the microscope, it must be many hundreds of atomic spacings in thickness.

In the age-hardening silver-aluminium alloys, the sequence of changes is the same as described above, namely the formation of plates, intermediate phase, final phase. In this case, however, the plates of silver-rich material form on the (111) planes of the parent lattice and the intermediate phase is a close-packed hexagonal structure, the basal plane of which fits accurately on to the (111) plane of aluminium. Since the axial ratio of the new phase is $1 \cdot 61$ which is appreciably different from the ideal value of $\sqrt{8/3}$ for close-packed spheres, there is a slight misfit in the direction at right angles to the plane of union of the two phases, which introduces strain into the parent lattice. With rise in temperature and prolongation of treatment, this intermediate phase is transformed into the final precipitate, also hexagonal close-packed, but with a lattice parameter which does not fit the aluminium lattice at all accurately.

Commercial aluminium alloys of the duralumin type contain appreciable quantities of magnesium and silicon in addition to copper. The age-hardening process is then further complicated by the precipitation of Mg_2Si.

CHAPTER XI

APPLICATION OF X-RAYS TO THE STUDY OF REFRACTORY MATERIALS

The Value of X-ray Methods. The ferrous and non-ferrous metallurgical industries are almost entirely dependent on refractory materials for winning metals from their ores and for the production of alloys. The demands made by each industry are highly specialized, and, in order to increase the range of available refractory materials and effect improvements in the quality of those already well established, the more important metallurgical companies are co-operating with the manufacturers of refractory materials in carrying out joint research programmes.

Several hundred natural and synthetic refractories are known, of which only a comparatively small number find use on a commercial scale. The materials which are in most common use are fire-clay, silica, kaolin, diaspore, alumina, and products of the electric furnace such as silicon carbide. Besides resistance to high temperatures, other qualities are demanded. Refractories must maintain their shape, strength and other physical properties. They must be resistant to erosion by ash-laden gases, their tendency to spall must be low, they must resist fluxing and be chemically inert. Needless to say, no refractory material is endowed with all these virtues, and a considerable amount of research is being done to obtain improved combinations of desirable properties.

Until recently, the more important methods of control and identification of the raw materials were carried out by microscopical examination and chemical analysis. X-ray methods, which have proven of such value in metallurgical studies, are now employed on an ever increasing scale in the investigation of refractory materials. Chemical analysis gives no information of the crystalline form of the material, while the microscope is limited to the examination of transparent crystals which are large enough to lie in the visible range. As we have already seen, an X-ray diffraction pattern is a characteristic product of the atomic arrangement in the diffracting crystal. It is therefore a rapid and certain means of compound identification, and in many cases offers a satisfactory alternative to the more direct and tedious methods of chemical analysis. Moreover, X-ray diffraction methods do not suffer from the many cramping limitations to which

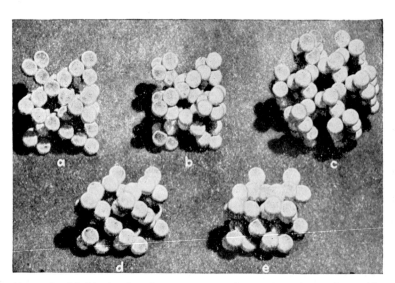

FIG. 216.—Models showing the arrangement of atoms in various polymorphic modifications of silica, SiO$_2$.

(*a*) High cristobalite, (*b*) low cristobalite, (*c*) high tridymite, (*d*) high quartz, (*e*) low quartz. The silicon atoms are not visible because they are small and nestle in a tetrahedron formed by four oxygen atoms. Note that the low-temperature forms are more closely packed than the high-temperature forms.

(F. H. NORTON, *Refractories*, McGraw-Hill Book Co.)

Facing page 301.]

the microscope is subject. As is the case in metallographic studies, the X-ray method is complementary to microscope technique, and, together, they form an extremely powerful combination.

In the industrial laboratory, the principal requirements are to classify the material by the identification of the constituents in the refractory, and, from the crystalline constitution developed during manufacture, to determine whether the product is likely to approach the requisite standards of performance in service. The X-ray attack on the problems is three-fold. Firstly, by single crystal methods, the internal arrangements of the atoms in a large number of refractory materials are worked out, thus putting the crystal chemistry of the subject on a solid foundation. Secondly, in the Debye-Scherrer powder method, we have an excellent means of compound identification. Finally, by the methods outlined in Chapters IX and X, it is possible to examine the crystal texture of the material. The identification of compounds and the determination of crystal texture are the methods simplest to apply, and are, therefore, most frequently applied in the industrial laboratory.

The Principal Refractory Raw Materials. 1. *Clays* form an important section of the raw materials for refractory manufacture. They are, generally speaking, composed of hydrated earth materials which contain a considerable amount of silica or alumina and have plastic properties. The constituents in clays from various localities differ widely. They consist of fine, mainly platy, fragments of definite minerals which range in size from 10^{-1} down to 10^{-5} cm. In refractory clays, the clay minerals which are found are predominantly kaolinite, diaspore and gibbsite, with such accessory minerals as quartz, feldspars, micas, iron oxides and sulphides, titanium minerals, calcite, dolomite, magnesite, gypsum, garnet and tourmaline.

2. *Silica* (SiO_2). One of the most important refractory materials, silica, occurs in nature as the mineral quartz and as ganisters, quartzites and sandstones in sedimentary rocks. Silica exists in a number of polymorphic forms, quartz, cristobalite and tridymite, each of which has a low and high temperature modification. Atomic models of some polymorphic forms of silica are shown in Fig. 216. These have been worked out by single crystal methods. The dominant feature in the atomic pattern in all the varieties is the tetrahedra formed by large tightly crammed oxygen atoms which are held together by a very much smaller atom of silicon at their centroid. These SiO_4 tetrahedral groups are linked together by their corners, so that on the whole the composition of the structure is SiO_2. On account of their small size and position, the Si atoms cannot be seen in the models.

It will be observed that cristobalite and tridymite are each more openly packed than quartz. The high-temperature forms have a higher symmetry than the low-temperature forms. We can see how the diagonal groups of tetrahedra of high-temperature cristobalite are linked to form an almost straight chain, while in low-temperature cristobalite the chain becomes distinctly puckered. The same sort of thing occurs in quartz. While the crystal structures of quartz, cristobalite and tridymite differ considerably from each other and require the breaking and reforming of chemical bonds to effect the polymorphic transformation, the high-low transitions in each polymorphic variety only require small atomic shifts and rotations. Consequently, the polymorphic transformations from the high temperature

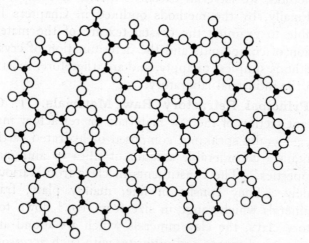

FIG. 217.—Random network in vitreous silica.
(After ZACHARIASEN.)

modification of silica, tridymite, to cristobalite and thence to quartz, take place so slowly that it is quite impossible to form the end product, quartz. On the other hand, the high-low transitions of each structural type are rapid and reversible.

When fused, silica does not regain its crystalline characteristics because of its high viscosity and remains an amorphous solid or *glass* on cooling. In the vitreous or glass-like state, the essential unit of the crystalline form, the SiO_4 tetrahedron, is still retained. What happens is that the neighbouring tetrahedra are linked together at slightly incorrect angles, and their neighbours in turn are wrongly inclined to them. Thus, although the correct interatomic distances between the nearest neighbours are accurately maintained, all trace of that orderly repetition of a fundamental unit of pattern, so char-

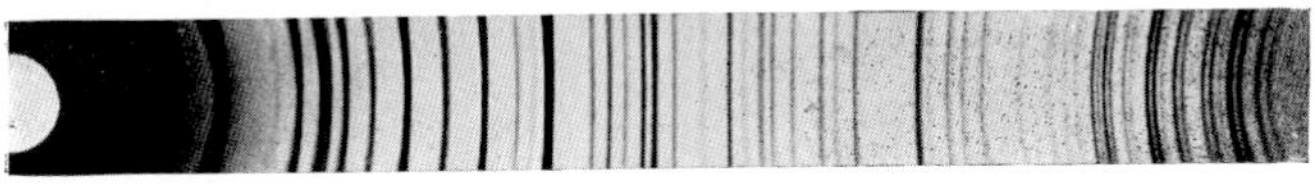

1. Quartz.

2. Cristobalite.

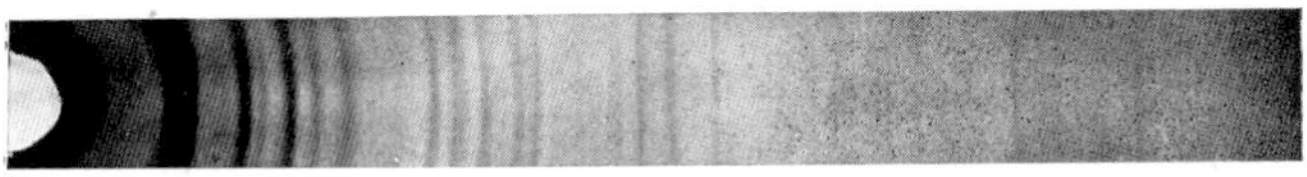

3. Tridymite.

4. Magnesia.

5. Alumina.

6. Spinel (MgO.Al$_2$O$_3$).

7. Chromite.

8. Mullite.

9. Forsterite.

FIG. 218.—Debye-Scherrer Identification Patterns for various minerals.

(A. H. JAY and J. H. CHESTERS, *Trans. Ceramic Soc.*, **37**, 209, 1938.)

[*Facing page* 302.

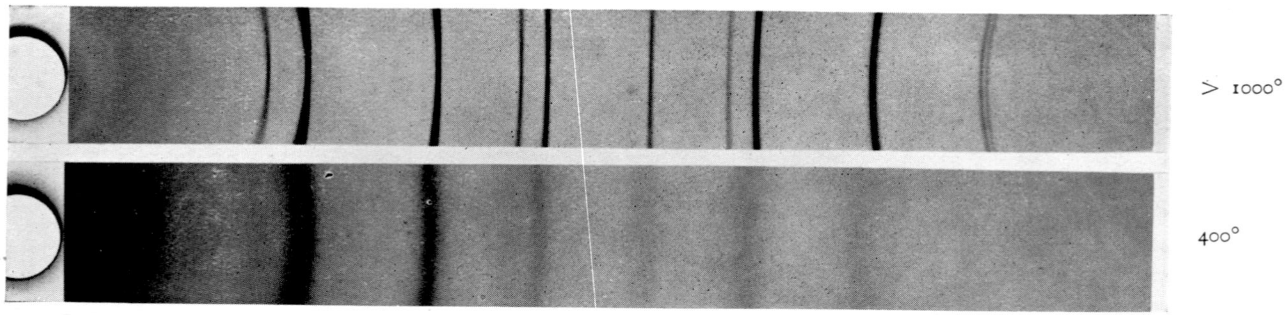

FIG. 219.—X-ray Powder Photographs showing increase in line width with decrease in crystal size of magnesium oxide.

The specimens were prepared by decomposition of $MgCO_3$ at different temperatures.

(H. P. ROOKSBY and J. H. PARTRIDGE, *Trans. Soc. Glass Tech.*, **24**, 110, 1940.)

acteristic of the crystalline state, is quickly lost after proceeding only a short distance from a lattice point (Fig. 217). The vitreous form is just as solid as the crystalline one, but on account of its random internal arrangement it behaves, in many ways, as an essentially non-crystalline material. Fused silica yields broad diffuse haloes very similar to the diffuse bands given by minute crystals which are of the order of 10^{-7} cm. in size.

X-ray patterns from some of the forms of quartz and other minerals are given in Fig. 218 (1) to (9).

3. *Alumina* (Al_2O_3). Alumina occurs in a number of polymorphic varieties. The α-form is identical with corundum, a natural mineral which is rhombohedral. It is very stable and is almost always formed from a cooling fusion. β-alumina is really a compound of the form $Na_2O.11Al_2O_3$ or $K_2O.11Al_2O_3$. It can be formed by heating a mixture of alumina with alkali in an electric arc furnace. γ-alumina is generally formed by heating hydrated alumina materials such as kaolin ($Al_2(Si_2O_5).(OH_4)$), or gibbsite ($Al(OH)_3$) at about 900° C. ζ-alumina only seems to occur in melts which contain lithium. It can be formed by heating alumina with lithium oxide as a flux in an electric arc furnace. The atomic structure is probably similar to β-alumina. A typical Debye-Scherrer photograph of α-alumina is shown in Fig. 218 (5).

4. *Magnesia* (MgO). There is only one crystalline form of magnesia, namely the cubic (NaCl) type. It occurs in nature as periclase. Commercially it is produced by the decomposition of magnesite $MgCO_3$, or the hydrate, brucite, $Mg(OH)_2$. A typical Debye-Scherrer pattern of magnesia is illustrated in Fig. 218 (4). The temperature of calcination plays a considerable part in the properties of magnesia. Some typical powder photographs showing the decrease in line width as the crystals of MgO increase in size with rising temperature are shown in Fig. 219.

5. *Chromite* (Cr_2FeO_4). This is a natural mineral of variable iron oxide and chromic oxide content. It is a spinel, part of the iron and chromic oxide being replaced by either magnesia or alumina. We may therefore give it the general formula $(Mg, Fe)O.(Al, Cr)_2O_3$. Although the ores vary considerably in analysis, they maintain their refractory properties. A powder photograph of chromite is illustrated in Fig. 218 (7).

6. *Carbon*. Carbon occurs naturally as flaky graphite in great abundance. It can also be manufactured by heating coke to a high temperature in the electric furnace. The graphitic carbon thrown out of solution from the molten iron tapped from a blast furnace is

known as kish. Graphite is almost completely chemically inert. Its chief use as a refractory is for crucibles for melting metals.

7. *Carborundum* (SiC). Carborundum is a trade name for a product which is synthesized in the electric furnace by heating together sand and coke at temperatures between 1,780° and 2,200° C. Above 2,300° carborundum decomposes. Some of the raw materials for commercial and special purpose refractories are listed below in Table XXVII.

TABLE XXVII

REFRACTORY MATERIALS

Material	Fusion Point, ° C.	Density
Alumina, Al_2O_3	3,722	3·97–4·03
Bauxite, $Al_2O_3.n.SiO_2.nH_2O$	3,722	2·0 –2·6
Beryllia, BeO	2,570	3·025
Brucite, $Mg(OH)_2$	2,800	2·38–2·39
Carborundum, SiC	> 2,300 (sublimes)	3·208
Chalcedony, SiO_2	1,715	2·55–2·63
Chromite, $FeCr_2O_4$	2,180	4·32–4·57
Corundum, Al_2O_3	3,722	3·97–4·03
Cristobalite, SiO_2	1,715	2·32–2·36
Diaspore, AlO(OH)	2,035	3·39
Dolomite, $CuMg(CO_3)_2$	2,570–2,800	2·83–2·99
Forsterite, Mg_2SiO_4	1,910	3·22–3·27
Ganister, SiO_2	1,715	2·65
Gibbsite, $Al(OH)_3$	2,035	2·3 –3·42
Graphite, C	3,527	2·22
Hematite, Fe_2O_3	1,565	5·17–5·26
Ilmenite, $FeTiO_3$		4·44–4·86
Kaolinite, $Al_2Si_2O_5(OH)_4$	1,785	2·6 –2·63
Limestone, $CaCO_3$	2,570	2·4 –2·8
Magnesite, $MgCO_3$	2,800	2·95–3·12
Mesitite, $(Fe,Mg)CO_3$	> 1,500	2·54
Montmorillonite, $(OH)_2Al_2[Si_2O_5]_2nH_2O$		2·04–2·52
Olivine, $(Mg,Fe)SiO_4$	1,700–1,910	3·2 –3·3
Periclase, MgO	2,800	3·64–3·67
Quartz, SiO_2	1,715	2·65–2·70
Rutile, TiO_2	1,900	4·12–4·27
Sillimanite, Al_2SiO_5	1,816	3·23–3·24
Spinel, $MgAl_2O_4$	2,135	3·68–3·92
Thoria, ThO_2	> 2,800	9·69
Tridymite, SiO_2	1,715	2·27
Zircon, $ZrSiO_4$	2,550	4·05–4·75
Zirconia, ZrO_2	2,700	5·49

Method of Ordered Aggregates. Powder diagrams of various clay minerals are very similar to each other and in mixtures many lines may coincide. Improvement may be effected by the use of 19 cm. diameter cameras. To overcome the difficulties presented by the lack of sufficient resolution, the method of *ordered aggregates* is used. That is, the platy constituents in the clay are given a high degree of preferred orientation in preparing the specimen, and the X-ray photograph which the aggregate produces corresponds to a fibre diagram. Now the crystal structures of most clay minerals can be considered as built up of sheets of various ions.   The composition of the sheets are all very similar, the main distinguishing feature being the number of sheets piled on top of each other.   This number corresponds to a characteristic of the lattice, namely the basal spacing.   The nature of the preferred orientation in the ordered aggregate is one which makes the basal plane reflexions predominate with the virtual exclusion of all other spectra, and provides a great simplification of the powder diagram.

The basal spacings can be identified and measured with much higher accuracy on the X-ray pattern from an ordered aggregate than is the case with an ordinary powder diagram, in which it is often impossible to decide whether a given diffraction line corresponds to a basal spacing or not.

There are several methods of preparing ordered aggregates. They can be made by slow sedimentation, or, more quickly, by centrifuging the clay suspension against a flat surface such as a microscope cover glass.   It is also useful to let the suspension settle on a thin mica plate and to use the sharp basal mica reflexions as fiducial marks. Ordered aggregates can be deposited on curved or flat surfaces and X-ray patterns can be taken in cylindrical or plate cameras.   The range of lattice spacings in clay diagrams varies from 1 to at least 20Å, and the X-ray camera should be large enough to allow accurate measurements of the larger (low angle) spacings.[114]

Thermal Equilibrium.   Equilibrium diagrams which are so essential to the development and control of modern alloys are proving of equal value in the manufacture of refractory materials.   The construction of an equilibrium diagram for refractory materials presents difficulties seldom encountered in the study of alloys.   The high temperatures, the small heat evolutions when phase changes take place and the serious under-cooling which is encountered owing to the sluggish attainment of equilibrium, all operate against the satisfactory employment of cooling or heating curve methods.   The most frequently employed technique is to soak the refractory material at a given temperature for a sufficient time to ensure the establishment of equilibrium, whereupon the material is quenched to retain the high temperature structure.   The final product is then subjected to a microscopic or X-ray examination to establish which crystalline phases are present. A typical ternary equilibrium diagram for the system SiO_2-MgO-Al_2O_3[115] is illustrated in Fig. 220.

In addition to the formation of new phase structures, the constituents of refractories very often have wide ranges of mutual solid solubility. This is mainly on account of the lattice structure possessed by the majority of refractory minerals. In most of these materials, it is the mode of packing the large oxygen atoms which controls the fabric of the lattice. The small metal atoms fit in the interstices binding the oxygen atoms together into their characteristic groups. As it does not matter a great deal whether, for example, a silicon or

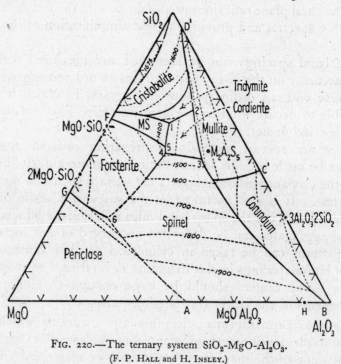

FIG. 220.—The ternary system SiO_2-MgO-Al_2O_3.
(F. P. HALL and H. INSLEY.)

an aluminium atom is actually present, the composition of the material can often vary within wide limits and allow of quite wide ranges of solid solubility.

Powder photographs of some of the phases present in the system SiO_2-MgO-Al_2O_3 are illustrated in Fig. 221.[116] By the powder method, as little as 1 per cent. by weight of α-quartz can be detected in aluminium silicate refractories made from fireclay material. The sensitivity of the method depends on the phases which are present. One factor which complicates the interpretation of the powder pattern is a glassy phase which is generally present to a greater or

Fiduciary
mark
↓

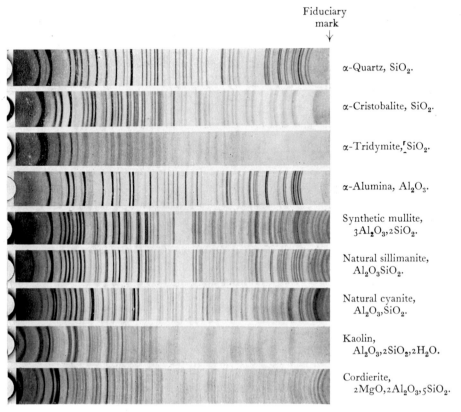

α-Quartz, SiO$_2$.

α-Cristobalite, SiO$_2$.

α-Tridymite, SiO$_2$.

α-Alumina, Al$_2$O$_3$.

Synthetic mullite,
    3Al$_2$O$_3$,2SiO$_2$.

Natural sillimanite,
    Al$_2$O$_3$SiO$_2$.

Natural cyanite,
    Al$_2$O$_3$,SiO$_2$.

Kaolin,
    Al$_2$O$_3$,2SiO$_2$,2H$_2$O.

Cordierite,
    2MgO,2Al$_2$O$_3$,5SiO$_2$.

Fig. 221.—X-ray powder photographs of various Alumina-Silica substances.

10-cm. camera.   Cu Kα radiation.

(H. P. Rooksby and J. H. Partridge, *Trans. Soc. Glass Tech.*, **24**, 110, 1940.)

[*Facing page* 306.

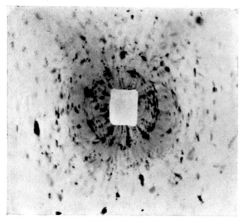

Welsh Quartzite.

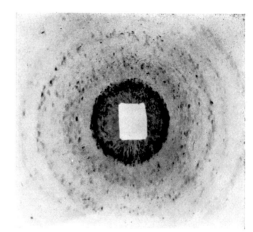

Sheffield Ganister.

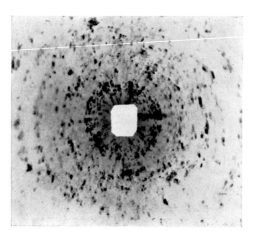

American Quartz Schist.

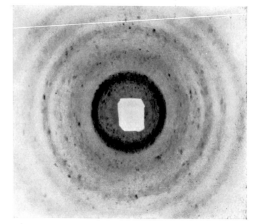

German Findlings Quartzite.

FIG. 222.—Transmission patterns of silica from various localities.

(A. H. JAY and J. H. CHESTERS, *Trans. Ceramic Soc.*, **37**, 209, 1938.)

lesser degree. This can be identified by the presence of broad diffraction haloes on the powder diagram. Any quantitative determinations will only give the ratio of the crystalline constituents.

Mullite. Sillimanite is a natural mineral having a (approximate) composition $SiO_2Al_2O_3$. When heated above $1,555°$ C., it transforms to mullite, $3Al_2O_3 . 2SiO_2$, and silica SiO_2. There is a great similarity between the X-ray diffraction patterns of sillimanite and mullite which indicates a similarity in the atomic arrangements. It has been pointed out by W. H. Taylor [117] that in view of the similarity between the (SiO_4) and (AlO_4) atomic groups, a replacement of an (SiO_4) group in the sillimanite structure by an (AlO_4) group would give the mullite structure if one oxygen atom in forty were removed.

It is possible to synthesize mullites by heating finely powdered alumina and silica in the correct proportions for the formula $3Al_2O_3 . 2SiO_2$, to a temperature of $1,750°$ C. for two hours. The X-ray patterns from the synthesis differs in only small details from natural mullites from North America and the Isle of Mull. From the slight variations in the high-order reflexions, H. P. Rooksby and J. H. Partridge [118] have been able to distinguish three separate, though closely similar, crystalline varieties of mullite which they designate the α-, β- and γ-forms. They also found that by adding increasing amounts of alumina in the synthesis it was possible to obtain a gradual transition from the α- to the β-variety, which can be regarded as the result of solid solution of alumina in α-mullite. Additions of quite small amounts of impurity such as Fe_2O_3 or TiO_2 with alumina in the synthesis were capable of producing large variations in lattice spacing of α-mullite and ultimately converted it to the γ-variety, which is typical of the natural mineral found at Ormsaig in the Isle of Mull.

Crystal Texture of Refractory Materials. The principles of examining the crystal texture of refractory materials are precisely the same as those employed in the case of metals. To obtain information regarding the size of crystals and their orientation, we pass a beam of X-rays through a section of the refractory ground to a thin plate $0·2$ mm. thick. The diffraction pattern is recorded on a flat film placed behind the specimen. Alternatively, a back-reflexion technique may be employed. The radiation is usually unfiltered, so that we obtain a pattern of Laue spots from the white radiation in addition to the reflexions produced from the strong $K\alpha$ and $K\beta$ components.

Crystal size can vary considerably from one variety of silica to another, depending on the place of origin and even from point to point within a given sample.   These differences are illustrated by the transmission patterns shown in Fig. 222.   The crystal size and amount of impurity present each exert a considerable influence on the rate and temperature at which the conversion from quartz to cristobalite and tridymite takes place on heating.   Examination of a large number of patterns from various quartzites taken before and after firing reveal that it is the smallest crystals which invert most readily.

Chromite ores from different sources reveal considerable variations in crystal size and in the degree of preferred orientation.   Grecian chromite and certain African ores contain fairly large crystals. A number of African deposits yield chromites having very fine textures, with little or no preferred orientation, as shown in Fig. 223 (a). Chromites from Turkish, Cuban and Indian sources show fairly small crystals having a considerable degree of preferred orientation.   An X-ray pattern from a Turkish chrome ore is illustrated in Fig. 223 (b).

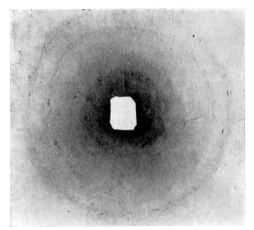 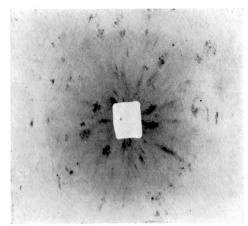

(a) African Chrome Ore.   (b) Turkish Chrome Ore.

FIG. 223.—Transmission patterns of chrome ores from various localities.

(A. H. JAY and J. H. CHESTERS, *Trans. Ceramic Soc.*, **37**, 209, 1938.)

[*Facing page* 308.

FIG. 225 (a).—Microporosity in aluminium alloy casting (L 33).

Positive print, full-size. Casting ¼ in. thick. 80 Kv. 5 Milliamps, 63 seconds. Tube-film distance, 42 in.
Kodak Industrex D film. No intensifying screens. Victor 220-Kv. oil-immersed tube.

(*Courtesy, English Electric Co., Ltd.*)

CHAPTER XII

RADIOGRAPHY AND MICRORADIOGRAPHY

General Principles. The foundations of medical and industrial radiography were laid by Röntgen when he discovered that X-rays could travel through matter and be recorded photographically. Gradations in blackness which correspond to fluctuations in density or defects in the material are obtained on the film. Such a pattern or shadow photograph of the internal macrostructure is termed a radiograph. The pattern may be rendered directly visible to the naked eye by screens of zinc blende, calcium tungstate or barium platinocyanide which have the property of fluorescing under the action of the rays.

Fig. 224 illustrates the principles of making a radiograph. Fundamentally the method is very simple. A permanently evacuated X-ray tube, generally of the incandescent filament type, fitted with a water-cooled tungsten target is normally employed. The rays travel out in straight lines from a small focal spot of projected area approximately $1\frac{1}{2}$ mm. square, and strike the object placed a suitable distance away. Close behind the object is a fluorescent screen or the thin

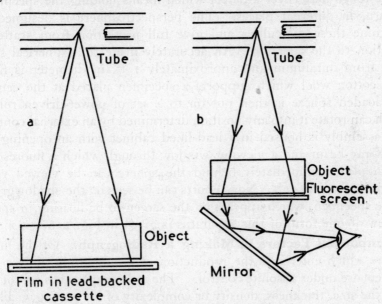

FIG. 224.—(a) Principle of making a radiograph.
(b) Screening. Image is generally viewed via a mirror inclined at 45° to fluorescent screen.

aluminium cassette containing the photographic film upon which the record is made. Although the technique appears to be simple and straightforward, very great care is necessary to obtain radiographs which convey the maximum amount of detail and information.

Screening is usually employed for the smaller castings of light alloys which are easily penetrated by X-rays. The castings are usually held by means of suitable tongs behind the fluorescent screen which is mounted as a "window" in a lead-lined cabinet which shields the operator from the direct beam and scattered rays. The operator holding the tongs wears protective gloves of leaded rubber and takes great care *never* to get his gloved hands in the direct beam. The specimen is manipulated into several positions with regard to the incident radiation so that it can be examined from every aspect. Screening is suitable only for the coarser types of defect such as blowholes and pipes. For the more subtle flaws and fine detail such as hair-line cracks or micro-porosity (Fig. 225), the much more sensitive method of photographic radiography must be resorted to. With a complicated casting the best angle at which to radiograph the specimen is not always immediately obvious and it is very useful to screen the specimen in advance, for by this means the most suitable aspect can be quickly established.

The Perspectrosphere. Manipulating castings by means of tongs causes the operator a great deal of fatigue. Moreover, the ends of the tongs may cover a defect which means holding the specimen, in turn, in different places. The perspectrosphere is designed to overcome these difficulties and give full protection from scattered radiation to the operator. An accurately made thin spherical shell spun from duralumin and approximately 1 ft. in diameter is filled with cotton wool which supports a specimen placed at the centre. The loaded sphere is then put on to a set of power-driven rollers which can rotate it into any position determined by an external control. The assembly is housed in a lead-lined cabinet with an opening for the X-ray beam and a viewing window through which a fluorescent screen placed immediately behind the sphere can be viewed via a mirror inclined at 45°. No supports can be seen on the shadowgraph of the specimen, which appears on the screen to be floating in space. A view of one form of this apparatus is given in Fig. 226.

Important Factors in Making a Radiograph. Of the many factors which enter into the production of a radiograph, only a few of them are under absolute control. The radiographer has no control over the size, thickness, density or complexity of his casting. These must be accepted in advance and he must do the best he can to surmount the difficulties presented by each individual case. As far

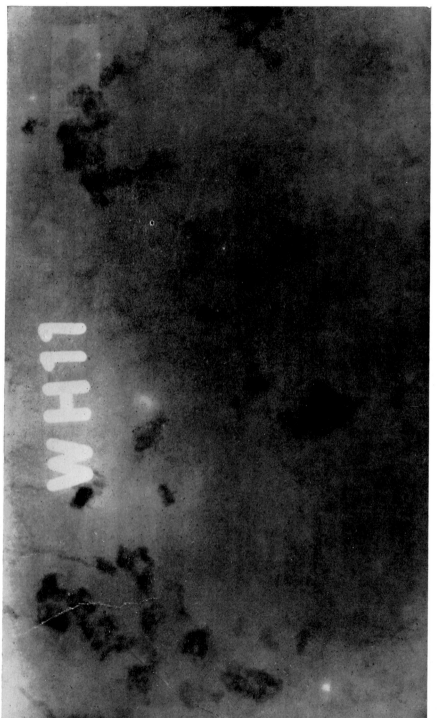

Fig. 225 (b).—Large gas cavities and microporosity in cast steel Pelton wheel bucket.

Positive print, full-size. Film in flexible cassette curved to circular contour of casting. Thickness of metal, 1 in. 215 Kv., 2 milliamps, 130 seconds. Tube film distance, 36 in. Kodak Industrex S film, two intensifying screens. Note outline of penetrameter in top right-hand corner. Taken with Victor 400-Kv. oil-immersed tube.

(Courtesy, English Electric Co., Ltd.)

[Facing page 310.

Fig. 226.—The Perspectrosphere Machine.   Tunnicliffe Model.
(Siemens-Schuckert Ltd.)

as the X-ray tube is concerned, the operator has full control over the kilovoltage which governs the thickness of the material which can be penetrated by the radiation, and over the tube current which exerts a control over the exposure period. Assuming the kilovoltage on the tube is sufficient to ensure penetration, the exposure period is inversely proportional to the tube current and inversely proportional to the square of the distance from the target to the film. Partial control may also be effected over the film. The radiographer now has at his disposal a limited range of films with varying degrees of contrast and speed which are adequate to cover the majority of the problems which are to be encountered.

The X-ray Film. The effective action of X-rays upon the emulsion of the film is intimately connected with absorption. Thus

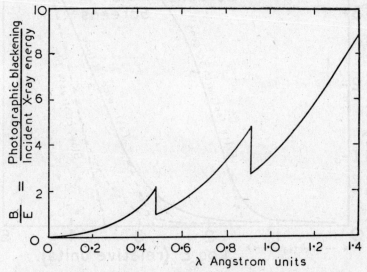

FIG. 227.—Effects of X-rays of different wavelengths on film emulsion. The short and long wavelength discontinuities correspond to the absorption edges of Ag and Br respectively.

"hard" X-rays of short wavelength produced by very high tube potentials do not have as great an effect upon the film emulsion as rays of longer wavelength which are more easily absorbed. This is illustrated in Fig. 227, where a curve connecting photographic effect with wavelength is drawn. It will be noted that the curve shows two sharp discontinuities. These correspond to the K absorption edges of the silver and bromine constituents in the emulsion.

The density of blackening, $B = \log_{10} \dfrac{i_0}{i}$, of photographic film (page 98) is a function of the wavelength, the intensity of the radiation and a power, p, of the exposure time.   In the X-ray region the Schwartzschild constant p is substantially equal to unity and therefore the density of blackening is a linear function of the exposure time. The *characteristic curve* of the film (Fig. 228) is obtained when the density of blackening is plotted as a function of $\log_{10} E$ where $E =$ intensity of X-ray beam $\times$ exposure time.   If the intensity is kept constant, the logarithm of the exposure *time* may be plotted horizontally.   This is rather different from the calibration curve of Fig. 58, where the simple exposure time is plotted as abscissa.

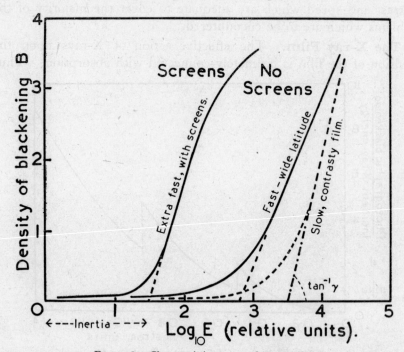

FIG. 228.—Characteristic curves of X-ray films.

A normal radiograph has a density of about 0·7 to 1·0.   For a density of 2·0 only $\frac{1}{100}$ of the light from an ordinary viewing lantern passes through the film and the film appears too dark to see any detail.   The range may be considerably extended beyond 2·0 if a special high-powered lamp is used to view small regions of the film at a time.   It is then possible to radiograph a casting possessing large variations in thickness in one shot, and by viewing the denser portions of the film with the high-powered lamp, to economize in time and amount of film used.

The characteristic curve has three distinct sections.   At low intensities the curve rises slowly and merges, at a density of about 0·4, into the steep linear portion of the curve which, in turn, bends over near the reversal point. The *inertia* is a measure of the speed of the film. The slope, or γ, of the linear portion is a measure of the *contrast* of the film. If the γ is high, the film will readily distinguish between slightly different X-ray intensities and therefore between slight variations in the thickness of the specimen, but the range of specimen thickness which will keep the density of blackening within a reasonable range, say 0·5 to 1·5, is small. On the other hand, if the curve has a low slope, the film will have a wide *latitude* and will give a correct rendering for big differences in thickness, but the contrast for detecting small defects will be low (Fig. 228). In practice, a compromise must be sought between latitude and contrast, and it may be necessary to take several radiographs to cover the range of thicknesses presented by the specimen.

Only a small amount of the radiant energy actually participates in blackening the film. In order to employ as much of the energy as possible and thereby reduce the exposure times, use is made of intensifying screens. They are generally thin layers of calcium tungstate powder on a cardboard backing placed in contact with the film during the exposure. These may be used in pairs, one in front of the film and one behind, with the calcium tungstate in contact with the film. The calcium tungstate fluoresces under the influence of the X-rays and emits a bluish light which has a strong action on the film. The speed can be increased by a factor of two, but since longer wavelengths are now influencing the emulsion of the film, the γ of the film is also somewhat modified and the Schwartzschild constant p is no longer equal to unity. There is also some loss of fine detail owing to the finite size of the particles of the fluorescent powder of which the intensifying screens are composed. For light alloys of small section, where exposure times are relatively short and the finest detail is required, intensifying screens are seldom employed.

For many purposes where the cost of film is high in relation to the product to be radiographed, it is often possible to substitute special X-ray papers which may be used with or without intensifying screens. The detail these papers can record is exceptionally fine, and excellent results can be obtained within a limited range of application, but in general radiographs on paper are inferior to those recorded on film.

Exposure Charts. In Chapter II we described how the intensity I of the X-ray beam was reduced according to the relation $I = I_0 e^{-\mu d}$, after passing through material of thickness d. The absorption coefficient μ is a function of the wavelength and the

L*

material, so that for the continuous radiation emitted by a radiographic tube, the absorption will be a relatively complicated function, but will, in general, increase with the wavelength and the atomic weight and thickness of the material. Of the continuous spectrum emitted at a given tube potential, only the shorter wavelengths will succeed in getting through the material ; the remainder will be scattered and absorbed. The total energy in the X-ray beam is proportional to the square of the tube potential. The position of the maximum of

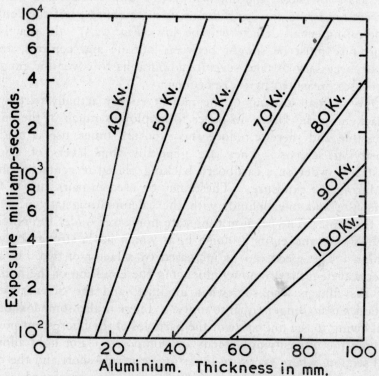

FIG. 229.—Typical exposure curves for Aluminium. Tungsten target, full-wave rectification, tube-film distance, 30 in. No intensifying screens.

Note.—Every tube has its own particular set of characteristic curves.

the emission spectrum moves in the direction of *decreasing* wavelength as the tube potential is raised, and the short-wave limit set by the quantum condition also decreases as shown in Fig. 2, page 8. Thus, with higher tube potentials, the penetrative power of the rays will be much greater.

In making a radiograph it is important to use a sufficiently high tube potential to ensure adequate penetration of the specimen, *but no more.* Using too high a voltage increases the penetrating power of the radiation to such an extent that little if any discrimination will be effected between portions of the specimen having different densities.

For aluminium and magnesium alloy castings, an X-ray tube designed to carry 150 Kv. will be sufficient for almost all industrial purposes, while for the examination of heavy metals, tubes running at potentials of 300–350 Kv. capable of penetrating some $4\frac{1}{2}$ in. of steel are employed. For greater thicknesses of steel, special tubes running at 1,000 Kv. have been designed, and γ-rays emitted by radium salts or radium emanation are employed.

When large quantities of specimens have to be radiographed, the time factor in making a radiograph becomes of considerable importance and necessitates cutting down the exposure period to a maximum of not more than two or three minutes. Usually this can only be achieved by increasing the penetrative power of the rays, which in turn, lessens the sensitivity. In practice a compromise must be reached between the desirability of speed and the attainment of radiographic perfection.

To achieve correct exposure, it is customary to draw up a series of charts relating thickness of material, kilo-voltage and exposure in terms of milliampere-seconds for a given anode-film distance. Such a chart for aluminium drawn on semi-logarithmic paper is illustrated in Fig. 229. Each chart is characteristic of the tube for which it is drawn as no two tubes with their rectifying units are quite alike.

Influence of Geometry and Scattering. The distance between the X-ray tube and the specimen, the size of the focal spot and the depth of the flaw in the specimen each influences the sharpness with which the defect can be registered (Fig. 230). The finer the focal spot, the sharper will be the X-ray shadows which are produced. The distance between the X-ray tube and the specimen should be made as large as possible without unduly increasing the exposure time. The minimum tube-film distance should not be less than 30 in. with the specimen not more than 1 in. from the film. To observe the fine detail present in the microporous castings of light alloys a tube-film distance of 4 to 5 ft. should be used.

Even with correct geometrical factors and exposure conditions, the clarity of definition in the radiograph is greatly influenced by internal scattering as shown in Fig. 231. Scatter not only lessens the sharpness of definition, it materially adds to the background level since the scattered wavelengths are much longer than the directly transmitted rays and have a much greater influence on the film. This trouble may be overcome to a large extent by using a filter of gauge

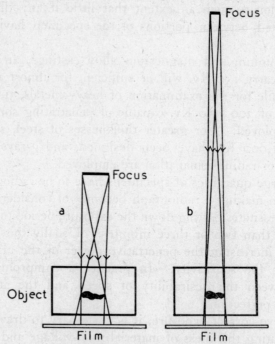

FIG. 230.—Geometric factors which govern the sharpness of detail in a radiograph.

(a) Large focus and short focus-film distance.

(b) Sharp focus and long focus-film distance.

20 brass sheet between the specimen and the film, which preferentially absorbs the softer scattered rays. An alternative device known as the Potter-Bucky grid originally employed in medical work is now finding industrial application for heavy sections of metal. It consists of thin wooden slats separated by thin lead strips. The primary rays pass straight through the light wooden slats while the scattered rays which travel at oblique angles are entirely cut off by the lead as shown in Fig. 231 (b). The grid must be moved slowly across the plate by a cam mechanism during the exposure period. The use of a Potter-Bucky grid increases the exposure period roughly 500 per cent.

Still further improvements in the clarity of the radiograph can be effected by the use of a thin sheet of lead placed over the window of the X-ray tube. This absorbs the longer wavelength radiation but transmits the useful shorter wavelengths with little reduction in intensity. Secondary radiation also arises from the walls of the room and other objects which rescatter the rays scattered by the specimen and its surrounds. This is minimized by covering the walls of the room with thin lead sheet or a layer of barium plaster which absorbs the scattered radiation. To prevent any fogging of the film from

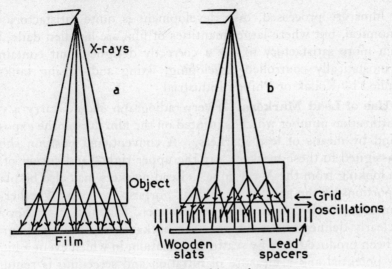

FIG. 231.—(*a*) Effect of internal scatter.
(*b*) Potter-Bucky grid cutting out scattered rays.

such extraneous radiation, the back and edges of the cassette are protected by thin lead sheet.

The use of thin lead or lead-alloy foil as a combined filter and intensifying screen is slowly coming into vogue. The foil, which must be perfectly smooth and free from scratches, is laid in direct contact with the front of the X-ray film. The foil not only prevents scattered radiation from reaching the film, but also produces secondary electrons under the action of the primary rays which activate the film emulsion. With a tube potential of 150 Kv., sufficient secondary electrons are liberated to reduce the exposure time by a factor of 2, but at lower tube potentials the intensifying action is much less.

Processing. Ranking equal in importance to correct exposure conditions is darkroom technique. All films, without exception, should be processed under conditions of standard time, temperature and developer concentration. "Snatching" films from the developer before the correct processing time has elapsed is very bad practice and leads to endless trouble in interpretation. Messrs. Kodak Ltd. and Ilford Ltd. each manufacture correctly blended developers and fixers for their films and issue full instructions as to their use.

The films should be held in scrupulously clean frames of stainless steel for developing and fixing, and after rinsing for at least 30 minutes in running water they should be removed from the frames and hung by the corner with special clips to dry in a dust-free cabinet, preferably one which is fitted with a hot-air drier. In a small laboratory where few films are processed, dish development is quite satisfactory and economical, but where large quantities of film are handled daily, it is much more satisfactory to use a correctly designed unit containing thermostatically controlled developing, fixing and rinsing tanks as supplied by Kodak or Philips Industrial.

Use of Lead Markers. Every radiograph should carry a code identification number which is printed on the film during the exposure period by means of lead markers. A conventional position should be assigned to these markers, say the upper right-hand corner of the film looking from the X-ray tube. Lead markers may also be placed on portions of the specimen. Their purpose is to test whether the beam has actually penetrated the specimen, in which case they will be clearly delineated, or whether the background of the radiograph has been produced only by scattered radiation, in which event a higher tube potential and a measure of filtration and screening is required. Stepped wedges built up of layers of the same material as the specimen and known as penetrameters are also used for the same purpose.

Part of the scatter may have been produced by the direct beam passing through holes in the specimen or around it and then being scattered by the X-ray film itself. A putty of red-lead in linseed oil may be used to plug up the holes if they lie in such a direction as to permit the direct ray to pass through. Alternatively, small lead shot may be used, or the specimen immersed in an aqueous solution of lead acetate and lead nitrate.

Foundry Applications. The main object of casting inspection by X-ray methods should be the prevention of faults by the development of a sound casting and alloying technique, rather than the rejection of unsound castings. For this reason, the correct place for the X-ray equipment is in the foundry itself rather than in the purchaser's testing laboratory.

The first few of a new type of casting should invariably be tested by radiography, and, if necessary, by breaking up some of the faulty castings in order to assist in the interpretation of the radiographs. It is most important that the radiographer in charge of interpreting the photographs should have had a sound training in foundry methods. Not only will he be able to discern the types of flaw present in the castings, but as a result of his apprenticeship in the foundry he will probably be able to suggest at once the corrections to be made in the temperature of pouring and in the dispositions of the runners, risers and ingates of the mould.

The most common forms of imperfection are shrinkage cavities, blowholes from the mould or metal gases, cracks, inclusions, pro-

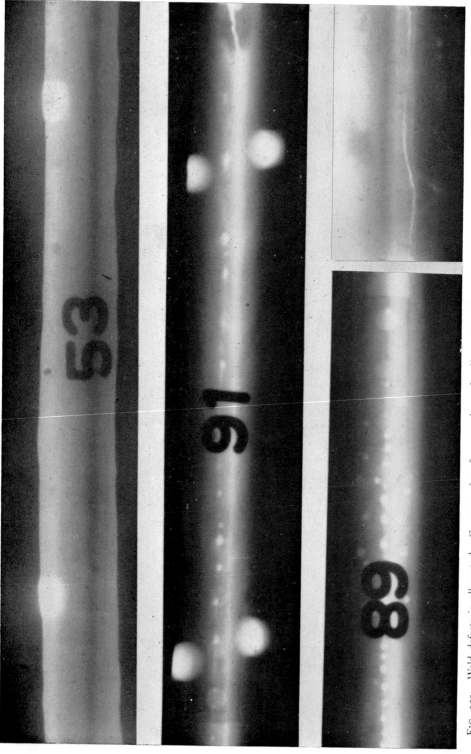

FIG. 232.—Weld defects in alloy steel. Contact prints from portions of radiographs. Reproduced full-size. (*Courtesy, English Electric Co., Ltd.*)

(*a*) A perfect weld. 1½ in. thick, 200 Kv., 10 milliamps., 120 secs., tube-film distance 36 in., Kodak Industrex S film, two intensifying screens.
(*b*) Slag inclusions and crack formation. 1 in. thick, 170 Kv., 10 milliamps., 30 secs., tube-film distance 36 in., Kodak Industrex S film, two intensifying screens.
(*c*) Large gas cavities. 1¼ in. thick, 170 Kv., 10 milliamps., 120 secs., tube-film distance 36 in., Kodak Industrex S film, two intensifying screens.
(*d*) Formation of large crack in basis metal near end of weld. 2 in. thick, 220 Kv., 8 milliamps., 45 secs., tube-film distance 26 in., Kodak Industrex S film, two

nounced dendritic formations, cold shuts and microporosity. Each is recognizable in the radiograph by its characteristic features. Microporosity, which is very prevalent in light alloys, is mainly caused by insufficient feed or by turbulence and is not easy to eliminate. It cannot be seen by screening and resort must be made to photographic radiography and the use of fine-grained film. Kodak "Crystallex" film is exceptionally good for this purpose and should always be used even though the slow speed of the emulsion increases the exposure period by a factor of three.

For routine inspection, a perspective drawing of each casting should be provided on which numbered arrows indicating the various angles of shot, and data concerning the correct exposure conditions, are given. Setting up the specimen may be very awkward, and it is convenient to have a number of wooden cubes of various sizes constructed and also a number of small inclined planes on which to rest the cassette and specimen at the correct angle. For awkward sections, flexible rubber cassettes may be used which allow the film to bend round the contour of the specimen. In difficult cases, it may even be necessary to cut the film to shape and to insert the pieces inside the casting.

Attention should be drawn to all defects by marking the finished radiograph in white ink. A good viewing lantern such as the Philips Philora lantern fitted with mercury vapour lamp and dimming device is necessary for satisfactory inspection. It is good practice to make sliding screens whereby the area of the illuminated panel of the lantern may be cut down to the size of the radiograph under inspection.

Radiography of Welds. X-ray methods provide the most reliable means of examining welds and has been an approved method of inspection of all Class 1 welded high-pressure vessels for a number of years. Butt welds, which have the highest mechanical strength and are most frequently used, are ideal for X-ray examination, for their thickness is fairly even and allows for maximum sensitivity of the X-ray method. The other forms of weld, such as fillet and lap welds, cannot be X-rayed with quite the same high degree of precision.

Almost all the types of defect which can arise in modern welding are capable of being revealed by X-ray methods. These are (a) lack of penetration or fusion between the weld and the parent metal, (b) blowholes or porosity due to gas, (c) slag inclusions, (d) shrinkage cracks. In most cases these are quite easy to identify. Blowholes are usually rounded and may easily be distinguished from slag inclusions which have irregular contours. Typical weld radiographs are shown in Fig. 232.

If a serious defect is found in a weld, it may be necessary to locate its exact depth in order to decide from which side of the metal the defect should be cut out and repaired. This is easily done by the method of triangulation. Two separate photographs of the weld are taken with slightly different positions of the X-ray tube. The image of the flaw on the film is different in position with respect to the images of fixed lead markers on the top and underside of the weld. From the amount of shift and the focus-film distance it is a relatively straightforward matter to find the position of the defect by simple triangulation. Alternatively, special stereoscopic viewers may be employed. This practice is only really necessary for welds above 1 in. in thickness and is of more use in double V welds than in the more usual simple V- or U-shaped weld.

When examining welds in large boilers, the general practice is to take films about 15 in. long on longitudinal seams. When examining circumferential seams, it is better to put the tube inside the boiler with the X-rays directed radially outwards. With this technique it is possible to radiograph 15 in. of weld with one shot, while if the tube is on the outside of the boiler, only about 10 inches of weld can be radiographed with the same high standard of perfection. Philips have designed special short anode and hollow anode tubes for the radiography of boiler welds. For thicknesses of steel up to $2\frac{3}{8}$ in., X-ray units with a maximum potential of 150 Kv. are used. By using two 150 Kv. generators with a Philips "Macro 300" 300 Kv. tube, illustrated in Fig. 233, it is possible to penetrate $4\frac{3}{8}$ to $4\frac{1}{2}$ in. of steel in an economic time. Portability is an important feature of the equipment which enables it to be used under the most adverse circumstances on the construction site.

The Victor X-ray Corporation have recently constructed a 1,000 Kv. unit capable of penetrating up to 7 in. of steel. The unit employs a 180-cycle resonant transformer connected to a self-rectified multi-section Coolidge tube, the whole assembly being immersed in "freon" gas which is contained in an earthed metal tank. Running at 3·0 milliamperes and at 1,000 Kv. peak it takes only 27 minutes' exposure period for 7 in. of steel at a distance of 32 in. from the tube.[119] The equipment is illustrated in Fig. 234. Being a hollow anode tube, it can be inserted inside a boiler and used for radiographing entire circumferential seams in one shot.

X-ray Planigraphy. In a radiograph, no defect can stand out with perfect sharpness since the pattern is formed by the more or less confused superposition of X-ray shadows cast from different layers in the radiographed object. By methods known variously as "plani-

FIG. 233 (a).—Inspection of a boiler under field conditions with the Philips "Macro 150".

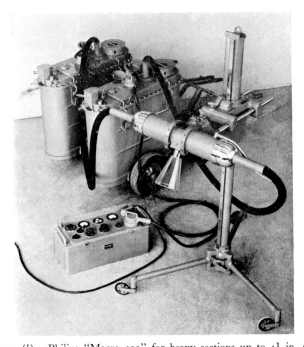

FIG. 233 (b).—Philips "Macro 300" for heavy sections up to $4\frac{1}{2}$ in. of steel.

Note the two 150 Kv. high tension transformers connected in series, and the lead-glass applicator cone which confines the scattered radiation.

[*Facing page* 320.

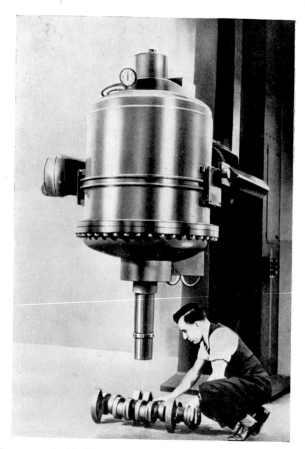

FIG. 234.—G. E. Victor 1,000,000-volt gas-insulated X-ray unit.

(*Courtesy, Victor X-ray Corporation.*)

graphy", "tomography" or "stratigraphy", it is possible to examine any given stratum of the specimen and thus bring out with the greatest clarity the detail confined to the layer under observation. The essential principles underlying these methods are illustrated in Fig. 235.

The planigraph is made by moving the tube and film in opposite directions while keeping the specimen stationary. In position (1), Fig. 235, B is the shadow on the film of the point P within the specimen. The X-ray tube is now moved slowly from A to A' while

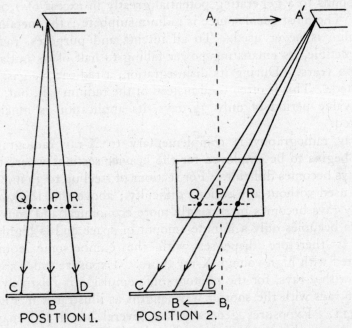

POSITION 1.   POSITION 2.

FIG. 235.—Principle of Planigraphy. The image of plane QPR remains sharply defined during the movement of film and tube.

the film is moved a proportionate amount in a parallel line in the opposite direction in such a manner that the shadow of P always falls on B. Thus no matter how big the movement, the image of P is always perfectly sharp. The same will be true for all points in the plane PQ lying parallel to the movement, and these too will be recorded with perfect definition, while layers in the specimen above and below this favoured plane will only record as a diffuse background.

Which stratum in the specimen is recorded depends on the relative movements of tube and specimen. In practice the object is generally kept much nearer to the film than to the tube. Variation on the method keep the tube stationary while moving the object and the film by predetermined amounts.

Gamma–Ray Radiography. The construction of X-ray equipment for the radiography of extremely thick steel sections is one which presents considerable difficulties. Fortunately, in radium there exists a natural source of X-rays, the so-called γ-rays, which are emitted along with α-particles and electrons during the spontaneous disintegration of the element. The enormous penetrating power of γ-rays is due to their extremely short wavelength which corresponds to a generating potential greatly in excess of 1,000,000 volts. The most usual source is radium sulphate ; the metallic form of radium is never used. To all intents and purposes, radium is indestructible, its emanating power falling to half of its initial value in 1,580 years. During its disintegration, a radioactive gas, radon, is emitted. This is often used instead of the radium salt, but, having a half-value period of only $3\frac{1}{2}$ days, its application is much more restricted.

γ-ray radiography is complementary to X-ray radiography in that it begins to be employed for the heavier sections where the use of X-rays becomes difficult. For sections of steel up to $3\frac{1}{2}$ in., X-rays can be used without any serious difficulty ; above this thickness the use of γ-rays becomes increasingly more economical and convenient. Radium occupies only a minute amount of space and is highly portable. It therefore dispenses with the cumbersome equipment associated with high voltage X-ray tubes. Exposure times are much longer with γ-rays, for the photographic emulsion is relatively insensitive to rays with the shorter wavelengths as illustrated in Fig. 227, page 311. Exposures generally last several hours and may even run into many days according to the nature of the problem. Intensifying screens of thin lead may be used to cut down the exposure period somewhat. The intensity of the rays may be increased by adding to the amount of radium at the source. This in turn increases the size of the source and tends to form less sharp images on the radiograph. Special exposure charts are drawn corresponding to the mass of radium in the source.

The apparatus required for γ-ray radiography is very simple. By arranging several specimens in a circle with films strapped to their backs in light-tight containers, it is possible to radiograph them all simultaneously by using a single radium source placed in the centre. It is always advisable to use duplicate films as a faint marking seen on both films confirms the existence of a small defect.

Radium and its salts are very dangerous to handle, and a special technique must be used to ensure the safety of the operator. The effects on the body are to some extent cumulative, making it necessary to have frequent blood counts as a check on the operator's health. The salts are carefully sealed in small silver capsules which are kept in egg-shaped duralumin containers to minimize loss or damage. These containers are manipulated by long strings or tongs which enable the operator to keep at a safe distance, which is at least 10 ft., unless he is shielded from the rays by lead or heavy castings. Finally, when not in use, the capsules should be kept in safes lined on all sides with a minimum of 6 in. of lead.

Microradiography. Radiography only allows us to examine extensive zones of the irradiated object, and, while revealing the presence of defects such as cracks and cavities, it gives no information of the finer texture of the examined object. By using a specialized technique, known as microradiography, it is possible to obtain detailed information of the microstructure of a metal.

In microradiography, we radiograph a heterogeneous object of very small size and then enlarge the picture by projection or view it under the microscope. The specimen, in the form of a thin plate some hundredths or thousandths of a millimetre thick, is placed in contact with the film and the whole is irradiated by X-rays of convenient wavelength, the radiograph afterwards being enlarged.

The microradiograph does not depend on the etching characteristics of the metal, and therefore the information which it gives is rather different and is not confined to the surface layer. Since the mass absorption coefficient

$$\frac{\mu}{\rho} = CN^4\lambda^3$$

where N is the atomic number of the element, λ the wavelength and C a constant between two absorption edges, it follows that the absorption for a given wavelength increases very rapidly with the atomic number of the element, whatever its state of combination.

On account of the fine detail which is to be examined, ordinary films with their coarse-grained emulsions are quite useless and it is necessary to use Lipmann emulsions which enable enlargements of the order of $\times 600$ to be made. Kodak have developed a special maximum resolution plate and fine-grain developer which are suitable for this purpose. On account of their fine grain, the emulsions of these plates are about 1,000 times less sensitive to X-rays than those of commercial coarse-grained films.

One can only use very thin specimens of uniform thickness, from $\frac{1}{100}$ to $\frac{5}{100}$ of a millimetre at the most, if it is desired to avoid the confusion produced by superimposed shadows. To get really good specimens is not at all easy. Thinning by acid attack is not very satisfactory, for specimens prepared in this manner are invariably of irregular thickness and are often perforated in places. Slow grinding and filing are quite satisfactory provided the specimen is kept cool to avoid structural changes, and a final finish is given on graded emery papers. The high polish required for ordinary microscopic examination is not required.

The specimen is placed in contact with the photographic film and a lead screen with a hole about ⅛ in. diameter is placed over it as shown in Fig. 236. The assembly is then fixed to the window of a fine-focus X-ray tube so as to be as near to the target as possible. The exposure time is naturally very variable, depending as it does on the thickness of the specimen, its composition and the wavelength of the

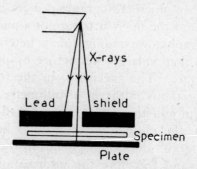

FIG. 236.—Preparation of a microradiograph.

radiation. With light alloys the exposure period is only a few minutes, while for alloy steels it is a few hours. The wavelength of the radiation should be chosen on the basis of alloy composition in such a way as to accentuate the contrasts by preferential absorption. By studying the positions of the absorption edges of the constituents, one easily arrives at a choice of wavelength. Suitable radiations for this sort of work are Cr Kα, Fe Kα, Co Kα and Cu Kα employing rectified current and a potential ranging from 10 to 20 Kv. The tube should be designed to pass a high current at these low potentials in order to reduce the exposure time to a minimum.

A few typical microradiographs are illustrated in Fig. 237 at a magnification of 100. Figs. 237 (b) and 237 (d) and their corresponding photomicrographs (a) and (c) are of copper-aluminium alloys. The copper-rich areas which have the greater absorbing power appear as the lighter areas in the microradiographs, while the aluminium appears as the dark areas. The obvious interpretation

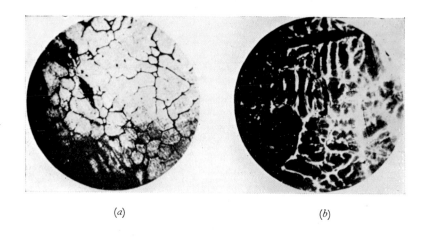

(a)   (b)

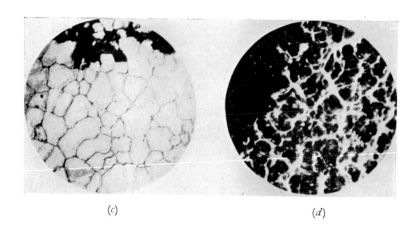

(c)   (d)

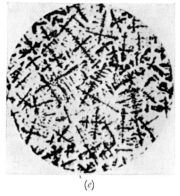

(e)

(a) Photomicrograph of Al-Cu alloy used in
   aeroplane parts.

(b) Microradiograph of same section.

(c) Photomicrograph of Al-Cu alloy. Etched
   with NaOH solution. Al light, Cu
   dark, apparently homogeneous solid
   solution.

(d) Corresponding microradiograph.

(e) Microradiograph of Lead-bronze.

FIG. 237.

(G. L. CLARK, *Photo Technique*, p. 20, 1939.)

Facing page 325.]

of the microradiographs is that the alloys are heavily cored, but the corresponding photomicrographs make no such disclosure. The dendritic structure in lead-bronze is very beautifully brought out by the microradiograph in Fig. 237 (e). Cracks, porosity, inclusions and precipitated particles are easily shown by microradiographs.

By far the most informative photographs are obtained with light elements to which are alloyed elements of much higher atomic weight. Brasses give no result at all in spite of the ease with which specimens can be prepared. The reason is that the copper (29) and the zinc (30) have similar atomic numbers and therefore similar absorption co-efficients. Apart from the few rare cases where the contrast between constituents is too low, microradiography, used in conjunction with microscopy, should be capable of yielding much valuable information.

REFERENCES

[1] W. C. Röntgen, *Sitzungsber. der Würzburger Physik-Medic. Gesellsch. Jahrg*, 1895; *Ann. der Physik*, **64**, 1, 1898.

[2] W. Friedrich, P. Knipping, and M. von Laue, *Sitzungsberichte der Königlich Bayerischen Akademie der Wissenschaften*, 303, June, 1912.

[3] W. L. Bragg, *Proc. Camb. Phil. Soc.*, **17**, 43, 1912

[4] W. Hume-Rothery, *J. Inst. Metals*, **35**, 295, 1926.

[5] H. Jones, *Proc. Roy. Soc.* (A), **144**, 225, 1934.

[6] O. S. Edwards and H. Lipson, *J. Scientific Instruments*, **18**, 131, 1941.

[7] H. Lipson and D. P. Riley, *Nature*, **151**, 251, 1943.

[8] J. E. de Graaf and W. J. Oosterkamp, *J. Scientific Instruments*, **15**, 293, 1938.

[9] G. L. Clark, *Applied X-Rays* (McGraw-Hill Book Co.).

[10] J. D. Hanawalt, *Industrial and Engineering Chemistry*, **10**, 457, 1938.

[11] A. W. Hull, *Phys. Rev.*, **17**, 571, 1921.

[12] A. J. Bradley, H. Lipson, and N. J. Petch, *J. Scientific Instruments*, **18**, 216, 1941.

[13] A. J. C. Wilson, *Proc. Phys. Soc.*, **53**, 235, 1941.

[14] H. Lipson and A. J. C. Wilson, *J. Scientific Instruments*, **18**, 145, 1941.

[15] A. J. Bradley and A. H. Jay, *Proc. Phys. Soc.*, **44**, 563, 1932.

[16] M. U. Cohen, *Rev. Scientific Instruments*, **6**, 68, 1935; *Zeits. Krist. A.*, **94**, 288, 1936

E. Jette and F. Foote, *J. Chem. Physics*, **3**, 616, 1935.

[17] C. S. Barrett, *Symposium on Radiography and X-Ray Diffraction* (A.S.T.M.), 1936.

[18] G. W. Brindley, *Phil. Mag.*, **21**, 778, 1936.

[19] A. J. Bradley, *Proc. Phys. Soc.*, **47**, 879, 1935.

[20] G. M. B. Dobson, *Proc. Roy. Soc.* (A), **104**, 248, 1923.

[21] A. Westgren and G. Phragmén, *J. Iron and Steel Inst.*, **105**, 241, 1922.

[22] P. W. Bridgeman, *Proc. Amer. Acad.*, **60**, 342, 1925.

[23] H. Lipson and O. Edwards, *Proc. Roy. Soc.* (A), **180**, 268, 1942.
A. J. C. Wilson, *Proc. Roy. Soc.* (A), **180**, 277, 1942.

[24] A. J. Bradley and A. Taylor, *Proc. Roy. Soc.* (A), **159**, 56, 1937.

[25] J. Willard Gibbs, *Collected Works*, Vol. **1**.

[26] Ryn van Alkemade, *Zeits. für Physik., Chem.*, **11**, 289.

[27] H. W. Hume-Rothery, *J. Inst. Met.*, **35**, 295, 1926.

[28] H. W. B. Roozeboom, *Zeits. für Physik., Chem.*, **15**, 147, 1894.

[29] J. Willard Gibbs, *Collected Works*, Vol. **1**.

[30] C. G. Stokes, *Proc. Roy. Soc.* (A), **49**, 174, 1891.

[31] H. W. B. Roozeboom and Schreinemakers, *Die Ternäre Gleichgewichte*, 1911.

[32] C. S. Barrett, *Symposium on Radiography and X-Ray Diffraction* (A.S.T.M.), 1936.

[33] A. J. Bradley and A. Taylor, *Proc. Roy. Soc.* (A), **159**, 56, 1937.

[34] W. O. Alexander and N. B. Vaughan, *J. Inst. Met.*, **61**, 247, 1937.

[35] A. J. Bradley and S. S. Lu, *J. Inst. Met.*, **60**, 319, 1937.

[36] A. J. Bradley and J. Thewliss, *Proc. Roy. Soc.* (A), **112**, 678, 1926.

[37] H. Jones, *Proc. Roy. Soc.* (A), **144**, 225, 1934.

[38] H. Lipson and N. J. Petch, *J. Iron and Steel Inst.*, p. 95, 1940.

[39] G. Tammann, *Zeits. Anorg. Chemie*, **107**, 1, 1919.

[40] C. H. Johansonn and J. O. Linde, *Ann. Physik.*, **78**, 439, 1925.

[41] U. Dehlinger and L. Graf, *Zeits. Physik.*, **64**, 359, 1930.

[42] C. Sykes and F. W. Jones, *Proc. Roy. Soc.* (A), **161**, 440, 1937.

[43] A. J. Bradley and A. H. Jay, *Proc. Roy. Soc.* (A), **136**, 210, 1932.

[44] A. J. Bradley and J. W. Rodgers, *Proc. Roy. Soc.* (A), **144**, 340, 1934.

[45] F. C. Nix and W. Shockley, *Rev. Modern Physics*, **10**, 2, 1938.

(46) W. L. Bragg and E. J. Williams, *Proc. Roy. Soc.* (A), **145**, 699, 1934.

(47) P. D. Merica, *National Metals Handbook*, p. 607, 1930.

(48) A. G. H. Anderson and E. R. Jette, *Trans. Am. Soc. Metals*, **24**, 375, 1936.

(49) H. Lipson, *Reports on Progress in Physics* (The Physical Society), **6**, 361, 1939.

(50) J. S. Marsh, *Principles of Phase Diagrams* (Alloys of Iron Research).

(51) T. Mishima, *Stahl und Eisen*, **53**, 79, 1933.
W. Köster, *Archiv. für das Eisenhüttenwesen*, **7**, 257, 1933/4.

(52) A. J. Bradley and A. Taylor, *Proc. Roy. Soc.* (A), **166**, 253, 1938; *J. Inst. Met.*, **66**, 53, 1940.

(53) A. J. Bradley and C. S. Cheng, *Zeits. Krist.*, **99**, 480, 1938.

(54) W. G. Burgers and J. L. Snoek, *Physica*, **2**, 1064, 1935.

(55) A. J. Bradley and A. Taylor, *Physics in Industry—Magnetism*.   Institute of Physics, 1937.

(56) A.Westgren and G. Phragmén, *J. Iron and Steel Inst.*, **109**, 159, 1924.

(57) N. J. Petch, *J. Iron and Steel Inst.*, **145**, 111, 1942.

(58) E. Öhman, *J. Iron and Steel Inst.*, **123**, 445, 1931.

(58A) H. Lipson and Audrey M. B. Parker, *J. Iron and Steel Inst.*, November, 1943. (Advance copy.)

(59) A. B. Greninger and A. R. Troiano, *Trans. Am. Inst. Min. and Met. Eng.*, **7**, 1940; *Tech. Pub.* 1212, *Metals Technology*.

(60) H. Lipson and N. J. Petch, *J. Iron and Steel Inst.*, p. 95, 1940.
N. J. Petch, *J. Iron and Steel Inst.*, March, 1944.   (Advance copy.)

(61) A. Westgren, *Am. Inst. Min. and Met. Eng.*, Inst. Met. Div. (B), 1931.

(62) C. A. Edwards and L. B. Pfeil, *J. Iron and Steel Inst.*, **112**, 129, 1925.

(63) T. Ishigaki, *Sci. Rep. Tohoku*, **16** (2), 1927.

(64) J. D. Jevons, *The Metallurgy of Pressing and Deep Drawing* (Chapman & Hall).

(65) T. Berglund, A. Hultgren, and G. Phragmén, *Jernkontorets Annales*, **121**, 600, 1937.

(66) E. C. Bain, *J. Iron and Steel Inst.*, 1938.

(67) J. J. B. Rutherford, R. H. Aborn, and E. C. Bain, *Metals and Alloys*, **8**, 345, 1937.

(68) H. P. Rooksby, *Royal Society of Arts*, **90**, 673, 1942.

(69) W. Bass, *Glocker—Materialprüfung mit Röntgenstrahlen*.

(70) G. L. Clark and Zimmer, *Clark—Applied X-Rays* (McGraw-Hill Book Co.).

(71) H. S. Schdanow, *Zeits. Krist.*, **90**, 82, 1935.

(72) R. A. Stephen and R. J. Barnes, *J. Inst. Metals*, **60**, 285, 1937.

(73) G. L. Clark, *Applied X-Rays* (McGraw-Hill Book Co.).

(74) P. Scherrer, *Zigmondy Kolloidchemie*, 3rd ed., 387, 1920.

(75) M. von Laue, *Zeits. Kristallographie*, **64**, 115, 1926.

(76) F. W. Jones, *Proc. Roy. Soc.* (A), **166**, 16, 1938.

(77) A. L. Patterson, *Phys. Rev.*, **56**, 972, 1939; **56**, 978, 1939.

(78) A. Taylor, *Phil. Mag.*, **31**, 339, 1941.

(79) H. Lipson, D. S. Schoenberg, and G. V. Stupart, *J. Inst. Metals*, **67**, 333, 1941.

(80) W. A. Wood, *Proc. Roy. Soc.* (A), **172**, 231, 1939.
S. L. Smith and W. A. Wood, *Proc. Roy. Soc.* (A), **174**, 310, 1940.

(81) W. A. Wood, *Phil. Mag.*, **15**, 553, 1933.

(82) F. Wever and B. Pfarr, *Mitteilungen Inst. Eisenforschung*, **15**, 137, 1933.

(83) S. L. Smith and W. A. Wood, *Proc. Roy. Soc.* (A), **179**, 450, 1942.

(84) E. Orowan and K. J. Pascoe, *Nature*, **148**, 467, 1941.

(85) D. E. Thomas, *J. Scientific Instruments*, **18**, 135, 1941.
F. Wever and H. Möller, *Archiv. für das Eisenhüttenwesen*, **4**, 215, 1931.
R. Glocker, *Zeits. für tech. Phys.*, 289, 1938.

(86) E. Schiebold and G. Sachs, *Zeits. Krist.*, **63**, 34, 1926.

(87) J. Czochralski, *Moderne Metallkunde in Theorie und Praxis* (Julius Springer, Berlin).

(88) H. C. H. Carpenter and C. F. Elam, *Proc. Roy. Soc.* (A), **100**, 329, 1921.

(89) A. F. Joffe, *The Physics of Crystals*.
Ewald, Pöschl, and Prandl, *The Physics of Solids and Fluids* (Blackie).

(90) E. N. Da C. Andrade, *Proc. Phys. Soc.*, **52**, 1, 1940.

(91) M. Polanyi, H. Mark, and E. Schmid, *Zeits. f. Physik.*, **12**, 58, 1922.

(92) E. Orowan, *Nature*, **147**, 452, 1941.
   G. I. Taylor, *Proc. Roy. Soc.* (A), **145**, 379, 1934.

(93) H. Mark, M. Polanyi and E. Schmid, *Zeits. für Physik*, **5**, 58, 1922.

(94) C. F. Elam, *Distortion of Metal Crystals* (Oxford University Press), 1935.

(95) E. Orowan, *Nature*, **149**, 643, 1942.

(96) S. Nishikawa and S. Ono, *Proc. Math. Phys. Soc.* Tokyo, **7**, 131, 1913.

(97) N. Uspenskij and S. Konobejewski, Lecture to the Russian Lebedev Society, Moscow, 30th April, 1920.

(98) K. Becker, R. O. Herzog, W. Jancke, and M. Polanyi, *Zeits. für Physik*, **5**, 61, 1921.

(99) R. M. Bozorth, *Phys. Rev.*, **26**, 390, 1925.

(100) E. Schmid and G. Wassermann, *Zeits. Physik.*, **42**, 779, 1927; *Naturwissenschaft*, **17**, 321, 1929.

(101) W. R. D. Jones and L. Powell, *J. Inst. Metals*, **66**, 331, 1940.

(102) C. E. Ransley and H. P. Rooksby, *J. Inst. Met.*, **62**, 205, 1938.

(103) D. E. Thomas, *J. Inst. Met.*, **67**, 173, 1941; *Phil. Mag.*, **31**, 425, 1941.

(104) F. Wever, *Mitt. Kaiser-Wilhelm Inst. für Eisenforsch.*, **11**, 109, 1929; **5**, 69, 1924.

(105) C. S. Barrett, *Am. Inst. Min. and Met. Eng.*, Inst. Met. Div., **29**, 124, 1937.

(106) C. S. Barrett, *Metals and Alloys*, **8**, 13, 1937.

(107) C. S. Barrett and L. H. Levenson, *Trans. Am. Inst. Mech. and Met. Eng.*, **137**, 76, 1940.

(108) J. T. Norton and R. E. Hiller, *Trans. A.I.M.M.E.*, **99**, 190, 1932.

(109) L. Hermann and G. Sachs, *Metallwirtschaft*, **13**, 745, 1934.

(110) C. S. Barrett and R. E. Mehl, *Trans. A.I.M.M.E.*, 78, 1931, *et seq.*

(111) J. Young, *Proc. Roy. Soc.* (A), **112**, 630, 1926.

(112) P. D. Merica, *Trans. Am. Inst. Min. and Met. Eng.*, Inst. Met. Div., **99**, 13, 1932.

(113) G. D. Preston, *J. Scientific Instruments*, **18**, 155, 1941; *Proc. Phys. Soc.*, **52**, 77, 1940; *Phil. Mag.*, **26**, 855, 1938.

(114) G. Nagelschmidt, *J. Agric. Science*, **29**, 477, 1939.

(115) F. P. Hall and H. Insley, *J. Am. Ceram. Soc.*, **16**, 1933; **21**, 113, 1938.

(116) H. P. Rooksby and J. H. Partridge, *Trans. Soc. Glass. Tech.*, **24**, 110, 1940.

(117) W. H. Taylor, *Trans. Soc. Glass Tech.*, **16**, 111, 1932.

(118) H. P. Rooksby and J. H. Partridge, *Trans. Soc. Glass. Tech.*, **24**, 110, 1940.

(119) A. J. Moses, *Metal Progress*, 771, 1941.

(120) C. H. Mathewson, *Trans. Am. Inst. Min. and Met. Eng.*, 7, 1928.
   C. H. Mathewson and G. H. Edmunds, *Trans. Am. Inst. Min. and Met. Eng.*, 311, 1928.

APPENDIX

MAKING LINDEMANN GLASS AND CELLOPHANE CAPILLARY TUBES FOR CYLINDRICAL DEBYE-SCHERRER POWDER SPECIMENS

In making cylindrical powder specimens, the method of filling thin-walled capillary tubes which have a low absorption factor for X-rays is sometimes preferable to mounting the grains on a hair by means of Canada balsam. To make Lindemann glass for specimen tubes, mix 17·8 parts by weight of lithium carbonate with 5·8 parts of beryllium carbonate and 76·4 of boric acid. These ingredients are finely powdered, well mixed and fused in a platinum basin. Heating is prolonged until all the CO_2 is driven off and the melt left perfectly clear and homogeneous. The temperature is allowed to fall until the viscosity becomes great enough to allow the fused mass to be drawn into capillary tubing. A silica tube 5·0 mm. in diameter is then dipped into the melt and withdrawn again, pulling after it a thin-walled tube which necks down into a capillary some 0·3 to 0·5 mm. in diameter. These tubes can be sealed off to maintain a vacuum.

Thin cellophane tubes are also very satisfactory and are easily made. Dissolve cellophane clippings in a fifty-fifty solution of acetone and amyl acetate until the liquid is fairly viscous. A piece of soft copper wire of the required diameter is dipped in the cellophane solution and hung up to harden for two days. When quite dry, the cellophane is scraped away from both ends with a razor blade and the wire is stretched by holding one end in a vice· and pulling the other end with a pair of pliers. The wire is reduced in diameter on stretching, leaving the cellophane sleeve loose enough to slide off. The cellophane tube is then cut into suitable lengths and may be sealed with the solution.

MAKING Kβ FILTERS

Filters to cut out the Kβ component are made with a mass per square centimetre of filtering element given in Table I, page 14. Iron filters are best made from standard feeler-gauge steel $\frac{1}{1000}''$ thick rubbed down to 0·018 mm. on 00 emery paper. Dissolving in acid tends to make the filter uneven and full of pinholes. Nickel and copper filters are similarly made from thin, rolled sheet, or by electrodeposition.

Filters of metals which cannot readily be obtained as thin foil can be made by sieving the finely ground metal powder through 350 mesh. The powder is then mixed with collodion solution and allowed to settle and dry on a clean glass plate. The collodion-bonded powder strips away very easily as a thin sheet which is then cut into convenient pieces $1\frac{1}{2}$–2 cm. square. Portions are tested with standard powder specimens in a Debye-Scherrer camera until a piece is found which yields a diffraction pattern free from $K\beta$ in a reasonable period of time. This period is about 2–3 times as long as that required to take a photograph of the same density with unfiltered radiation. An oxide of the metal may also be used, but the extra absorption of the $K\alpha$ component by the oxygen still further increases the exposure period.

If a rock-salt or pentaerythritol crystal is used as a monochromatizer, it is, of course, quite unnecessary to employ a β-filter in addition.

TABLE XXVIII

INDICES FOR CUBIC CRYSTALS

The following table gives values of $h^2 + k^2 + l^2$, $\sqrt{h^2 + k^2 + l^2}$ and $\log (h^2 + k^2 + l^2)$ with a degree of accuracy sufficient for spacing determinations. h, k and l are written in descending order of magnitude for convenience, but it must be remembered that h, k and l can be interchanged without altering the value of $h^2 + k^2 + l^2$. Numbers of the form $4^p(8n + 7)$ cannot be expressed as the sum of three squares. Their absence is noted by marking the succeeding integer with an asterisk.

$h^2 + k^2 + l^2$	$\sqrt{h^2 + k^2 + l^2}$	$\log (h^2 + k^2 + l^2)$	h k l
1	1·000 000	0·000 0000	1 0 0
2	1·414 214	0·301 0300	1 1 0
3	1·732 051	0·477 1213	1 1 1
4	2·000 000	0·602 0600	2 0 0
5	2·236 068	0·698 9700	2 1 0
6	2·449 490	0·778 1513	2 1 1
8*	2·828 427	0·903 0900	2 2 0
9	3·000 000	0·954 2425	3 0 0; 2 2 1
10	3·162 278	1·000 0000	3 1 0
11	3·316 625	1·041 3927	3 1 1
12	3·464 102	1·079 1812	2 2 2
13	3·605 551	1·113 9434	3 2 0
14	3·741 657	1·146 1280	3 2 1
16*	4·000 000	1·204 1200	4 0 0
17	4·123 106	1·230 4489	4 1 0; 3 2 2
18	4·242 641	1·255 2725	4 1 1; 3 3 0
19	4·358 899	1·278 7536	3 3 1
20	4·472 136	1·301 0300	4 2 0
21	4·582 576	1·322 2193	4 2 1
22	4·690 416	1·342 4227	3 3 2
24*	4·898 979	1·380 2112	4 2 2
25	5·000 000	1·397 9400	5 0 0; 4 3 0
26	5·099 020	1·414 9733	5 1 0; 4 3 1
27	5·196 152	1·431 3638	5 1 1; 3 3 3
29*	5·385 165	1·462 3980	5 2 0; 4 3 2
30	5·477 226	1·477 1213	5 2 1

TABLE XXVIII (*continued*)

$h^2 + k^2 + l^2$	$\sqrt{h^2 + k^2 + l^2}$	$\log(h^2 + k^2 + l^2)$	$h \quad k \quad l$
32*	5·656 854	1·505 1500	4 4 0
33	5·744 563	1·518 5139	5 2 2; 4 4 1
34	5·830 952	1·531 4789	5 3 0; 4 3 3
35	5·916 080	1·544 0680	5 3 1
36	6·000 000	1·556 3025	6 0 0; 4 4 2
37	6·082 763	1·568 2017	6 1 0
38	6·164 414	1·579 7836	6 1 1; 5 3 2
40*	6·324 555	1·602 0600	6 2 0
41	6·403 124	1·612 7839	6 2 1; 5 4 0; 4 4 3
42	6·480 741	1·623 2493	5 4 1
43	6·557 439	1·633 4685	5 3 3
44	6·633 250	1·643 4527	6 2 2
45	6·708 204	1·653 2125	6 3 0; 5 4 2
46	6·782 330	1·662 7578	6 3 1
48*	6·928 203	1·681 2412	4 4 4
49	7·000 000	1·690 1961	7 0 0; 6 3 2
50	7·071 068	1·698 9700	7 1 0; 5 5 0; 5 4 3
51	7·141 428	1·707 5702	7 1 1; 5 5 1
52	7·211 103	1·716 0033	6 4 0
53	7·280 110	1·724 2759	7 2 0; 6 4 1
54	7·348 469	1·732 3938	7 2 1; 6 3 3; 5 5 2
56*	7·483 315	1·748 1880	6 4 2
57	7·549 834	1·755 8749	7 2 2; 5 4 4
58	7·615 773	1·763 4280	7 3 0
59	7·681 146	1·770 8520	7 3 1; 5 5 3
61*	7·810 250	1·785 3298	6 5 0; 6 4 3
62	7·874 008	1·792 3917	7 3 2; 6 5 1
64*	8·000 000	1·806 1800	8 0 0
65	8·062 258	1·812 9134	8 1 0; 7 4 0; 6 5 2
66	8·124 038	1·819 5439	8 1 1; 7 4 1; 5 5 4
67	8·185 353	1·826 0748	7 3 3
68	8·246 211	1·832 5089	8 2 0; 6 4 4
69	8·306 624	1·838 8491	8 2 1; 7 4 2
70	8·366 600	1·845 0980	6 5 3

TABLE XXVIII (*continued*)

$h^2 + k^2 + l^2$	$\sqrt{h^2 + k^2 + l^2}$	$\log(h^2+k^2+l^2)$	$h \quad k \quad l$
72*	8·485 281	1·857 3325	8 2 2; 6 6 0
73	8·544 004	1·863 3229	8 3 0; 6 6 1
74	8·602 325	1·869 2317	8 3 1; 7 5 0; 7 4 3
75	8·660 254	1·875 0613	7 5 1; 5 5 5
76	8·717 798	1·880 8136	6 6 2
77	8·774 964	1·886 4907	8 3 2; 6 5 4
78	8·831 761	1·892 0946	7 5 2
80*	8·944 272	1·903 0900	8 4 0
81	9·000 000	1·908 4850	9 0 0; 8 4 1; 7 4 4; 6 6 3
82	9·055 385	1·913 8139	9 1 0; 8 3 3
83	9·110 434	1·919 0781	9 1 1; 7 5 3
84	9·165 151	1·924 2793	8 4 2
85	9·219 544	1·929 4189	9 2 0; 7 6 0
86	9·273 618	1·934 4985	9 2 1; 7 6 1; 6 5 5
88*	9·380 832	1·944 4827	6 6 4
89	9·433 981	1·949 3900	9 2 2; 8 5 0; 8 4 3; 7 6 2
90	9·486 833	1·954 2425	9 3 0; 8 5 1; 7 5 4
91	9·539 392	1·959 0414	9 3 1
93*	9·643 651	1·968 4829	8 5 2
94	9·695 360	1·973 1279	9 3 2; 7 6 3
96*	9·797 959	1·982 2712	8 4 4
97	9·848 858	1·986 7717	9 4 0; 6 6 5
98	9·899 495	1·991 2261	9 4 1; 8 5 3; 7 7 0
99	9·949 874	1·995 6352	9 3 3; 7 7 1; 7 5 5
100	10·000 000	2·000 0000	10 0 0; 8 6 0
101	10·049 88	2·004 3214	10 1 0; 9 4 2; 8 6 1; 7 6 4
102	10·099 50	2·008 6002	10 1 1; 7 7 2
104*	10·198 04	2·017 0333	10 2 0; 8 6 2
105	10·246 95	2·021 1893	10 2 1; 8 5 4
106	10·295 63	2·025 3059	9 5 0; 9 4 3
107	10·344 08	2·029 3838	9 5 1; 7 7 3
108	10·392 30	2·033 4238	10 2 2; 6 6 6
109	10·440 31	2·037 4265	10 3 0; 8 6 3
110	10·488 09	2·041 3927	10 3 1; 9 5 2; 7 6 5

TABLE XXVIII (*continued*)

$h^2 + k^2 + l^2$	$\sqrt{h^2 + k^2 + l^2}$	$\log(h^2 + k^2 + l^2)$	$h\ \ k\ \ l$
113**	10·630 15	2·053 0784	10 3 2; 9 4 4; 8 7 0
114	10·677 08	2·056 9049	8 7 1; 8 5 5; 7 7 4
115	10·723 81	2·060 6978	9 5 3
116	10·770 33	2·064 4580	10 4 0; 8 6 4
117	10·816 65	2·068 1859	10 4 1; 9 6 0; 8 7 2
118	10·862 78	2·071 8820	10 3 3; 9 6 1
120*	10·954 45	2·079 1812	10 4 2
121	11·000 00	2·082 7854	11 0 0; 9 6 2; 7 6 6
122	11·045 36	2·086 3598	11 1 0; 9 5 4; 8 7 3
123	11·090 54	2·089 9051	11 1 1; 7 7 5
125*	11·180 34	2·096 9100	11 2 0; 10 5 0; 10 4 3; 8 6 5
126	11·224 97	2·100 3705	11 2 1; 10 5 1; 9 6 3
128*	11·313 71	2·107 2100	8 8 0
129	11·357 82	2·110 5897	11 2 2; 10 5 2; 8 8 1; 8 7 4
130	11·401 75	2·113 9434	11 3 0; 9 7 0
131	11·445 52	2·117 2713	11 3 1; 9 7 1; 9 5 5
132	11·489 13	2·120 5739	10 4 4; 8 8 2
133	11·532 56	2·123 8516	9 6 4
134	11·575 84	2·127 1048	11 3 2; 10 5 3; 9 7 2; 7 7 6
136*	11·661 90	2·133 5389	10 6 0; 8 6 6
137	11·704 70	2·136 7206	11 4 0; 10 6 1; 8 8 3
138	11·747 34	2·139 8791	11 4 1; 8 7 5
139	11·789 83	2·143 0148	11 3 3; 9 7 3
140	11·832 16	2·146 1280	10 6 2
141	11·874 34	2·149 2191	11 4 2; 10 5 4
142	11·916 38	2·152 2883	9 6 5
144*	12·000 00	2·158 3625	12 0 0; 8 8 4
145	12·041 59	2·161 3680	12 1 0; 10 6 3; 9 8 0
146	12·083 05	2·164 3529	12 1 1; 11 5 0; 11 4 3; 9 8 1; 9 7 4
147	12·124 36	2·167 3173	11 5 1; 7 7 7
148	12·165 53	2·170 2617	12 2 0
149	12·206 56	2·173 1863	12 2 1; 10 7 0; 9 8 2; 8 7 6
150	12·247 45	2·176 0913	11 5 2; 10 7 1; 10 5 5
152*	12·328 83	2·181 8436	12 2 2; 10 6 4

INDEXING OF LINES IN POWDER PHOTOGRAPHS BY THE METHOD OF HULL AND DAVEY

Tetragonal and hexagonal crystals involve a cell edge (a) and an axial ratio (c/a). It is therefore possible to index their Debye-Scherrer reflexions by means of special charts devised by A. W. Hull and W. P. Davey (*Physical Review*, **17**, 549, 1921).

In the case of a hexagonal crystal, the spacing d of the family of planes with Miller indices (hkl) is given by the Bragg relation

$$\sin \theta = \frac{n\lambda}{2d} = \frac{n\lambda}{2a}\sqrt{\frac{4}{3}(h^2 + hk + k^2) + l^2/\left(\frac{c}{a}\right)^2} \qquad . \quad (1)$$

If we let

$$x = \log\left(\frac{d}{na}\right) = -\log n \sqrt{\frac{4}{3}(h^2 + hk + k^2) + l^2/\left(\frac{c}{a}\right)^2} \quad . \quad (2)$$

we obtain from (1) on taking logarithms

$$-\log \sin \theta = x - \log \frac{\lambda}{2a} \quad . \qquad . \qquad . \quad (3)$$

For each set of *Miller* indices (hkl) equation (2) or (3) yields one curve, which is indicated on the Hull-Davey charts with its appropriate indices. The plots show the spacings of all possible planes (within the range of the plot) as a function of the axial ratio $\frac{c}{a}$. The scale of abscissæ is logarithmic so that if the planar spacings d calculated from the Debye-Scherrer photograph are plotted on the same logarithmic scale shown on the bottom of each plot, they may be compared directly with the theoretical values without regard to the absolute length of the unit axes.

In order to compare the observed spacings with the theoretical values of the plots, a strip of paper is placed beneath the logarithmic scale of abscissæ of the chart, and the values of the interplanar spacings d laid off along its edge. The strip with its pattern of lines is then moved about over the plot with its edge always parallel to the axis of abscissa, until a position is found where its pattern coincides exactly with that of the chart.

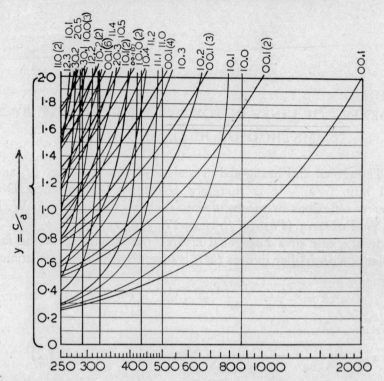

FIG. 238.—Hull-Davey Curves for the hexagonal system.

Fig. 238 shows a typical Hull-Davey chart for the hexagonal system. Similar curves are also drawn for tetragonal lattices. The plots have only a limited usefulness as they tend to become very crowded at small values of log d/na, which makes it difficult to be sure that a coincidence does not belong to one of many curves. To be really useful, the Hull-Davey charts must be drawn on a very large scale.

INDICES FOR THE HEXAGONAL SYSTEM

The values of θ at which the X-ray reflexions from a hexagonal crystal appear are given by the relation

$$\sin^2 \theta = \left(\frac{\lambda}{2}\right)^2 \left\{ \frac{4(h^2 + hk + k^2)}{3a^2} + \frac{l^2}{c^2} \right\}$$

$$= \left(\frac{\lambda}{2}\right)^2 \left\{ \frac{4s}{3a^2} + \frac{l^2}{c^2} \right\}$$

where

$$s = h^2 + hk + k^2 = h^2 + ki + i^2 = i^2 + ih + h^2 \; ; \; i = -(h + k).$$

TABLE XXIX

Values of $s = h^2 + hk + k^2$ and $\dfrac{4}{3}s$ for Hexagonal Crystals

s	$\dfrac{4}{3}s$	h	k	i	s	$\dfrac{4}{3}s$	h	k	i
1	1·3	1	0	$\bar{1}$	100	133·3	10	0	$\overline{10}$
3	4·0	1	1	$\bar{2}$	103	137·3	9	2	$\overline{11}$
4	5·3	2	0	$\bar{2}$	108	144·0	6	6	$\overline{12}$
7	9·3	2	1	$\bar{3}$	109	145·3	7	5	$\overline{12}$
9	12·0	3	0	$\bar{3}$					
12	16·0	2	2	$\bar{4}$	111	148·0	10	1	$\overline{11}$
13	17·3	3	1	$\bar{4}$	112	149·3	8	4	$\overline{12}$
16	21·3	4	0	$\bar{4}$	117	156·0	9	3	$\overline{12}$
19	25·3	3	2	$\bar{5}$					
					121	161·3	11	0	$\overline{11}$
21	28·0	4	1	$\bar{5}$	124	165·3	10	2	$\overline{12}$
25	33·3	5	0	$\bar{5}$	127	169·3	7	6	$\overline{13}$
27	36·0	3	3	$\bar{6}$	129	172·0	8	5	$\overline{13}$
28	37·3	4	2	$\bar{6}$					
					133	177·3	11	1	$\overline{12}$
31	41·3	5	1	$\bar{6}$	133	177·3	9	4	$\overline{13}$
36	48·0	6	0	$\bar{6}$	139	185·3	10	3	$\overline{13}$
37	49·3	4	3	$\bar{7}$					
39	52·0	5	2	$\bar{7}$	144	192·0	12	0	$\overline{12}$
					147	196·0	11	2	$\overline{13}$
43	57·3	6	1	$\bar{7}$	147	196·0	7	7	$\overline{14}$
48	64·0	4	4	$\bar{8}$	148	197·3	8	6	$\overline{14}$
49	65·3	7	0	$\bar{7}$					
49	65·3	5	3	$\bar{8}$	151	201·3	9	5	$\overline{14}$
					156	208·0	10	4	$\overline{14}$
52	69·3	6	2	$\bar{8}$	157	209·3	12	1	$\overline{13}$
57	76·0	7	1	$\bar{8}$					
					163	217·3	11	3	$\overline{14}$
61	81·3	5	4	$\bar{9}$	169	225·3	13	0	$\overline{13}$
63	84·0	6	3	$\bar{9}$	169	225·3	8	7	$\overline{15}$
64	85·3	8	0	$\bar{8}$					
67	89·3	7	2	$\bar{9}$	171	228·0	9	6	$\overline{15}$
					172	229·3	12	2	$\overline{14}$
73	97·3	8	1	$\bar{9}$	175	233·3	10	5	$\overline{15}$
75	100·0	5	5	$\overline{10}$					
76	101·3	6	4	$\overline{10}$	181	241·3	11	4	$\overline{15}$
79	105·3	7	3	$\overline{10}$	183	244·0	13	1	$\overline{14}$
					189	252·0	12	3	$\overline{15}$
81	108·0	9	0	$\bar{9}$					
84	112·0	8	2	$\overline{10}$	192	256·0	8	8	$\overline{16}$
					193	257·3	9	7	$\overline{16}$
91	121·3	6	5	$\overline{11}$	196	261·3	14	0	$\overline{14}$
91	121·3	9	1	$\overline{10}$	196	261·3	10	6	$\overline{16}$
93	124·0	7	4	$\overline{11}$	199	265·3	13	2	$\overline{15}$
97	129·3	8	3	$\overline{11}$					

M

TABLE XXX

Number of Co-operating Planes for Powder Photographs

CUBIC SYSTEM

Space-Groups			hkl	hhl	okl	okk	hhh	ool
O_h	O	T_d	48	24	24	12	8	6
T_h	T		2.24	24	2.12	12	8	6

HEXAGONAL AND RHOMBOHEDRAL SYSTEMS

Space-Groups			$hkil$	$hh\overline{2h}l$	$ok\overline{k}l$	$hkio$	$hh\overline{2h}o$	$ok\overline{k}o$	$ooo l$
D_{6h}	D_6	C_{6v} D_{3h}	24	12	12	12	6	6	2
C_{6h}	C_6	C_{3h}	2.12	12	12	2.6	6	6	2
D_{3d}	D_3	C_{3v}	2.12	12	2.6	12	6	6	2
C_{3i}	C_3		4.6	2.6	2.6	2.6	6	6	2

TETRAGONAL SYSTEM

Space-Groups			hkl	hhl	okl	hko	hho	oko	ool
D_{4h}	D_4	C_{4v} V_d	16	8	8	8	4	4	2
C_{4h}	C_4	S_4	2.8	8	8	2.4	4	4	2

ORTHORHOMBIC SYSTEM

Space-Groups			hkl	okl	hol	hko	hoo	oko	ool
V_h	V	C_2	8	4	4	4	2	2	2

MONOCLINIC SYSTEM

Space-Groups			hkl	hol	oko
C_{2h}	C_2	C_s	4	2	2

EMISSION SPECTRA AND ABSORPTION EDGES

The tables of the strongest lines in the K, L, and M spectra and absorption edges given below are from Siegbahn's *Spektroskopie der Röntgenstrahlen*. The most pronounced edges of the L and M series only are given. The X-unit of wavelength used in the tables below is very nearly equal to 10^{-11} cm. or 10^{-3} Angstrom units.[*] It is based upon an assumed value of the (200) spacing of calcite which is taken to be 3029·45 X-units. Correcting for refraction, the actual value of the spacing taken for the 200 order in the calculation is 3029·04 X-units.

It is possible to use these emission spectra as a means of identifying elements in an unknown substance. The unknown is made the target of the X-ray tube and the emitted X-rays are reflected from the face of a calcite crystal which acts as an analyser. From the spacing of the reflecting planes and the angle at which a reflexion appears, the wavelength emitted by the tube can be calculated and the element responsible for it determined by looking up the tables.

In taking X-ray diffraction patterns, it must be remembered that if the radiation lies just on the *short* wave side of an absorption edge of the specimen, it will be heavily absorbed and rescattered as incoherent radiation with longer wavelength which produces a dense background on the photograph. This may be avoided by choosing a radiation which lies well away from the absorption edge on the short wave side, or just beyond the edge on the long wave side.

[*] Cf. footnote on page 15.

TABLE XXXI

K Emission Spectra and Absorption Edges

Element	Atomic No.	α_2	α_1	β_3	β_1	β_2	Absorption Edge
Sodium . .	11	11885			11594		
Magnesium .	12	9869			9539		9496·2
Aluminium .	13	8320·5			7965		7935·6
Silicon . .	14	7111·06			6754·5		6731·0
Phosphorus .	15	6142·5			5792·1		5774·9
Sulphur . .	16	5363·7	5361·3		5021·1		5008·8
Chlorine . .	17	4721·2	4718·2		4394·2		4383·8
Potassium .	19	3737·07	3733·68		3446·8		3431·0
Calcium . .	20	3354·95	3351·69		3083·4		3064·3
Scandium .	21	3028·40	3025·03		2773·9		2751·7
Titanium. .	22	2746·81	2743·17		2509·0		2491·2
Vanadium .	23	2502·13	2498·35		2279·7		2263·0
Chromium .	24	2288·91	2285·03		2080·6		2065·9
Manganese .	25	2101·49	2097·51		1906·20		1891·6
Iron . . .	26	1936·012	1932·076		1753·013		1739·4
Cobalt . .	27	1789·19	1785·29		1617·44		1604·0
Nickel . .	28	1658·35	1654·50		1497·05	1485·61	1483·9
Copper . .	29	1541·232	1537·395		1389·35	1378·24	1377·4
Zinc . . .	30	1436·03	1432·17		1292·55	1281·07	1280·5
Gallium . .	31	1340·87	1337·15		1205·20	1193·8	1190·2
Germanium .	32	1255·21	1251·30		1126·71	1114·59	1114·6
Arsenic . .	33	1177·43	1173·44		1055·10	1042·81	1042·63
Selenium . .	34	1106·52	1102·48		990·13	977·91	977·73
Bromine . .	35	1041·66	1037·59		930·87	918·53	918·09
Krypton . .	36	978			875		
Rubidium .	37	927·76	923·64	827·49	826·96	814·76	814·10
Strontium .	38	877·61	873·45	781·83	781·30	769·21	768·37
Yttrium . .	39	831·32	827·12	739·72	739·19	727·13	725·5
Zirconium .	40	788·51	784·30	700·83	700·28	688·50	687·38
Columbium .	41	748·89	744·65	664·96	664·38	652·80	651·58
Molybdenum	42	712·105	707·831	631·543	630·978	619·698	618·48
Ruthenium .	44	646·06	641·74	571·93	571·31	560·51	558·4
Rhodium .	45	616·37	612·02	545·09	544·49	533·96	533·03
Palladium .	46	588·63	584·27	520·09	519·47	509·18	507·95
Silver . .	47	562·67	558·28	496·65	496·01	486·03	484·48

Note in β_3 column: β_3 and β_1 not resolved.

Note in β_2 column: For atomic numbers below 42, β_2 decreases rapidly in intensity. It is not observed below nickel.

TABLE XXXI (*continued*)

Element	Atomic No.	α_2	α_1	β_3	β_1	β_2	Absorption Edge
Cadmium .	48	538·32	533·90	474·71	474·08	464·20	463·13
Indium . .	49	515·48	511·06	454·23	453·58	444·08	442·98
Tin . . .	50	494·02	489·57	434·95	434·30	424·99	423·94
Antimony .	51	473·87	469·31	416·23		407·10	406·09
Tellurium .	52	454·91	450·37	399·26		390·37	389·26
Iodine . .	53	437·03	432·49	383·92	383·15	374·71	373·44
Xenon . .	54	417		360			
Cæsium . .	55	404·11	399·59	354·36	353·62	345·16	344·04
Barium . .	56	388·99	384·43	340·89	340·22	332·22	330·70
Lanthanum .	57	374·66	370·04	328·09	327·26	319·66	318·14
Cerium . .	58	361·10	356·47	315·72	315·01	307·70	306·26
Praseodymium	59	348·05	343·40	304·39	303·60	296·25	295·1
Neodymium .	60	335·95	331·25	293·51	292·75	285·73	284·58
Samarium .	62	313·02	308·33	273·25	272·50	265·75	264·4
Europium .	63	302·65	297·90	263·86	263·07	256·45	254·8
Gadolinium .	64	292·61	287·82	254·71	253·94	247·62	246·2
Terbium . .	65	282·86	278·20	246·29	245·51	239·12	237·6
Dysprosium .	66	273·75	269·03	237·87	237·10	231·28	230·1
Holmium .	67	264·99	260·30	—	—	—	222·64
Erbium . .	68	256·64	251·97	223·00	222·15	216·71	
Thulium . .	69	248·61	243·87	215·58	214·87	—	208·5
Ytterbium .	70	240·98	236·28	209·16	208·34	203·22	201·6
Lutecium .	71	233·58	228·82	202·52	201·71	196·49	195·1
Hafnium . .	72	226·53	221·73	195·83	195·15	190·42	190·1
Tantalum .	73	219·73	214·88	189·91		184·52	183·6
Tungsten .	74	213·45	208·62	184·22		178·98	178·22
Osmium . .	76	201·31	196·45	173·61		168·75	167·55
Iridium . .	77	195·50	190·65	168·50		163·76	162·09
Platinum .	78	190·04	182·23	163·70		158·87	157·70
Gold . . .	79	184·83	179·96	159·02		154·26	153·20
Thallium .	81	174·66	169·80	150·11		145·39	144·41
Lead . . .	82	170·04	165·16	146·06		141·25	140·49
Bismuth . .	83	165·25	160·41	142·05		136·21	136·78
Thorium . .	90	136·8	132·3	116·9		113·4	112·70
Uranium . .	92	130·95	126·40	111·87		108·42	106·58 ?
Approximate relative intensities }		50	100	7	14	< 5	

TABLE XXXII

L Emission Spectra and L_{III} Absorption Edges

Element	Atomic Number	l	η	α_2	α_1	β_1	β_2	β_3	β_4	β_6	γ_1	Absorption Edge L_{III}
Copper	29	15190	14830	13306	13306	13030	—	12100	12100			
Zinc	30	13950	13610	12230	12230	11960	—	11160	11160			
Gallium	31	12890	12560	11270	11270	11010						
Germanium	32	11922	11587	10415	10415	10153						
Arsenic	33	11048	10711	9652	9652	9395	—		8912			
Selenium	34	10272	9939	8972	8972	8718						
Bromine	35	9564	9235	8358	8358	8109						
Rubidium	37	—	7506			6610.0	—	6769.4	6800.9	6968.1	—	6841.3
Strontium	38	7822	7031.0	6848.6	6848.6	6203.9	—	6358.2	6391.8	6508.1	—	6362.0
Yttrium	39	—		6435.7	6435.7		—	5974.1	6007.7	6085.7		5944.4
Zirconium	40	6899	6593.9	6056.7	6056.7	5823.6	5574.2	5618.6	5651.7	5692.7	5373.8	5561.0
Columbium	41	6510	6196	5718	5712	5480.3	5226.0	5297.1	5330.6	5347.1	5024.8	5212.1
Molybdenum	42	5486.4	5836	5401	5395.0	5166.5	4910.0	5004.7	5041.0	—	—	4904.2
Ruthenium	44	5207.0	4911.2	4843.7	4835.7	4611.0	4361.9	4476.4	4512.6	4476.4	4172.8	4360.4
Rhodium	45			4595.6	4587.8	4364.0	4122.1	4244.7	4280.2	4232.8	3935.7	4121.2
Palladium	46	4939.6	4650.2	4366.6	4358.5	4137.3	3900.7	4025.7	4062.3	4007.0	3716.4	3903.9
Silver	47	4697.6	4410.1	4153.8	4145.6	3926.6	3693.8	3824.5	3861.1	3798.6	3514.9	3690.8
Cadmium	48	4471.3	4187.5	3956.4	3947.8	3730.1	3506.4	3636.4	3674.3	3607.3	3328.0	3496.3
Indium	49	4259.3	3976.1	3772.4	3763.7	3547.8	3331.2	3461.9	3499.0	3428.0	3155.3	3315.5
Tin	50	4063.3	3781.8	3601.1	3592.2	3377.9	3167.9	3298.9	3336.3	3262.2	2994.9	3149.3
Antimony	51	3880.3	3599.6	3440.8	3431.8	3218.4	3016.6	3145.1	3184.3	3107.8	2845.1	2990.7
Tellurium	52	3710.1	—	3291.0	3282.0	3070.0	2876.1	3001.3	3040.0	2964.4	2706.5	2845.7
Iodine	53	3549.7		3150.9	3141.7	2930.9	2746.1	2868.2	2905.9	2830.5	2577.5	2713.9
Cæsium	55	3259.6	2983.3	2895.6	2886.1	2677.8	2506.4	2622.9	2660.5	2587.5	2342.5	2467.4
Barium	56	3128.7	2857.1	2779.0	2769.6	2562.2	2399.3	2511.0	2549.8	2477.2	2236.6	2356.8
Lanthanum	57	3000	2734	2668.9	2659.7	2453.3	2298.0	2405.3	2443.8	2373.9	2137.2	2253.7
Cerium	58	2885.7	2614.7	2565.1	2556.0	2351.0	2204.1	2305.9	2344.2	2276.9	2044.3	2159.5
Praseodymium	59	2778.1	2507	2467.6	2457.7	2253.9	2114.8	2212.4	2250.1	2185.9	1956.8	2072.8
Neodymium	60	2670.3	2404.2	2375.3	2365.3	2162.2	2021.4	2122.1	2162.2	2099.3	1873.8	1999.7

		3	2	12	100	50	25	10	5	1	10	
63	Europium	2390·3	—	2127·3	2116·3	1916·3	1808·2	1882·7	1922·1	1870·5	1654·3	1771·7
64	Gadolinium	2307·1	—	2052·6	2041·9	1842·5	1741·9	1810·9	1849·3	1803·1	1588·6	1706·0
65	Terbium	2229·0	—	1982·3	1971·5	1772·7	1679·0	1742·5	1781·4	1737·5	1526·6	1645·3
66	Dysprosium	2154·0	1892·2	1915·6	1904·6	1706·6	1619·8	1677·7	1716·7	1677·7	1469·7	1576
67	Holmium	2082·1	1822·0	1852·1	1841·0	1643·5	1563·7	1616·0	1655·3	1618·8	1414·2	1532·2
68	Erbium	2015·1	1754·8	1791·4	1780·4	1583·4	1510·6	1557·9	1596·4	1563·6	1362·3	1479·19
69	Thulium	1951·1	1692·3	1733·9	1722·8	1526·8	1460·2	1502·3	1541·2	1511·5	1312·7	1429·9
70	Ytterbium	1890	1631	1678·9	1667·8	1472·5	1412·8	1449·4	1488·2	1462·7	1264·8	1382·64
71	Lutecium	1831·8	1573·8	1626·36	1615·51	1420·7	1367·2	1398·2	1437·2	1414·3	1220·3	1337·5
72	Hafnium	1777·4	1519·7	1577·04	1566·07	1371·1	1323·5	1349·7	1389·3	1371·1	1176·5	1293·0
73	Tantalum	1724·9	1467·9	1529·78	1518·85	1324·23	1281·90	1304·09	1343·07	1328·4	1135·58	1251·7
74	Tungsten	1675·0	1418·1	1484·38	1473·36	1279·17	1242·03	1259·92	1298·79	1287·0	1096·30	1212·9
75	Rhenium	1627·3	1370·6	1441·0	1429·97	1236·03	1204·1	1217·6	1256·3	1248·1	1058·7	1175·5
76	Osmium	—	—	1398·66	1388·59	1194·90	1168·84	—	—	—	1022·96	1139·0
77	Iridium	—	1281·7	1359·8	1348·47	1155·40	1132·97	1138·47	1177·15	1175·45	988·76	1103·8
78	Platinum	1496·4	1240·3	1321·55	1310·33	1117·58	1099·74	1101·65	1139·86	1141·00	955·99	1071·0
79	Gold	1456·9	1200·3	1285·02	1273·77	1081·28	1068·01	1065·50	1104·22	1108·63	924·61	1038·2
80	Mercury	1418·41	1161·6	1249·51	1238·63	1046·52	1037·70	1030·46	1069·2	1076·8	894·6	1007·5
81	Thallium	1381·9	1125·4	1216·26	1204·93	1012·99	1008·22	998·50	1036·99	1047·48	865·71	977·8
82	Lead	1347·4	1090·0	1184·08	1172·58	980·83	980·83	967·21	1005·63	1019·06	838·01	949·2
83	Bismuth	1313·7	1056·5	1153·01	1141·50	950·02	953·24	936·66	975·01	991·31	811·43	922·1
90	Thorium	1112·8	852·8	965·85	954·05	763·56	791·92	753·24	791·92	826·46	651·76	760·0
91	Protoactinium	1088·5	827·8	942·7	930·9	740·7	772·1	730·7	768·3	806·2	632·5	—
92	Uranium	1064·9	803·5	920·62	908·74	718·51	753·07	708·79	746·4	786·79	613·59	720·8
	Approximate relative intensities for elements of high atomic number	3	2	12	100	50	25	10	5	1	10	

TABLE XXXIII

M Emission Spectra and M_V Absorption Edges

Element	Atomic Number	α_2	α_1	β	γ	M_V Absorption Edge
Tantalum . .	73	—	7237	7008	6299	—
Tungsten . .	74	—	6969	6743	6076	6702
Rhenium . .	75	—	6715	6491	5875	—
Osmium . .	76	—	6477	6254	5670	6194
Iridium. . .	77	6262	6249	6025	5490	5961
Platinum . .	78	6045	6034	5816	5309	5746
Gold . . .	79	5842	5828	5612	5135	5529
Thallium . .	81	5461	5450	5239	4815	5136
Lead . . .	82	5288	5274	5065	4665	4945
Bismuth . .	83	5119	5108	4899	4522	4762
Thorium . .	90	4143	4130	3934	3672	3722
Uranium . .	92	3916	3902	3708	3473	3491

TABLES OF X-RAY ATOMIC SCATTERING FACTORS

The following tables of atomic scattering factors are for atoms at rest. For convenience they are given as a function of $\dfrac{\sin \theta}{\lambda}$, which makes them adaptable for radiation of any wavelength. They must be corrected for heat motion by means of the Debye-Waller temperature factor $e^{-B\frac{\sin^2\theta}{\lambda^2}}$.

Table XXXIV is based upon the Hartree model of the electron distribution in light atoms which is obtained by the method of self-consistent fields. For atoms heavier than Rb, the atomic scattering factors may be computed from the more approximate Thomas-Fermi electron distribution. The f_0 values of Cs, atomic number 55, are first calculated, and, for an atom of atomic number Z, each value of f_0 is multiplied by $Z/55$ and each value of $\dfrac{\sin \theta}{\lambda}$ by $(55/Z)^{\frac{1}{3}}$. The resulting values are given in Table XXXV.

The f-factors in the tables are computed making no allowance for possible variations with wavelength. In the region of an absorption edge of the scattering atom, the value of f_0 decreases by several units. We may obtain the true value of the scattering factor f for radiation of wavelength λ from the expression

$$f = f_0 - \Delta f.$$

Values of the decrement Δf calculated by Hönl are given in Table XXXVI. They are tabulated in terms of the ratio λ/λ_κ, where λ_κ is the wavelength of the K absorption edge of the scattering element.

TABLE XXXIV

Atomic Scattering Factors f_o for Atoms at Rest

(R. W. James and G. W. Brindley, *Zeitschrift für Kristallographie*, **78**, 470, 1931)

$\frac{\sin\theta}{\lambda} \times 10^{-8}$	0	0·1	0·2	0·3	0·4	0·5	0·6	0·7	0·8	0·9	1·0	1·1	Remarks
H	1·0	0·81	0·48	0·25	0·13	0·07	0·04	0·03	0·02	0·01	0·00	0·00	W
He	2·0	1·88	1·46	1·05	0·75	0·52	0·35	0·24	0·18	0·14	0·11	0·09	H
Li+	2·0	1·96	1·8	1·5	1·3	1·0	0·8	0·6	0·5	0·4	0·3	0·3	H
Li (neut.)	3·0	2·2	1·8	1·5	1·3	1·0	0·8	0·6	0·5	0·4	0·3	0·3	H
Be++	2·0	2·0	1·9	1·7	1·6	1·4	1·2	1·0	0·9	0·7	0·6	0·5	I
Be (neut.)	4·0	2·9	1·9	1·7	1·6	1·4	1·2	1·0	0·9	0·7	0·6	0·5	I
Be+++	2·0	2·0	1·9	1·8	1·7	1·6	1·4	1·3	1·2	1·0	0·9	0·7	I
B (neut.)	5·0	3·5	2·4	1·9	1·7	1·5	1·6	1·2	1·2	1·0	0·9	0·7	I
C	6·0	4·6	3·0	2·2	1·9	1·7	1·6	1·4	1·3	1·2	1·0	0·9	I
N+5	2·0	2·0	2·0	1·9	1·9	1·8	1·7	1·6	1·5	1·4	1·3	1·16	I
N+3	4·0	3·7	3·0	2·4	2·0	1·8	1·65	1·55	1·5	1·4	1·3	1·15	I
N (neut.)	7·0	5·8	4·2	3·0	2·3	1·9	1·65	1·55	1·5	1·4	1·3	1·15	H
O (neut.)	8·0	7·1	5·3	3·9	2·9	2·2	1·8	1·6	1·5	1·4	1·35	1·25	I+H
O−2	10·0	8·0	5·5	3·8	2·7	2·1	1·8	1·6	1·5	1·4	1·35	1·25	H
F−	10·0	8·7	6·7	4·8	3·5	2·8	2·2	1·9	1·7	1·55	1·5	1·35	I
F (neut.)	9·0	7·8	6·2	4·45	3·35	2·65	2·15	1·9	1·7	1·6	1·5	1·35	H
Ne	10·0	9·3	7·5	5·8	4·4	3·4	2·65	2·2	1·9	1·65	1·55	1·5	I
Na+	10·0	9·5	8·2	6·7	5·25	4·05	3·2	2·65	2·25	1·95	1·75	1·6	H
Na	11·0	9·65	8·2	6·7	5·25	4·05	3·2	2·65	2·25	1·95	1·75	1·6	H
Mg++	10·0	9·75	8·6	7·25	5·05	4·8	3·85	3·15	2·55	2·2	2·0	1·8	I
Mg	12·0	10·5	8·6	7·22	5·05	4·8	3·85	3·15	2·55	2·2	2·0	1·8	I
Al+++	10·0	9·7	8·9	7·8	6·65	5·5	4·45	3·65	3·1	2·65	2·3	2·0	H
Al++	11·0	10·3	9·0	7·75	6·6	5·5	4·5	3·7	3·1	2·65	2·3	2·0	H
Al+	12·0	10·9	9·0	7·75	6·6	5·5	4·5	3·7	3·1	2·65	2·3	2·0	H
Al	13·0	11·0	8·95	7·75	6·6	5·5	4·5	3·7	3·1	2·65	2·3	2·0	H+I

M*

TABLE XXXIV (continued)

$\frac{\sin \theta}{\lambda} \times 10^{-8}$	0	0·1	0·2	0·3	0·4	0·5	0·6	0·7	0·8	0·9	1·0	1·1	Remarks
Si+4	10·0	9·75	9·15	8·25	7·15	6·05	5·05	4·2	3·4	2·95	2·6	2·3	H
Si++	12·0	11·1	9·55	8·2	7·15	6·05	5·05	4·2	3·4	2·95	2·6	2·3	H + I
Si	14·0	11·35	9·4	8·2	7·15	6·1	5·1	4·2	3·4	2·95	2·6	2·3	H + I
P+5	10·0	9·8	9·25	8·45	7·5	6·55	5·65	4·8	4·05	3·4	3·0	2·6	I
P (neut.)	15·0	12·4	10·0	8·45	7·45	6·5	5·65	4·8	4·05	3·4	3·0	2·6	I
P−3	18·0	12·7	9·8	8·4	7·45	6·5	5·65	4·85	4·05	3·4	3·0	2·6	I
S (neut.)	16·0	13·6	10·7	8·95	7·85	6·85	6·0	5·25	4·5	3·9	3·35	2·9	I
S+6	10·0	9·85	9·4	8·7	7·85	6·85	6·05	5·25	4·5	3·9	3·35	2·9	I
S−2	18·0	14·3	10·7	8·9	7·85	6·85	6·0	5·25	4·5	3·9	3·35	2·9	I
Cl	17·0	14·6	11·3	9·25	8·05	7·25	6·5	5·75	5·05	4·4	3·85	3·35	H + I
Cl−	18·0	15·2	11·5	9·3	8·05	7·25	6·5	5·75	5·05	4·4	3·85	3·35	H
A	18·0	15·9	12·6	10·4	8·7	7·8	7·0	6·2	5·4	4·7	4·1	3·6	I
K+	18·0	16·5	13·3	10·8	8·85	7·75	7·05	6·44	5·9	5·3	4·8	4·2	H
Ca++	18·0	16·8	14·0	11·5	9·3	8·1	7·35	6·7	6·2	5·7	5·1	4·6	H
Sc+3	18·0	16·7	14·0	11·4	9·4	8·3	7·6	6·9	6·4	5·8	5·35	4·75	I
Ti+4	18·0	17·0	14·4	11·9	9·9	8·5	7·85	7·3	6·7	6·15	5·65	5·05	I
Ti++	20·0	18·7	15·5	12·5	10·1	8·5	7·8	7·25	6·7	6·15	5·65	5·05	I
Cu+	28·0	27·0	24·0	20·7	17·3	14·0	11·3	9·4	8·0	7·3	7·0	6·7	I
Cu+	28·0	26·3	23·0	19·2	15·8	13·0	11·2	9·7	8·4	7·4	6·7	6·5	H approx.
Cu	29·0	25·8	21·4	17·8	15·2	13·3	11·7	10·2	9·1	8·1	7·3	6·7	T
Rb+	36·0	33·6	28·7	24·6	21·4	18·9	16·7	14·6	12·8	11·2	9·9	8·9	H }
Rb	37·0	33·4	28·2	23·6	20·4	17·9	15·9	14·0	12·4	11·2	10·2	9·3	T }

I = calculated by method of interpolation.   T = calculated from Thomas model.
H = calculated from Hartree distribution.   W = calculated from hydrogen wave-function (ground state).

TABLE XXXV

Thomas-Fermi Scattering Factors f_0 for Heavy Atoms

(Internationale Tabellen)

$10^{-8} \times \dfrac{\sin\theta}{\lambda}$		0.0	0.1	0.2	0.3	0.4	0.5	0.6	0.7	0.8	0.9	1.0	1.1	1.2
K . . .	19	16.5	13.3	10.8	9.2	7.9	6.7	5.9	5.2	4.6	4.2	3.7	3.3
Ca . .	20	17.5	14.1	11.4	9.7	8.4	7.3	6.3	5.6	4.9	4.5	4.0	3.6
Sc . .	21	18.4	14.9	12.1	10.3	8.9	7.7	6.7	5.9	5.3	4.7	4.3	3.9
Ti . .	22	19.3	15.7	12.8	10.9	9.5	8.2	7.2	6.3	5.6	5.0	4.6	4.2
V . .	23	20.2	16.6	13.5	11.5	10.1	8.7	7.6	6.7	5.9	5.3	4.9	4.4
Cr . .	24	21.1	17.4	14.2	12.1	10.6	9.2	8.0	7.1	6.3	5.7	5.1	4.6
Mn .	25	22.1	18.2	14.9	12.7	11.1	9.7	8.4	7.5	6.6	6.0	5.4	4.9
Fe . .	26	23.1	18.9	15.6	13.3	11.6	10.2	8.9	7.9	7.0	6.3	5.7	5.2
Co . .	27	24.1	19.8	16.4	14.0	12.1	10.7	9.3	8.3	7.3	6.7	6.0	5.5
Ni . .	28	25.0	20.7	17.2	14.6	12.7	11.2	9.8	8.7	7.7	7.0	6.3	5.8
Cu . .	29	25.9	21.6	17.9	15.2	13.3	11.7	10.2	9.1	8.1	7.3	6.6	6.0
Zn . .	30	26.8	22.4	18.6	15.8	13.9	12.2	10.7	9.6	8.5	7.6	6.9	6.3
Ga . .	31	27.8	23.3	19.3	16.5	14.5	12.7	11.2	10.0	8.9	7.9	7.3	6.7
Ge . .	32	28.8	24.1	20.0	17.1	15.0	13.2	11.6	10.4	9.3	8.3	7.6	7.0
As . .	33	29.7	25.0	20.8	17.7	15.6	13.8	12.1	10.8	9.7	8.7	7.9	7.3
Se . .	34	30.6	25.8	21.5	18.3	16.1	14.3	12.6	11.2	10.0	9.0	8.2	7.5
Br . .	35	31.6	26.6	22.3	18.9	16.7	14.8	13.1	11.7	10.4	9.4	8.6	7.8
Kr . .	36	32.5	27.4	23.0	19.5	17.3	15.3	13.6	12.1	10.8	9.8	8.9	8.1
Rb . .	37	33.5	28.2	23.8	20.2	17.9	15.9	14.1	12.5	11.2	10.2	9.2	8.4
Sr . .	38	34.4	29.0	24.5	20.8	18.4	16.4	14.6	12.9	11.6	10.5	9.5	8.7
Y . .	39	35.4	29.9	25.3	21.5	19.0	17.0	15.1	13.4	12.0	10.9	9.9	9.0
Zr . .	40	36.3	30.8	26.0	22.1	19.7	17.5	15.6	13.8	12.4	11.2	10.2	9.3
Cb . .	41	37.3	31.7	26.8	22.8	20.2	18.1	16.0	14.3	12.8	11.6	10.6	9.7
Mo .	42	38.2	32.6	27.6	23.5	20.8	18.6	16.5	14.8	13.2	12.0	10.9	10.0
Ma .	43	39.1	33.4	28.3	24.1	21.3	19.1	17.0	15.2	13.6	12.3	11.3	10.3
Ru . .	44	40.0	34.3	29.1	24.7	21.9	19.6	17.5	15.6	14.1	12.7	11.6	10.6
Rh . .	45	41.0	35.1	29.9	25.4	22.5	20.2	18.0	16.1	14.5	13.1	12.0	11.0
Pd . .	46	41.9	36.0	30.7	26.2	23.1	20.8	18.5	16.6	14.9	13.6	12.3	11.3
Ag . .	47	42.8	36.9	31.5	26.9	23.8	21.3	19.0	17.1	15.3	14.0	12.7	11.7
Cd . .	48	43.7	37.7	32.2	27.5	24.4	21.8	19.6	17.6	15.7	14.3	13.0	12.0
In . .	49	44.7	38.6	33.0	28.1	25.0	22.4	20.1	18.0	16.2	14.7	13.4	12.3
Sn . .	50	45.7	39.5	33.8	28.7	25.6	22.9	20.6	18.5	16.6	15.1	13.7	12.7
Sb . .	51	46.7	40.4	34.6	29.5	26.3	23.5	21.1	19.0	17.0	15.5	14.1	13.0
Te . .	52	47.7	41.3	35.4	30.3	26.9	24.0	21.7	19.5	17.5	16.0	14.5	13.3
I . .	53	48.6	42.1	36.1	31.0	27.5	24.6	22.2	20.0	17.9	16.4	14.8	13.6
Xe . .	54	49.6	43.0	36.8	31.6	28.0	25.2	22.7	20.4	18.4	16.7	15.2	13.9
Cs . .	55	50.7	43.8	37.6	32.4	28.7	25.8	23.2	20.8	18.8	17.0	15.6	14.5
Ba . .	56	51.7	44.7	38.4	33.1	29.3	26.4	23.7	21.3	19.2	17.4	16.0	14.7
La . .	57	52.6	45.6	39.3	33.8	29.8	26.9	24.3	21.9	19.7	17.9	16.4	15.0
Ce . .	58	53.6	46.5	40.1	34.5	30.4	27.4	24.8	22.4	20.2	18.4	16.6	15.3
Pr . .	59	54.5	47.4	40.9	35.2	31.1	28.0	25.4	22.9	20.6	18.8	17.1	15.7
Nd . .	60	55.4	48.3	41.6	35.9	31.8	28.6	25.9	23.4	21.1	19.2	17.5	16.1

TABLE XXXV (*continued*)

$10^{-8} \times \dfrac{\sin \theta}{\lambda}$		0.0	0.1	0.2	0.3	0.4	0.5	0.6	0.7	0.8	0.9	1.0	1.1	1.2
Il . . .	61	56.4	49.1	42.4	36.6	32.4	29.2	26.4	23.9	21.5	19.6	17.9	16.4
Sm . . .	62	57.3	50.0	43.2	37.3	32.9	29.8	26.9	24.4	22.0	20.0	18.3	16.8
Eu . . .	63	58.3	50.9	44.0	38.1	33.5	30.4	27.5	24.9	22.4	20.4	18.7	17.1
Gd . . .	64	59.3	51.7	44.8	38.8	34.1	31.0	28.1	25.4	22.9	20.8	19.1	17.5
Tb . . .	65	60.2	52.6	45.7	39.6	34.7	31.6	28.6	25.9	23.4	21.2	19.5	17.9
Dy . . .	66	61.1	53.6	46.5	40.4	35.4	32.2	29.2	26.3	23.9	21.6	19.9	18.3
Ho . . .	67	62.1	54.5	47.3	41.1	36.1	32.7	29.7	26.8	24.3	22.0	20.3	18.6
Er . . .	68	63.0	55.3	48.1	41.7	36.7	33.3	30.2	27.3	24.7	22.4	20.7	18.9
Tu . . .	69	64.0	56.2	48.9	42.4	37.4	33.9	30.8	27.9	25.2	22.9	21.0	19.3
Yb . . .	70	64.9	57.0	49.7	43.2	38.0	34.4	31.3	28.4	25.7	23.3	21.4	19.7
Lu . . .	71	65.9	57.8	50.4	43.9	38.7	35.0	31.8	28.9	26.2	23.8	21.8	20.0
Hf . . .	72	66.8	58.6	51.2	44.5	39.3	35.6	32.3	29.3	26.7	24.2	22.3	20.4
Ta . . .	73	67.8	59.5	52.0	45.3	39.9	36.2	32.9	29.8	27.1	24.7	22.6	20.9
W . . .	74	68.8	60.4	52.8	46.1	40.5	36.8	33.5	30.4	27.6	25.2	23.0	21.3
Re . . .	75	69.8	61.3	53.6	46.8	41.1	37.4	34.0	30.9	28.1	25.6	23.4	21.6
Os . . .	76	70.8	62.2	54.4	47.5	41.7	38.0	34.6	31.4	28.6	26.0	23.9	22.0
Ir . . .	77	71.7	63.1	55.3	48.2	42.4	38.6	35.1	32.0	29.0	26.5	24.3	22.3
Pt . . .	78	72.6	64.0	56.2	48.9	43.1	39.2	35.6	32.5	29.5	27.0	24.7	22.7
Au . . .	79	73.6	65.0	57.0	49.7	43.8	39.8	36.2	33.1	30.0	27.4	25.1	23.1
Hg . . .	80	74.6	65.9	57.9	50.5	44.4	40.5	36.8	33.6	30.6	27.8	25.6	23.6
Tl . . .	81	75.5	66.7	58.7	51.2	45.0	41.1	37.4	34.1	31.1	28.3	26.0	24.1
Pb . . .	82	76.5	67.5	59.5	51.9	45.7	41.6	37.9	34.6	31.5	28.8	26.4	24.5
Bi . . .	83	77.5	68.4	60.4	52.7	46.4	42.2	38.5	35.1	32.0	29.2	26.8	24.8
Po . . .	84	78.4	69.4	61.3	53.5	47.1	42.8	39.1	35.6	32.6	29.7	27.2	25.2
— . . .	85	79.4	70.3	62.1	54.2	47.7	43.4	39.6	36.2	33.1	30.1	27.6	25.6
Em (Rn, Nt)	86	80.3	71.3	63.0	55.1	48.4	44.0	40.2	36.8	33.5	30.5	28.0	26.0
	87	81.3	72.2	63.8	55.8	49.1	44.5	40.7	37.3	34.0	31.0	28.4	26.4
Ra . . .	88	82.2	73.2	64.6	56.5	49.8	45.1	41.3	37.8	34.6	31.5	28.8	26.7
Ac . . .	89	83.2	74.1	65.5	57.3	50.4	45.8	41.8	38.3	35.1	32.0	29.2	27.1
Th . . .	90	84.1	75.1	66.3	58.1	51.1	46.5	42.4	38.8	35.5	32.4	29.6	27.5
Pa . . .	91	85.1	76.0	67.1	58.8	51.7	47.1	43.0	39.3	36.0	32.8	30.1	27.9
U . . .	92	86.0	76.9	67.9	59.6	52.4	47.7	43.5	39.8	36.5	33.3	30.6	28.3

TABLE XXXVI

VALUES OF THE DECREMENT $\triangle f$ AT VARIOUS WAVELENGTHS

(H. HÖNL, *Annalen der Physik*, **18**, 625, 1933)

(a) Short Wavelength Side of the Limit

$\dfrac{\lambda}{\lambda_\kappa} =$	0·2	0·5	0·667	0·75	0·9	0·95
26 Fe	— 0·17	— 0·30	— 0·03	0·28	1·47	2·40
42 Mo	— 0·16	— 0·26	0·01	0·31	1·48	2·32
74 W	— 0·15	— 0·25	0·01	0·30	1·40	2·18

(b) Long Wavelength Side of the Limit

$\dfrac{\lambda}{\lambda_\kappa} =$	1·05	1·11	1·2	1·33	1·5	2·0	inf.
26 Fe	3·30	2·60	2·20	1·90	1·73	1·51	1·32
42 Mo	3·08	2·44	2·06	1·77	1·61	1·43	1·24
74 W	2·85	2·26	1·91	1·65	1·49	1·31	1·15

X-RAY ABSORPTION

Absorption Coefficients. In traversing a thickness x of material, the intensity I_0 of the incident beam is reduced to a value I according to the expression

$$I = I_0 e^{-\mu x}$$

where μ is the linear absorption coefficient of the material for the particular wavelength of the radiation.   Now since it is mass of matter traversed which is important and not its distribution in space, it is simpler to express the reduced intensity by the equation

$$I = I_0 e^{-\frac{\mu}{\rho}\rho x}$$

where $\frac{\mu}{\rho}$ is the mass absorption coefficient and ρx the mass per square centimetre of the absorbing material.

The mass absorption coefficient for a substance of mixed composition is given by the expression

$$\frac{\mu}{\rho} = \sum \left(\frac{\mu}{\rho}\right)_i x_i$$

where ρ is the mean density of the substance and x_i is the proportion by weight of a constituent element of mass absorption coefficient $\left(\frac{\mu}{\rho}\right)_i$.

The mass absorption coefficients listed in Table XXXVII include a small constant coefficient for scattering of the rays.   If we multiply the mass absorption coefficient by the atomic weight, a quantity is obtained proportional to the absorption per atom of the element. Atomic Absorption Coefficients are listed in Table XXXVIII.

Absorption Factors for Debye–Scherrer Powder Specimens. In Chapter V we outlined the Claassen-Bradley method of deriving the absorption factor for a cylindrical Debye-Scherrer powder specimen of radius r and linear absorption coefficient μ.   The assumption was tacitly made that the reflecting particles of powder were so small that absorption within them could be neglected.   A more detailed analysis, amplifying the paper by A. Taylor (*Phil. Mag.*, **35**, 215, 1944), shows that we must take the size of the particles into account, since in general the linear absorption coefficient μ_p of the particle is much greater than μ, the mean linear absorption coefficient of the powder-Canada Balsam mixture, and the texture of the specimen is essentially discontinuous.

We may look upon the absorption factor A as consisting of two parts. The first part corresponds to the absorption within the bulk of the specimen and may be termed the "macro-absorption factor" α. This is the factor given by the integral $\alpha = \iint e^{-\mu rx} ds$. Values of 100α computed by Bradley in terms of μr are given in Tables XXXIX and XL.

The second part of the absorption factor reveals the "contrast" in absorption between the polycrystalline reflecting particles and the surrounding non-reflecting powder and Canada Balsam mixture. We term this the "micro-absorption factor" τ. The true absorption factor is thus the product $A = \tau\alpha$.

Values of τ are computed in terms of $(\mu_p - \mu)a$ where a is the effective radius of the polycrystalline particles and $(\mu_p - \mu)$ is the difference between the linear absorption coefficient of the particles and the mean linear absorption coefficient of the powder-Canada Balsam mixture. Values of τ are listed in Table XLI.

Since τ approaches unity (or 100 per cent. as in the tables) as the radius of the particles is reduced, it is advantageous to make them very small, although a practical limit is set by the Scherrer line-broadening effect which sets in when the reflecting crystallites are below 10 cm^{-4}. in diameter.

TABLE XXXVII

Mass Absorption Coefficient of Elements $\frac{\mu}{\rho}$, including Scattering

(*Internationale Tabellen*)

Radiation		Ag Kα λ 0·5604	Rh Kα 0·6149	Mo Kα 0·7097	Cu Kα 1·5392	Ni Kα 1·6565	Fe Kα 1·9344	Cr Kα 2·2869
Absorber	Z							
He	2	0·16	0·16	0·18				
Li	3	0·18	0·20	0·22				
Be	4	0·22	0·25	0·30	1·35	1·80	3·24	4·74
B	5	0·30	0·35	0·45	3·06	3·79	5·80	9·37
C	6	0·42	0·51	0·70	5·50	6·76	10·73	17·9
N	7	0·60	0·70	1·10	8·51	10·7	17·3	27·7
O	8	0·80	1·00	1·50	12·7	16·2	25·2	40·1
F	9	1·00	1·32	1·93	17·5	21·5	33·0	51·6
Ne	10	1·41	1·80	2·67	24·6	30·2	46·0	72·7
Na	11	1·75	2·25	3·36	30·9	37·9	56·9	92·5
Mg	12	2·27	2·93	4·38	40·6	47·9	75·7	120·1
Al	13	2·74	3·60	5·30	48·7	58·4	92·8	149
Si	14	3·44	4·52	6·70	60·3	75·8	116·3	192
P	15	4·20	5·36	7·98	73·0	90·5	141·1	223
S	16	5·15	6·65	10·03	91·3	111·5	175	273
Cl	17	5·86	7·50	11·62	103·4	125·6	199	308
A	18	6·40	8·00	12·55	112·9	141	217	341
K	19	8·05	10·7	16·7	143	179	269	425
Ca	20	9·66	12·8	19·8	172	210	317	508
Sc	21	10·5	13·8	21·1	185	222	338	545
Ti	22	11·8	15·8	23·7	204	247	377	603
V	23	13·3	17·7	26·5	227	275	422	77·3
Cr	24	15·7	20·4	30·4	259	316	490	89·9
Mn	25	17·4	22·6	33·5	284	348	63·6	99·4
Fe	26	19·9	25·8	38·3	324	397	72·8	114·6
Co	27	21·8	28·1	41·6	354	54·4	80·6	125·8
Ni	28	25·0	32·3	47·4	49·2	61·0	93·1	145
Cu	29	26·4	34·0	49·7	52·7	65·0	98·8	154
Zn	30	28·2	37·7	54·8	59·0	72·1	109·4	169
Ga	31	30·8	39·7	57·3	63·3	76·9	116·5	179
Ge	32	33·5	42·8	63·4	69·4	84·2	128·4	196
As	33	36·5	46·0	69·5	76·5	93·8	142	218
Se	34	38·5	49·0	74·0	82·8	100·6	152	235
Br	35	42·3	53·5	82·2	92·6	112·4	169	264
Kr	36	45·0	57·5	88·1	100·4	121·9	182	285
Rb	37	48·2	62·8	94·4	109·1	132·9	197	309
Sr	38	52·1	68·3	101·2	119	145	214	334
Y	39	55·5	74·0	108·9	129	158	235	360
Zr	40	61·1	80·9	17·2	143	173	260	391

TABLE XXXVII (*continued*)

Radiation	Z	Ag $K\alpha$ λ 0·5604	Rh $K\alpha$ 0·6149	Mo $K\alpha$ 0·7097	Cu $K\alpha$ 1·5392	Ni $K\alpha$ 1·6565	Fe $K\alpha$ 1·9344	Cr $K\alpha$ 2·2869
Absorber								
Cb	41	65·8	86·0	18·7	153	183	279	415
Mo	42	70·7	91·6	20·2	164	197	299	439
Ru	44	$\alpha_1$79·9 $\alpha_2$12·2	15·4	23·4	185	221	337	*488*
Rh	45	13·1	16·6	25·3	198	240	361	*522*
Pd	46	13·8	17·6	26·7	207	254	376	*585*
Ag	47	14·8	19·1	28·6	223	276	402	*608*
Cd	48	15·5	20·1	29·9	234	289	417	*648*
In	49	16·5	21·7	31·8	252	307	440	*681*
Sn	50	17·4	22·9	33·3	265	322	457	*727*
Sb	51	18·6	24·6	35·3	284	342	482	*742*
Te	52	19·1	25·0	36·1	289	347	488	*808*
I	53	20·9	27·3	39·2	314	375	527	*852*
Xe	54	22·1	28·5	41·3	330	392	552	*844*
Cs	55	23·6	30·0	43·3	347	410	579	*819*
Ba	56	24·5	31·1	45·2	359	423	599	*218*
La	57	26·0	33·0	47·9	378	444	632	*235*
Ce	58	28·4	35·8	52·0	407	476	*624*	*251*
Pr	59	29·4	37·2	54·5	422	493	*651*	*263*
Nd	60	30·5	38·8	57·0	437	510	183	*289*
Sm	62	33·1	41·2	62·3	467	*519*	193	*306*
Eu	63	35·0	44·5	65·9	*461*	*498*	199	*316*
Gd	64	35·8	45·7	68·0	*470*	*509*	211	333
Tb	65	37·5	47·9	71·7	*435*	140	220	345
Dy	66	39·1	49·9	75·0	*462*	146	232	361
Ho	67	41·3	52·7	79·3	128	153	242	370
Er	68	42·6	54·6	82·0	133	159	257	387
Tm	69	44·8	57·6	86·3	139	168	265	396
Yb	70	46·1	59·4	88·7	144	174	281	414
Lu	71	48·4	62·6	93·2	151	184	291	426
Hf	72	50·6	65·0	96·9	157	191	305	440
Ta	73	52·2	67·70	100·7	164	200	320	456
W	74	54·6	70·7	105·4	171	209	346	480
Os	76	58·6	76·3	112·9	186	226	362	498
Ir	77	61·2	80·0	117·9	194	237	376	518
Pt	78	64·2	83·8	123	205	248	390	537
Au	79	66·7	87·1	128	214	260	404	552
Hg	80	69·3	90·1	132	223	272	416	568
Tl	81	71·7	92·4	136	231	282	429	585
Pb	82	74·4	95·8	141	241	294	448	612
Bi	83	78·1	100·4	145	253	310	476	657
Nt	86	84·7	109·1	159	278	341	509	708
Ra	88	91·1	117	172	304	371	536	755
Th	90	97·0	*119*	*143*	327	399	566	805
U	92	104·2	*129*	*153*	352	423		

TABLE XXXVIII

ATOMIC ABSORPTION COEFFICIENTS OF THE ELEMENTS

(*Internationale Tabellen*)

$$\mu_\alpha = \frac{\mu}{\rho} \times \frac{\text{ATOMIC WT.}}{\text{LOSCHMIDT'S NUMBER}}$$

Radiation		Ag $K\alpha$	Rh $K\alpha$	Mo $K\alpha$	Cu $K\alpha$	Ni $K\alpha$	Fe $K\alpha$	Cr $K\alpha$
Absorber	Z				$\mu_\alpha \times 10^{23}$			
He	2	0·11	0·12	0·12				
Li	3	0·21	0·23	0·34				
Be	4	0·33	0·37	0·45	2·02	2·70	4·85	7·04
B	5	0·54	0·63	0·81	5·50	6·72	10·43	16·86
C	6	0·83	1·01	1·38	10·87	13·36	21·4	35·4
N	7	1·39	1·62	2·54	19·6	24·9	39·8	63·8
O	8	2·13	2·56	4·00	33·6	42·5	66·4	105·5
F	9	3·13	4·13	6·05	54·7	67·3	103·2	160
Ne	10	4·70	6·00	8·90	81·9	100	153	242
Na	11	6·65	8·5	12·8	117	143	215	350
Mg	12	9·1	11·7	17·6	163	192	303	481
Al	13	12·2	16·1	23·6	217	260	414	655
Si	14	16·6	21·0	31·2	281	353	542	896
P	15	21·5	27·4	40·8	373	462	721	1140
S	16	27·2	35·1	53·0	482	589	926	1441
Cl	17	34·2	43·8	68·0	604	734	1160	1800
A	18	42·0	52·6	82·5	742	924	1427	2220
K	19	51·9	69·0	107·2	923	1151	1730	2640
Ca	20	63·9	84·6	131	1138	1390	2100	3360
Sc	21	78·0	102·6	157	1380	1650	2510	4050
Ti	22	93·5	125	188	1616	1960	2980	4780
V	23	111·8	149	222	1910	2310	3560	650
Cr	24	134	175	260	2220	2700	4190	769
Mn	25	157	204	303	2570	3240	576	900
Fe	26	183	237	352	2980	3650	669	1051
Co	27	212	272	404	3430	527	782	1220
Ni	28	242	312	458	475	590	900	1410
Cu	29	282	362	529	562	693	1051	1640
Zn	30	303	406	590	635	775	1180	1820
Ga	31	356	459	663	731	888	1350	2060
Ge	32	401	513	759	830	1010	1540	2340
As	33	450	568	858	945	1160	1750	2690
Se	34	503	640	967	1070	1320	1960	3070
Br	35	550	695	1067	1202	1460	2190	3440
Kr	36	610	780	1190	1360	1650	2460	3860
Rb	37	678	883	1330	1540	1870	2760	4350
Sr	38	751	985	1460	1710	2090	3090	4810
Y	39	815	1089	1600	1900	2320	3460	5300
Zr	40	911	1208	257	2120	2570	3880	5830
Cb	41	1008	1320	286	2340	2810	4270	6350
Mo	42	1118	1450	320	2600	3120	4730	6940

TABLE XXXVIII (*continued*)

Radiation		Ag Kα	Rh Kα	Mo Kα	Cu Kα	Ni Kα	Fe Kα	Cr Kα
Absorber	Z				$\mu_\alpha \times 10^{23}$			
Ru	44	α₁ 1340 / α₂ 203	255	392	3 090	3 700	5 650	8 100
Rh	45	222	282	429	3 360	4 060	6 110	8 840
Pd	46	242	309	469	3 640	4 460	6 600	9 580
Ag	47	263	339	507	3 960	4 900	7 140	10 400
Cd	48	288	373	555	4 340	5 360	7 730	11 290
In	49	312	410	600	4 760	5 800	8 310	12 240
Sn	50	340	446	650	5 160	6 290	8 930	13 300
Sb	51	373	493	706	5 690	6 850	9 650	14 550
Te	52	401	525	758	6 060	7 290	10 270	15 600
I	53	436	570	819	6 560	7 830	11 000	16 900
Xe	54	475	613	879	7 100	8 420	11 800	18 300
Cs	55	516	655	946	7 590	8 960	12 650	18 400
Ba	56	555	705	1022	8 130	9 600	13 560	18 500
La	57	595	755	1098	8 650	10 180	14 500	5 000
Ce	58	656	827	1200	9 410	11 000	14 700	5 420
Pr	59	682	864	1265	9 780	11 310	14 500	5 820
Nd	60	726	926	1360	10 400	12 150	15 500	6 260
Sm	62	820	1020	1540	11 580	12 900	4 540	7 160
Eu	63	876	1114	1650	11 560	12 500	4 840	7 660
Gd	64	930	1186	1760	12 200	13 200	5 160	8 200
Tb	65	985	1260	1880	11 400	3 680	5 540	8 740
Dy	66	1048	1335	2000	12 400	3 905	5 890	9 230
Ho	67	1113	1420	2140	3 450	4 120	6 250	9 710
Er	68	1177	1510	2260	3 690	4 390	6 680	10 210
Tm	69	1245	1600	2400	3 860	4 670	7 140	10 750
Yb	70	1320	1700	2530	4 100	4 960	7 560	11 310
Lu	71	1400	1810	2690	4 360	5 310	8 110	11 920
Hf	72	1490	1910	2850	4 610	5 610	8 550	12 500
Ta	73	1560	2020	3010	4 900	5 970	9 110	13 150
W	74	1656	2140	3200	5 180	6 340	9 700	13 800
Os	76	1840	2400	3540	5 850	7 100	10 900	15 100
Ir	77	1950	2540	3760	6 180	7 540	11 510	15 900
Pt	78	2060	2690	3960	6 600	7 980	12 100	16 650
Au	79	2160	2830	4160	6 950	8 450	12 700	17 450
Hg	80	2290	2970	4370	7 360	9 000	13 320	18 200
Tl	81	2410	3100	4560	7 760	9 500	14 000	19 100
Pb	82	2540	3270	4810	8 220	10 020	15 000	19 800
Bi	83	2680	3440	4970	8 680	10 630	15 400	21 000
Nt	86	3100	4000	5830	10 200	12 500	17 400	24 200
Ra	88	3400	4370	6400	11 340	13 800	19 000	26 400
Th	90	3710	4550	5460	12 500	15 300	20 500	28 800
U	92	4100	5070	6000	13 800	16 700	22 200	31 600

TABLE XXXIX

MACRO-ABSORPTION FACTORS 100α WHEN $\mu r < 5$ FOR CYLINDRICAL DEBYE-SCHERRER SPECIMENS

(A. J. Bradley, *Proc. Phys. Soc.*, **47**, 879, 1935)

$\sin^2\theta$ / θ / μr	0 / 0°	0·1464 / 22½°	0·3290 / 35°	0·5000 / 45°	0·6710 / 55°	0·8536 / 67½°	1·00 / 90°
0·0	100	100	100	100	100	100	100
0·1	84·70	84·80	—	84·9	—	85·0	85·1
0·2	71·20	71·60	—	71·9	—	72·4	72·9
0·3	60·00	60·60	—	61·4	—	62·7	63·5
0·4	51·00	51·70	—	52·7	—	54·5	55·6
0·5	43·50	44·20	—	45·8	—	47·8	49·0
0·6	36·90	37·80	—	39·8	—	42·3	43·6
0·7	31·40	32·40	—	34·8	—	37·8	39·3
0·8	26·80	27·85	—	30·5	—	33·7	35·6
0·9	23·00	24·10	—	27·1	—	30·5	32·4
1·0	19·77	20·95	—	24·2	—	27·85	29·5
1·1	16·98	18·28	—	21·70	—	25·50	27·15
1·2	14·59	16·00	—	19·54	—	23·50	25·10
1·3	12·56	14·03	—	17·70	—	21·70	23·35
1·4	10·84	12·33	—	16·11	—	20·10	21·80
1·5	9·38	10·91	—	14·69	—	18·66	20·50
1·6	8·11	9·73	—	13·52	—	17·46	19·32
1·7	7·10	8·71	—	12·47	—	16·41	18·24
1·8	6·15	7·80	—	11·54	—	15·42	17·30
1·9	5·37	7·02	—	10·74	—	14·59	16·44
2·0	4·71	6·35	—	10·05	—	13·84	15·67
2·1	4·16	5·79	—	9·44	—	13·15	14·93
2·2	3·67	5·31	—	8·89	—	12·50	14·26
2·3	3·24	4·86	—	8·38	—	11·89	13·65
2·4	2·865	4·47	—	7·91	—	11·35	13·09
2·5	2·55	4·12	—	7·50	—	10·86	12·56
2·6	2·27	3·82	—	7·11	—	10·40	12·11
2·7	2·02	3·55	—	6·75	—	9·98	11·67
2·8	1·803	3·30	—	6·41	—	9·62	11·27
2·9	1·607	3·08	—	6·10	—	9·25	10·89
3·0	1·436	2·885	4·43	5·82	7·24	8·89	10·54
3·1	1·288	2·705	4·22	5·58	6·97	8·57	10·21
3·2	1·159	2·55	4·02	5·35	6·72	8·30	9·90
3·3	1·049	2·415	3·84	5·14	6·48	8·04	9·61
3·4	0·955	2·29	3·68	4·95	6·26	7·78	9·33
3·5	0·871	2·17	3·525	4·77	6·05	7·55	9·06
3·6	0·796	2·06	3·385	4·60	5·85	7·33	8·81
3·7	0·729	1·968	3·255	4·44	5·66	7·11	8·58
3·8	0·670	1·875	3·14	4·29	5·49	6·92	8·36
3·9	0·617	1·787	3·03	4·15	5·33	6·73	8·15
4·0	0·568	1·706	2·925	4·02	5·17	6·53	7·94
4·1	0·525	1·629	2·825	3·89	5·02	6·35	7·74
4·2	0·488	1·563	2·73	3·77	4·88	6·18	7·55
4·3	0·453	1·500	2·645	3·66	4·75	6·02	7·38
4·4	0·420	1·445	2·555	3·56	4·62	5·87	7·21
4·5	0·391	1·390	2·485	3·47	4·50	5·73	7·05
4·6	0·364	1·343	2·41	3·38	4·39	5·61	6·89
4·7	0·340	1·300	2·34	3·29	4·28	5·47	6·75
4·8	0·316	1·259	2·275	3·21	4·18	5·35	6·61
4·9	0·2945	1·222	2·21	3·13	4·08	5·25	6·47
5·0	0·2755	1·189	2·155	3·05	3·99	5·14	6·35

TABLE XL

RELATIVE VALUES OF α FOR LARGE VALUES OF μr, FOR CYLINDRICAL DEBYE-SCHERRER SPECIMENS

(A. J. Bradley, *Proc. Phys. Soc.*, **47**, 879, 1935)

$\sin^2\theta$	0	0·1464	0·3290	0·5000	0·6710	0·8536	1·00
θ / μr	0°	22½°	35°	45°	55°	67½°	90°
5·0	4·34	18·71	33·93	48·00	62·8	81·0	100
5·5	3·50	17·78	32·95	47·05	62·0	80·4	100
6·0	2·91	17·01	32·10	46·25	61·3	79·9	100
6·5	2·44	16·40	31·40	45·60	60·7	79·5	100
7·0	2·12	15·89	30·80	45·05	60·2	79·2	100
7·5	1·83	15·46	30·30	44·50	59·8	78·9	100
8·0	1·61	15·09	29·85	44·05	59·4	78·6	100
9·0	1·26	14·45	29·10	43·35	58·7	78·1	100
10·0	1·02	13·98	28·55	42·75	58·2	77·7	100
11·0	0·84	13·59	28·10	42·25	57·8	77·4	100
12·0	0·69	13·26	27·70	41·85	57·4	77·2	100
13·0	0·59	13·00	27·40	41·50	57·1	77·0	100
14·0	0·50	12·78	27·15	41·25	56·9	76·8	100
15·0	0·44	12·59	26·90	41·00	56·7	76·7	100
20·0	0·25	11·93	26·05	40·20	55·9	76·2	100
25·0	0·16	11·55	25·60	39·70	55·4	75·8	100
30·0	0·11	11·29	25·25	39·35	55·1	75·6	100
40·0	0·06	10·97	24·85	38·95	54·8	75·3	100
50·0	0·04	10·79	24·60	38·70	54·5	75·1	100
75·0	0·02	10·54	24·30	38·40	54·2	74·9	100
100	0·01	10·42	24·10	38·20	54·0	74·8	100
200	0·00	10·18	23·90	38·00	53·8	74·6	100
∞	0·00	10·07	23·65	37·70	53·6	74·4	100

TABLE XLI

MICRO-ABSORPTION FACTORS 100τ FOR SPHERICAL CRYSTALS

(A. TAYLOR, *Philosophical Magazine*, **35**, 1944.)

$\sin^2\theta$ / θ / $(\mu_p-\mu)a$	0 / 0°	0·1464 / 22½°	0·5000 / 45°	0·8536 / 67½°	1·0000 / 90°
0·00	100·0	100·0	100·0	100·0	100·0
0·01	98·6	98·6	98·6	98·6	98·6
0·02	97·2	97·2	97·3	97·3	97·3
0·03	95·9	95·9	96·0	96·0	96·0
0·04	94·5	94·5	94·6	94·6	94·7
0·05	93·2	93·2	93·3	93·3	93·4
0·06	91·8	91·8	91·9	92·0	92·1
0·07	90·5	90·5	90·6	90·6	90·8
0·08	89·2	89·2	89·3	89·4	89·5
0·09	87·8	87·8	87·9	88·0	88·2
0·10	86·5	86·5	86·6	86·8	87·0
0·20	74·2	75·0	75·3	76·0	76·0
0·30	64·0	65·1	65·3	65·8	67·1
0·40	54·5	56·6	56·9	58·0	58·7
0·50	46·8	48·9	49·6	51·6	52·9
0·60	41·0	42·2	43·6	46·0	47·7
0·70	36·0	37·2	38·7	41·8	43·4
0·80	31·5	32·6	34·7	37·9	39·9
0·90	27·6	28·7	31·1	34·5	36·4
1·00	23·9	25·1	28·2	31·8	33·4
1·10	20·9	22·2	25·5	29·1	30·9
1·20	18·4	19·7	23·2	26·8	28·7
1·30	16·2	16·6	21·2	24·8	26·8
1·40	14·5	16·0	19·4	23·2	25·0
1·50	12·9	14·3	17·9	21·8	23·5
1·60	11·4	12·9	16·5	20·7	22·1
1·70	10·1	11·8	15·2	19·6	20·9
1·80	9·0	10·6	14·1	18·5	19·8
1·90	8·0	9·6	13·1	17·6	18·8
2·00	7·1	8·7	12·3	16·8	18·0
2·10	6·2	7·8	11·4	16·0	17·2
2·20	5·6	7·1	10·8	15·3	16·4
2·30	5·0	6·5	10·2	14·5	15·7
2·40	4·5	6·0	9·6	13·8	15·2
2·50	4·0	5·5	9·1	13·2	14·6
2·60	3·6	5·1	8·7	12·6	14·1
2·70	3·3	4·8	8·3	12·0	13·6
2·80	3·0	4·6	7·9	11·4	13·0
2·90	2·8	4·3	7·6	11·0	12·6
3·00	2·6	4·1	7·3	10·6	12·2
3·50	1·7	2·8	5·9	8·9	10·5
4·00	1·2	2·1	5·0	7·81	9·3
4·50	0·9	1·9	4·2	7·10	8·3
5·00	0·6	1·7	3·7	6·0	7·4

TABLE XLII

The Debye-Waller Temperature Factor $e^{-B\left(\frac{\sin\theta}{\lambda}\right)^2}$.

$10^{-8}\times\frac{\sin\theta}{\lambda}$	$B\times10^{16}=0\cdot0$	$0\cdot1$	$0\cdot2$	$0\cdot3$	$0\cdot4$	$0\cdot5$	$0\cdot6$	$0\cdot7$	$0\cdot8$	$0\cdot9$	$1\cdot0$	$1\cdot1$	$1\cdot2$
$0\cdot0$	$1\cdot000$	$1\cdot000$	$1\cdot000$	$1\cdot000$	$1\cdot000$	$1\cdot000$	$1\cdot000$	$1\cdot000$	$1\cdot000$	$1\cdot000$	$1\cdot000$	$1\cdot000$	$1\cdot000$
$0\cdot1$	$1\cdot000$	$0\cdot999$	$0\cdot996$	$0\cdot991$	$0\cdot984$	$0\cdot975$	$0\cdot964$	$0\cdot952$	$0\cdot938$	$0\cdot923$	$0\cdot905$	$0\cdot886$	$0\cdot866$
$0\cdot2$	$1\cdot000$	$0\cdot998$	$0\cdot992$	$0\cdot982$	$0\cdot968$	$0\cdot951$	$0\cdot931$	$0\cdot906$	$0\cdot880$	$0\cdot850$	$0\cdot819$	$0\cdot785$	$0\cdot750$
$0\cdot3$	$1\cdot000$	$0\cdot997$	$0\cdot988$	$0\cdot973$	$0\cdot953$	$0\cdot928$	$0\cdot898$	$0\cdot863$	$0\cdot826$	$0\cdot784$	$0\cdot741$	$0\cdot695$	$0\cdot649$
$0\cdot4$	$1\cdot000$	$0\cdot996$	$0\cdot984$	$0\cdot964$	$0\cdot938$	$0\cdot905$	$0\cdot866$	$0\cdot821$	$0\cdot774$	$0\cdot724$	$0\cdot670$	$0\cdot616$	$0\cdot562$
$0\cdot5$	$1\cdot000$	$0\cdot995$	$0\cdot980$	$0\cdot955$	$0\cdot924$	$0\cdot882$	$0\cdot834$	$0\cdot782$	$0\cdot726$	$0\cdot667$	$0\cdot607$	$0\cdot548$	$0\cdot487$
$0\cdot6$	$1\cdot000$	$0\cdot994$	$0\cdot976$	$0\cdot947$	$0\cdot909$	$0\cdot860$	$0\cdot804$	$0\cdot745$	$0\cdot681$	$0\cdot615$	$0\cdot549$	$0\cdot484$	$0\cdot421$
$0\cdot7$	$1\cdot000$	$0\cdot993$	$0\cdot972$	$0\cdot939$	$0\cdot894$	$0\cdot839$	$0\cdot776$	$0\cdot710$	$0\cdot639$	$0\cdot567$	$0\cdot497$	$0\cdot429$	$0\cdot365$
$0\cdot8$	$1\cdot000$	$0\cdot992$	$0\cdot968$	$0\cdot931$	$0\cdot880$	$0\cdot818$	$0\cdot750$	$0\cdot676$	$0\cdot599$	$0\cdot523$	$0\cdot449$	$0\cdot380$	$0\cdot314$
$0\cdot9$	$1\cdot000$	$0\cdot991$	$0\cdot964$	$0\cdot923$	$0\cdot866$	$0\cdot798$	$0\cdot724$	$0\cdot644$	$0\cdot561$	$0\cdot482$	$0\cdot406$	$0\cdot336$	$0\cdot273$
$1\cdot0$	$1\cdot000$	$0\cdot990$	$0\cdot960$	$0\cdot915$	$0\cdot852$	$0\cdot779$	$0\cdot698$	$0\cdot613$	$0\cdot527$	$0\cdot445$	$0\cdot368$	$0\cdot298$	$0\cdot236$
$1\cdot1$	$1\cdot000$	$0\cdot989$	$0\cdot957$	$0\cdot907$	$0\cdot839$	$0\cdot759$	$0\cdot672$	$0\cdot584$	$0\cdot494$	$0\cdot410$	$0\cdot333$	$0\cdot264$	$0\cdot205$
$1\cdot2$	$1\cdot000$	$0\cdot988$	$0\cdot953$	$0\cdot898$	$0\cdot826$	$0\cdot740$	$0\cdot649$	$0\cdot556$	$0\cdot464$	$0\cdot378$	$0\cdot301$	$0\cdot234$	$0\cdot178$
$1\cdot3$	$1\cdot000$	$0\cdot987$	$0\cdot950$	$0\cdot890$	$0\cdot813$	$0\cdot722$	$0\cdot626$	$0\cdot529$	$0\cdot435$	$0\cdot349$	$0\cdot273$	$0\cdot207$	$0\cdot154$
$1\cdot4$	$1\cdot000$	$0\cdot986$	$0\cdot946$	$0\cdot882$	$0\cdot800$	$0\cdot704$	$0\cdot604$	$0\cdot503$	$0\cdot408$	$0\cdot322$	$0\cdot247$	$0\cdot184$	$0\cdot133$
$1\cdot5$	$1\cdot000$	$0\cdot985$	$0\cdot942$	$0\cdot874$	$0\cdot787$	$0\cdot687$	$0\cdot582$	$0\cdot479$	$0\cdot383$	$0\cdot297$	$0\cdot223$	$0\cdot167$	$0\cdot116$
$1\cdot6$	$1\cdot000$	$0\cdot984$	$0\cdot938$	$0\cdot866$	$0\cdot774$	$0\cdot670$	$0\cdot562$	$0\cdot458$	$0\cdot359$	$0\cdot274$	$0\cdot202$	$0\cdot144$	$0\cdot100$
$1\cdot7$	$1\cdot000$	$0\cdot983$	$0\cdot935$	$0\cdot858$	$0\cdot762$	$0\cdot654$	$0\cdot543$	$0\cdot436$	$0\cdot337$	$0\cdot252$	$0\cdot183$	$0\cdot128$	$0\cdot086$
$1\cdot8$	$1\cdot000$	$0\cdot982$	$0\cdot931$	$0\cdot850$	$0\cdot750$	$0\cdot638$	$0\cdot523$	$0\cdot414$	$0\cdot316$	$0\cdot233$	$0\cdot165$	$0\cdot113$	$0\cdot075$
$1\cdot9$	$1\cdot000$	$0\cdot981$	$0\cdot927$	$0\cdot842$	$0\cdot739$	$0\cdot622$	$0\cdot505$	$0\cdot394$	$0\cdot296$	$0\cdot215$	$0\cdot149$	$0\cdot100$	$0\cdot065$
$2\cdot0$	$1\cdot000$	$0\cdot980$	$0\cdot924$	$0\cdot834$	$0\cdot727$	$0\cdot607$	$0\cdot487$	$0\cdot375$	$0\cdot278$	$0\cdot198$	$0\cdot135$	$0\cdot089$	$0\cdot056$

ANGULAR FACTORS FOR VARIOUS EXPERIMENTAL ARRANGEMENTS

The integrated intensity I of the diffracted beam from a mosaic crystal may be written in the form

$$I = \text{const. } I_0 . A . f(\theta) . p . \{F(hkl)\}^2 \ e^{-2B\frac{\sin^2\theta}{\lambda^2}} . \quad (1)$$

where I_0 is the intensity of the incident energy in ergs. per sec. per unit area, A the absorption factor, $f(\theta)$ a factor dependent on the Bragg angle, p the planar factor, $F(hkl)$ the structure factor, and $e^{-2B\frac{\sin^2\theta}{\lambda^2}}$ the Debye-Waller temperature factor.

Equation (1) takes the following forms:

(a) *Crystal element*

$$I = \text{const. } I_0 . \frac{1 + \cos^2 2\theta}{\sin 2\theta} . \{F(hkl)\}^2 \ e^{-2B\frac{\sin^2\theta}{\lambda^2}} .$$

(b) *Crystal face*

$$I = \text{const. } I_0 . \frac{1}{\mu} . \frac{1 + \cos^2 2\theta}{\sin 2\theta} . \{F(hkl)\}^2 \ e^{-2B\frac{\sin^2\theta}{\lambda^2}} .$$

(c) *Crystal section*

$$I = \text{const. } I_0 e^{-\mu t_0 \sec\theta} . \frac{1 + \cos^2 2\theta}{\sin\theta \cos^2\theta} . \{F(hkl)\}^2 \ e^{-2B\frac{\sin^2\theta}{\lambda^2}} .$$

(d) *Powder halo (full ring)*

$$I = \text{const. } I_0 . A . \frac{1 + \cos^2 2\theta}{\sin\theta} . p . \{F(hkl)\}^2 \ e^{-2B\frac{\sin^2\theta}{\lambda^2}} .$$

(e) *Debye-Scherrer lines on cylindrical film*

$$I = \text{const. } I_0 . A . \frac{1 + \cos^2 2\theta}{\sin^2\theta \cos\theta} . p . \{F(hkl)\}^2 \ e^{-2B\frac{\sin^2\theta}{\lambda^2}} .$$

(f) *Block of crystal powder*

$$I = \text{const. } I_0 . \frac{1}{\mu} \frac{1 + \cos^2 2\theta}{\sin^2\theta \cos\theta} . p . \{F(hkl)\}^2 \ e^{-2B\frac{\sin^2\theta}{\lambda^2}} .$$

(g) *Rotation pattern from minute single crystal on flat plate*

$$I = \text{const. } I_0 . \frac{1 + \cos^2 2\theta}{\sin 2\theta} . \frac{1}{\sin\beta} . p' \{F(hkl)\}^2 \ e^{-2B\frac{\sin^2\theta}{\lambda^2}} .$$

β is the angle between the lines OP and OA, where O is the centre spot, P the diffraction spot, and OA the projection of the rotation axis on the plate.

Values of $f(\theta)$ are given in Table XLIII for a number of these cases. It will be found more convenient to graph the functions against θ or $\sin^2\theta$ rather than to use them for numerical interpolation. Debye-Waller factors are given in Table XLII. For further details, the reader should consult the *Internationale Tabellen zur Bestimmung von Kristallstrukturen*.

TABLE XLIII

ANGULAR FACTORS

$\theta°$	$\sin^2\theta$	$\dfrac{1+\cos^2 2\theta}{\sin 2\theta}$	$\dfrac{1+\cos^2 2\theta}{\sin^2\theta\cos\theta}$	$\theta°$	$\sin^2\theta$	$\dfrac{1+\cos^2 2\theta}{\sin 2\theta}$	$\dfrac{1+\cos^2 2\theta}{\sin^2\theta\cos\theta}$
0	0·0000	∞	∞	45	0·5000	1·000	2·828
1	0·0003	57·272	6563	$47\frac{1}{2}$	0·5436	1·011	2·744
$1\frac{1}{2}$	0·0006	38·162	2916				
2	0·0011	28·601	1639·1	50	0·5868	1·046	2·731
$2\frac{1}{2}$	0·0019	22·860	1048				
3	0·0027	19·029	727·2				
$3\frac{1}{2}$	0·0037	16·289	533·6	$52\frac{1}{2}$	0·6294	1·105	2·785
4	0·0049	14·231	408·0	55	0·6710	1·189	2·902
$4\frac{1}{2}$	0·0061	12·628	321·9	$57\frac{1}{2}$	0·7113	1·300	3·084
5	0·0076	11·344	260·3				
6	0·0109	9·411	180·06	60	0·7500	1·443	3·333
7	0·0149	8·025	131·70				
8	0·0193	6·980	100·31				
9	0·0243	6·163	78·80	$62\frac{1}{2}$	0·7868	1·622	3·658
				65	0·8214	1·845	4·071
				$67\frac{1}{2}$	0·8536	2·121	4·592
10	0·0302	5·506	63·41				
				70	0·8830	2·469	5·255
12	0·0432	4·510	43·39				
14	0·0581	3·791	31·34				
16	0·0762	3·244	23·54	72	0·9045	2·815	5·920
18	0·0955	2·815	18·22	74	0·9240	3·244	6·749
				76	0·9415	3·791	7·814
20	0·1170	2·469	14·44	78	0·9568	4·510	9·221
				80	0·9698	5·506	11·182
$22\frac{1}{2}$	0·1465	2·121	11·086				
25	0·1786	1·845	8·730	81	0·9755	6·163	12·480
$27\frac{1}{2}$	0·2133	1·622	7·027	82	0·9806	6·980	14·097
				83	0·9851	8·025	16·17
30	0·2500	1·443	5·774	84	0·9891	9·411	18·93
				85	0·9924	11·344	22·78
				$85\frac{1}{2}$	0·9938	12·628	25·34
$32\frac{1}{2}$	0·2887	1·300	4·841	86	0·9951	14·231	28·53
35	0·3290	1·189	4·123	$86\frac{1}{2}$	0·9963	16·289	32·64
$37\frac{1}{2}$	0·3706	1·105	3·629	87	0·9973	19·029	38·11
				$87\frac{1}{2}$	0·9981	22·860	45·76
40	0·4131	1·046	3·255	88	0·9988	28·601	57·24
				$88\frac{1}{2}$	0·9993	38·162	76·35
				89	0·9997	57·272	114·56
$42\frac{1}{2}$	0·4564	1·011	2·994				
45	0·5000	1·000	2·828	90	1·0000	∞	∞

THE OPTIMUM THICKNESS OF A FLAT POWDER COMPACT

(A) Transmission Spectra. Consider the general case of a flat powder compact of mean linear absorption coefficient μ and thickness t, irradiated by a parallel beam of monochromatic X-rays which make an angle ψ with the normal to the plate (Fig. 239). Since the cross-section of the incident beam is fixed by the slit system of the camera, any volume dV of the specimen swept out by the incident beam will be proportional to the depth of penetration dx. We may therefore confine our attention to a single ray which is deviated through an angle 2θ at various points in its path by the crystallites in the specimen, θ being the Bragg angle.

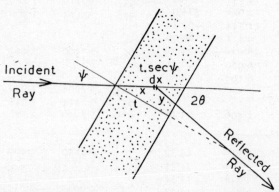

FIG. 239.—Paths of Incident and Transmitted Rays through Flat Powder Compact.

The transmitted intensity dI is proportional to the reflecting length dx and to $e^{-\mu(x+y)}$. Summing for all particles along the length $t \sec \psi$ swept out by the incident ray, the intensity of the transmitted reflexion becomes

$$I = \text{const.}\, I_0 \int_0^{t\sec\psi} e^{-\mu(x+y)} dx \qquad . \qquad . \qquad . \quad (1)$$

Now from the geometry of the figure

$$y = t \sec (2\theta - \psi) - x \cos \psi \sec (2\theta - \psi).$$

Writing

$$a = \sec (2\theta - \psi), \quad b = \sec \psi, \quad c = 1/b = \cos \psi$$

we obtain

$$I = \text{const.}\, I_0 \int_0^{bt} e^{-\mu(x - acx + at)} dx$$
$$= \frac{\text{const.}\, I_0}{\mu \cdot (ac - 1)} \{ e^{-\mu bt} - e^{-\mu at} \} \qquad . \qquad . \qquad . \quad (2)$$

The optimum thickness t^* occurs when $dI/dt = 0$, i.e. when

$$\mu t^* = \frac{1}{a - b} \, \log_e \frac{a}{b}$$

or

$$\mu t^* = \frac{1}{\sec (2\theta - \psi) - \sec \psi} \cdot \log_e \left\{ \frac{\sec (2\theta - \psi)}{\sec \psi} \right\}. \qquad . \qquad (3)$$

(a) *Special Case of Normal Incidence.*   When the incident beam is normal to the face of the specimen, $\psi = 0°$ and equation (3) takes the form

$$\mu t^* = \frac{1}{\sec 2\theta - 1} \, \log_e \sec 2\theta \quad . \qquad . \qquad . \qquad (4)$$

(b) *Special Case when $\psi = \theta$.*   In this case the plane of the specimen bisects the angle $180° - 2\theta$ between the incident and transmitted rays.   Equation (3) then reduces to

$$\mu t^* = \frac{1}{\sec \theta} \qquad . \qquad . \qquad . \qquad . \qquad (5)$$

(c) *Special Case when $\theta \to 0°$.*   For very small Bragg angles, we obtain

$$\mu t^* = 1 \, . \qquad . \qquad . \qquad . \qquad . \qquad (6)$$

(B) *Reflexion Spectra.*   In Fig. 240, let the incident ray strike the plate specimen at the grazing angle ϕ and be deviated through the angle 2θ after reflexion.

The total intensity I in the reflected ray is

$$I = \text{const. } I_0 \int_0^x e^{-\mu(x+y)} dx$$

and since $y = x \sin \phi / \sin (2\theta - \phi)$,

$$I = \text{const. } I_0 \int_0^x e^{-\mu x \left(1 + \frac{\sin \phi}{\sin (2\theta - \phi)}\right)} dx$$

$$= \frac{\text{const. } I_0}{\mu \left(1 + \dfrac{\sin \phi}{\sin (2\theta - \phi)}\right)} \left\{ 1 - e^{-\mu x \left(1 + \frac{\sin \phi}{\sin (2\theta - \phi)}\right)} \right\} \qquad . \qquad (7)$$

Thus I increases as x increases, reaching a limiting value when x is effectively "infinitely thick", in which case

$$I = \frac{\text{const. } I_0}{\mu} \cdot \frac{\sin (2\theta - \phi)}{[\sin (2\theta - \phi) + \sin \phi]} \qquad . \qquad . \qquad (8)$$

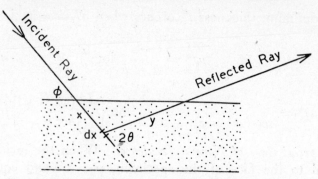

FIG. 240.—Paths of Incident and Reflected Rays in Surface
Reflexion Arrangement.

The criterion of infinite thickness is set by the sensitivity of the
X-ray film or recording device. For suppose the crystals at the
surface give rise to reflexions of intensity $I(s)$ and those at a depth x
give an intensity $I(x)$. The reflexions of $I(x)$ will not be visible if
$I(x)$ is less than $\dfrac{I(s)}{600}$ approximately. This ratio is taken on the
same basis as when the strongest $K\beta$ reflexion is invisible after
filtration has cut down the $K\beta$ component to $\dfrac{1}{600}$ of $K\alpha$ (page 12).
We thus have:

$$\frac{I(s)}{I(x)} = \frac{600}{1} = \frac{\text{const. } I_0 e^{-\mu.0}}{\text{const. } I_0 e^{-\mu(x + y)}}$$

$$= e^{+\mu x}\left(1 + \frac{\sin \phi}{\sin (2\theta - \phi)}\right)$$

Hence

$$\mu x = \frac{6\cdot4 \sin (2\theta - \phi)}{[\sin (2\theta - \phi) + \sin \phi]} \qquad . \qquad . \qquad . \qquad . \quad (9)$$

In back-reflexion patterns, $\phi = 90°$ and $\theta \to 90°$, in which
case the condition for infinite thickness is that x should exceed the
value given by

$$\mu x = 3\cdot2 \quad . \qquad . \qquad . \qquad . \qquad . \quad (10)$$

TABLE XLIV

List of Metal Compounds

Compound	System and Structure Type	Space Group	Lattice Constants				Mols. per Unit Cell
			a	b	c	Ax. Ang.	
Ag_3Al . .	Cubic, β-Mn	O^7	6·920				20 at.
	Cubic, f.c. 600–700° C.	—	3·24				2 at.
Ag_9As . .	Hexagonal, c.p.	D_{6h}^4	2·891	.....	4·722		2
$AgBe_2$ . .	Cubic, Cu_2Mg	O_h^7	6·287				8
$AgCa$ . .	Cubic, f.c.	—	9·07				—
Ag_3Ca . .	Tetragonal, f.c.	—	$c/a = 0.88$				—
$AgCd$ . .	Cubic, body-centred CsCl	O_h^1	3·32				I
Ag_2Cd_3 . .	Cubic	—	9·99				52 at.
$AgHg$ . .	Hexagonal, c.p.	D_{6h}^4	2·98	.....	4·94		2 at.
Ag_3Hg_4 . .	Cubic	O_h^9	10·09				4
$Ag_{10}Hg_{13}$.	Cubic, b.c.	—	10·0				2
Ag_3In . .	Hexagonal, c.p.	—	2·95	.....	4·79		2 at.
$AgLi$ . .	Cubic, CsCl	O_h^1	3·225				I
$AgMg$ . .	Cubic, b.c. CsCl	O_h^1	3·275				I
Ag_2S . .	Cubic, b.c. ?	—	4·84				2
	Cubic, 250° C.	—	3·465				I
$Ag(Sb, Bi)S_2$	Triclinic (deformed NaCl)	—	5·672	5·688	5·623		2
Ag_3Sb . .	Hexagonal, c.p.	—	2·985	.....	4·81		—
Ag_2Se . .	Cubic, b.c. 170° C.	—	4·983				2
Ag_3Sn . .	Hexagonal, c.p.	D_{6h}^4	2·98	.....	4·4		2 at.
Ag_2Te . .	Monoclinic	C_{2h}^1	5·98	6·31	5·56	75° 2′	3
	Cubic, f.c. > 170° C.	—	6·572	at 250° C.			4
$AgZn$ . .	Cubic, CsCl	O_h^1	3·156				I
Ag_5Zn_8 . .	Cubic, γ-brass	T_d^3	9·327				52 at.
$AlAs$ . .	Cubic, zinc blende	T_d^2	5·62				4
$AlAu_3$ . .	Cubic, β-Mn	O^7	6·909				20
Al_2Au . .	Cubic, CaF_2	O_h^5	6·00				4
AlB_2 . .	Hexagonal	D_{6h}^1	3·00	.....	3·24		I
Al_4Ba . .	Tetragonal	D_{4h}^{17}	4·530	.....	11·14		2
$AlB_{12}(?)$.	Tetragonal	D_{4h}^{12}	12·55	.....	10·18		16
Al_4C_3 . .	Rhombohedral	D_{3d}^5	8·53			$\alpha = 22°28′$	I
$AlCo$ . .	Cubic, CsCl	O_h^1	2·8565				I
Al_5Co_2 . .	Hexagonal	D_{6h}^4	7·656	.....	7·593		28 at.

TABLE XLIV (*continued*)

Compound	System and Structure Type	Space Group	Lattice Constants				Mols. per Unit Cell
			a	b	c	Ax. Ang.	
$AlCr_2$ . .	Tetragonal	D_{4h}^{17}	2·9984	.....	8·6303		2
Al_3Cr . .							
Al_7Cr . .	Orthorhombic, pseudo-hex.	—	19·99	34·51	12·47		—
Al_8Cr_5 . .	Rhombohedral, pseudo γ-brass		9·0	327		$\alpha=89°$ 16·4'	
$AlFe$ . .	Cubic, CsCl	O_h^1	2·9026				1
$AlFe_2$ . .	Cubic, b.c.	—	2·8887				2 at.
$AlFe_3$ . .	Cubic, b.c. superlattice .	—	2·8903				2 at.
	Random	—	2·8931				2 at.
Al_2Fe . .	Rhombohedral	—	6·314			$\alpha=74°9'$	
Al_3Fe . .	Orthorhombic	D_{2h}^{23}	47·43	15·46	8·08		400 at.
Al_5Fe_2 . .	Monoclinic	—	9·910	10·811	8·824	$\beta=124°$ 59'53"	
$AlMg$ (?) .	Low Symmetry						
Al_3Mg_2 . .	Hexagonal	—	11·38	.....	17·9		104 at.
Al_3Mg_4 . . ($\equiv Al_{12}Mg_{17}$)	Cubic, α-Mn	T_d^3	10·5				58 at.
AlN . . .	Hexagonal, wurtzite	C_{6v}^4	3·11	.....	4·98		2
$AlNi$ . . .	Cubic, CsCl	O_h^1	2·8814				1
Al_3Ni_2 . .	Hexagonal	D_{3d}^3	4·0282	.....	4·8906		1
Al_3Ni . .	Orthorhombic	V_h^{16}	6·5982	7·3515	4·8021		4
AlP . . .	Cubic, zinc blende	T_d^2	5·42				1
$AlSb$ . . .	Cubic, zinc blende	T_d^2	6·10				4
Al_3Ti . .	Hexagonal	D_{2d}^9	5·424	.....	8·574		4
As_2Cd_3 . .	Cubic Mg_3P_2	O_h^4	6·29				2
As_2Se_3 . .	pseudo-rhombohedral Bi_2Te_3						1 at.
$AsSn$ . .	Cubic, NaCl	O_h^5	5·681				4
$AuBe_5$ . .	Cubic, f.c.	T_d^2	6·685				4
Au_2Bi . .	Cubic, Cu_2Mg	O^4	7·942				24 at.
$AuCd$ . .	Orthorhombic	D_{2h}^5	3·144	4·851	4·745		2
$AuCu$ . .	Tetragonal (pseudo-cubic)	—	3·98	.....	3·72		4 at.
$AuCu_3$ . .	Cubic, f.c.	O_h^5	3·75				4 at.
$AuPb_2$ . .	Cubic, f.c.	—	16·14				—

TABLE XLIV (*continued*)

Compound	System and Structure Type	Space Group	a	b	c	Ax. Ang.	Mols. per Unit Cell
Au_2Pb . .	Cubic, f.c. Cu_2Mg	O_h^7	7·911				8
$AuSb_2$ . .	Cubic (pyrites)	T_h^6	6·647				4
$AuSn$ . .	Hexagonal, NiAs	D_{6h}^4	4·314	.....	5·512		2
$AuSn_2$ . .	Hexagonal, c.p.	D_{6h}^4	2·902	.....	4·775		2 at.
$AuSn_4$ . .	Hexagonal, c.p.	D_{6h}^4	2·932	.....	4·761		2 at.
$AuTe_2$ . .	Monoclinic	C_{2h}^3	7·18	4·40	5·07	90° ± 30′	2
$AuZn$ . .	Cubic, CsCl	O_h^1	3·146				1
Au_5Zn_8 . .	Cubic, γ-brass	T_d^3	9·268				52 at.
B_4C . . .	Rhombohedral	D_{3d}^5	5·62	.....	12·12		3
B_7C and B_6C	also possibilities						
BaB_6 . .	Cubic, CaB_6	O_h^1	4·28				1
BaC_2 . .	Tetragonal	O_{4h}^{17}	4·40	.....	7·06		2
Ba_3P_2 . .	Cubic, Mn_2O_3	T_h^7	≈ 10				16
BaS . . .	Cubic, NaCl	O_h^5	6·35				4
BaS_3 . .	Orthorhombic	D_2^3	8·32	9·64	4·82		4
$BaSe$ . . .	Cubic, NaCl	O_h^5	6·59				4
$BaTe$ . .	Cubic, NaCl	O_h^5	6·99				4
Be_2C . .	Cubic, CaF_2	O_h^5	4·33				4
Be_3P_2 . .	Cubic, Mn_2O_3	T_h^7	10·15				16
BeS . . .	Cubic, zinc blende	T_d^2	4·86				4
$BeSe$ . .	Cubic, zinc blende	T_d^2	5·13				4
$BeTe$ . .	Cubic, zinc blende	T_d^2	5·61				4
$BiNi$ . .	Hexagonal, NiAs	D_{6h}^4	4·072	.....	5·345		2
Bi_2S_3 . .	Orthorhombic, Sb_2S_3	D_{2h}^{16}	11·13	11·27	3·97		4
$BiSe$ . . .	Hexagonal	—	5·021	.....	8·034		3
Bi_2Se_3 . .	Hexagonal	—	6·702	.....	11·26		3
Bi_2Te_2S .	Rhombohedral	D_{3d}^5	10·31			α=24° 10′	1
Bi_2Te_3 . .	Isomorphous with Bi_2Se_3						
C_8Cs . .	Hexagonal	—	4·94	.....	≈ 22		
CaB_6 . .	Cubic	C_h^1	4·15				1
CaC_2 . .	Tetragonal	O_{4h}^{17}	5·48	.....	6·37		2
$CaPb_3$ . .	Cubic, $AuCu_3$	O_h^5	4·891				4 at.
$CaSn_3$ . .	Cubic, f.c.	O_h^5	4·732				4 at.
$CaTl_3$ . .	Cubic, f.c.	O_h^5	4·794				4 at.

TABLE XLIV (*continued*)

Compound	System and Structure Type	Space Group	Lattice Constants				Mols. per Unit Cell
			a	b	c	Ax. Ang.	
CaTl . .	Cubic, CsCl	O_h^1	3·847				1
CaS . . .	Cubic, NaCl	O_h^5	5·667				4
CaSe . .	Cubic, NaCl	O_h^5	5·912				4
CaSi$_2$ . .	Rhombohedral	D_{3d}^5	10·4			$\alpha = 21°$ 30′	2
CaTe . .	Cubic, NaCl	O_h^5	5·912				4
Cd$_3$As$_2$ . .	Tetragonal, Zn$_3$P$_2$	D_{4h}^{15}	8·945	.....	12·65		8
Cd$_3$Hg . .	Tetragonal, b.c.	—	16·53	.....	12·09		38
CdLi . .	Cubic, CsCl	O_h^1	3·32				1
CdLi$_3$ . .	Cubic, f.c.	—	4·250				4
Cd$_3$Li . .	Cubic, b.c.	—	8·62				8
CdP$_2$ . .	Tetragonal	D_4^4	5·28	.....	19·70		8
Cd$_3$P$_2$ . .	Cubic	O_h^4	6·06				2
	Hexagonal	D_{4h}^{15}	8·746	.....	12·28		8
CdS . . .	Cubic, zinc blende	T_d^2	5·82				4
	Hexagonal, wurtzite	C_{6v}^4	4·14	.....	6·72		2
CdSb . .	Orthorhombic	—	6·52	8·604	4·16		4
	Orthorhombic	D_{2h}	8·492	8·320	6·390		16 at.
Cd$_3$Sb$_2$ . .	Monoclinic	—	7·20	13·51	6·16	$\beta = 100°$ 14′	4
CdSe . .	Cubic, zinc blende	T_d^2	6·04				4
	Hexagonal, wurtzite	C_{6v}^4	4·30	.....	7·01		2
CdTe . . .	Cubic, zinc blende	T_d^2	6·464				4
CeB$_6$ . . .	Cubic	O_h^1	4·129				1
CeC$_2$ . .	Tetragonal	D_{4h}^{17}	3·87	.....	6·48		2
CeMg$_3$ . .	Cubic	O_h^7	7·373				8
CePb$_3$ . .	Cubic, f.c.	O_h^5	4·864				4 at.
CeSn$_3$ . .	Cubic, f.c.	O_h^5	4·711				4 at.
CoAs . .	Orthorhombic	D_{2h}^{16}	5·96	5·15	3·51		4
CoAs$_3$ . .	Cubic	T_h^5	8·18				8
CoAsS . .	Cubic	T^4	5·60				4
CoB . . .	Orthorhombic	D_{2h}^{16}	3·948	5·243	3·037		4
Co$_2$B . .	Tetragonal	D_{4h}^{18}	5·006	.....	4·212		4
CoCr . . .	Tetragonal	—	5·33	.....	7·20		8
Co$_2$CuS$_4$.	Cubic, spinel, Al$_2$MgO$_4$	O_h^7	9·46				8
CoP . . .	Orthorhombic	D_{2h}^{16}	5·588	5·066	3·274		4

TABLE XLIV (*continued*)

Compound	System and Structure Type	Space Group	Lattice Constants				Mols. per Unit Cell
			a	b	c	Ax. Ang.	
CoBe . .	Cubic, CsCl	O_h^1	2·606				1
CoS . . .	Cubic, NiAs	D_{6h}^4	3·385	.....	5·213		2
CoS$_2$. . .	Cubic, FeS$_2$	T_h^6	5·64				4
Co$_3$S$_4$ . .	Cubic, spinel	O_h^7	8·4				8
Co$_6$S$_5$ . .	Cubic, f.c.	—	9·924				—
Co$_9$S$_8$ . .	Cubic	O_h^5	9·907				4
CoSb . .	Hexagonal, NiAs	D_{6h}^4	3·87	.....	5·19		2
CoSb$_2$ . .	Orthorhombic	V_h^{12}	3·208	5·780	6·415		—
CoSe . .	Hexagonal, NiAs	D_{6h}^4	3·59	.....	5·27		2
CoSe$_2$ . .	Cubic, FeS$_2$	T_h^6	6·022				4
CoSi . .	Cubic, FeSi	T^4	4·438				4
Co$_2$Si . .	Orthorhombic	D_{2h}^{16}	7·095	4·908	3·730		4
Co$_4$W$_3$C .	Cubic ?	—	11·01				—
CoTe . .	Hexagonal, NiAs	D_{6h}^4	3·89	.....	5·36		2
Co$_5$Zn$_{21}$. .	Cubic, γ-brass	T_d^3	8·9				52 at.
CrAs. . .	Hexagonal		3·76	.....	5·32		
CrBe$_2$ . .	Hexagonal, MgZn$_2$	D_{6h}^4	4·239	.....	6·919		4
Cr$_3$C$_2$ . .	Orthorhombic	D_{2h}^{16}	11·46	5·52	2·821		4
Cr$_4$C. . .	Cubic	—	10·638				24
Cr$_7$C$_3$ . .	Hexagonal (Trigonal)	C_{3v}^4	13·98	.....	4·523		8
Cr$_{23}$C$_6$ . .	Cubic	O_h^5	10·638				4
CrN . .	Hexagonal, c.p.	D_3^2	2·751	.....	4·415		2
Cr$_2$Ni . .	Tetragonal, b.c.	D_4^{10}	10·64	.....	11·07		96 at.
CrS . . .	Hexagonal, NiAs	D_3^4	3·44	.....	5·67		2
CrSb . .	Hexagonal, NiAs	D_{6h}^4	4·11	.....	5·46		2
CrSe. . .	Hexagonal, NiAs	D_{6h}^4	3·59	.....	5·80		2
CrSi . . .	Cubic	T^4	4·620				4
CrSi$_2$ . .	Hexagonal	D_6^4	4·422	.....	6·351		3
Cr$_3$Si . .	Cubic, β—W	O_h^3	4·555				2
Cr$_{21}$W$_2$C$_6$.	Cubic, Cr$_{23}$C$_6$	O_h^5	≈10·5				4
CrTe . .	Hexagonal, NiAs	D_{6h}^4	3·981	.....	6·211		2
CuAl$_2$ . .	Tetragonal, b.c.	D_{4h}^{18}	6·052	.....	4·878		4
Cu$_3$Al . .	Cubic, CsCl	O_h^1	3·650				1
Cu$_9$Al$_4$ . .	Cubic, Cu$_5$Zn$_8$	T_d^1	8·685				4
Cu$_3$AsS$_4$ . .	Orthorhombic	C_{2v}^7	6·46	7·43	6·18		2

TABLE XLIV (*continued*)

| Compound | System and Structure Type | Space Group | Lattice Constants | | | | Mols. per Unit Cell |
			a	b	c	Ax. Ang.	
CuBe . .	Cubic, CsCl	O_h^1	2·698				1
CuBe$_2$ . .	Cubic, f.c. MgCu$_2$	O_h^7	5·940				24 at.
CuBiS$_2$ . .	Orthorhombic	D_{2h}^{16}	6·125	3·890	14·512		4
Cu$_5$Cd$_8$ . .	Cubic, γ-brass	T_d^3	9·635				52 at.
CuFeS$_2$ . .	Tetragonal	D_2^{12}	5·24	.....	10·30		4
CuFeS$_3$ . .	Orthorhombic	D_{2h}^{16}	6·45	11·07	6·21		4
Cu$_3$FeS$_3$ or Cu$_5$FeS$_4$.	Cubic	O_h^7	10·93				80 at.
Cu$_3$Ge . .	Hexagonal, c.p.	D_{6h}^4	2·626	.....	4·204		2 at.
CuHg . .	Cubic, Cu$_5$Zn$_8$	T_d	9·406				52
CuMg$_2$ . .	Orthorhombic	—	5·27	9·05	18·21		48
Cu$_2$Mg . .	Hexagonal	—	5·281	.....	18·29		8
	Cubic, f.c.	—	7·066				8
Cu$_2$MnAl .	Cubic, f.c.	O_h^5	5·90				16 at.
Cu$_2$MnSn .	Cubic, f.c.	O_h^5	6·167				16 at.
CuPbSbS$_3$.	Orthorhombic	D_{2h}^{13}	8·10	8·65	7·75		4
CuPd . .	Cubic, CsCl	O_h^1	2·988				1
Cu$_3$Pd . .	Cubic, f.c. AuCu$_3$	O_h^5	~3·7				4 at.
CuPt . .	Rhombohedral, pseudo-cubic	D_{3d}^5	7·56	.....	.....	$\alpha=90°$ 54′	32 at.
	Cubic	O_h^7					
CuS . . .	Hexagonal	D_{3h}	6·66	.....	~9·0		—
Cu$_2$S . .	Cubic	T_h^6	5·59				4
Cu$_2$Sb . .	Tetragonal	D_{4h}^7	3·992	.....	6·091		2
Cu$_3$Sb . .	Hexagonal, c.p.	D_{6h}^4	2·766	.....	4·348		$\frac{1}{2}$
CuSbS$_2$ . .	Orthorhombic	D_{2h}^{16}	6·008	3·784	14·456		4
Cu$_3$SbS$_3$.	Cubic	T_d	10·3				8
Cu$_2$Se . .	Cubic, CaF$_2$	O_h^5	5·749				4
Cu$_5$Si . .	Cubic, β-Mn	O^7	6·210				20 at.
Cu$_{15}$Si$_4$.	Cubic, b.c.	T_d^6	9·694				4
CuSn . .	Hexagonal, NiAs	D_{6h}^4	4·19	.....	5·08		2
Cu$_3$Sn . .	Hexagonal c.p.	D_{6h}^4	2·755	.....	4·319		2 at.
Cu$_{20}$Sn$_6$ . .	Hexagonal	D_{3d}^1	7·316	.....	7·854		26 at.
Cu$_5$Sn . .	Cubic, CsCl	O_h^1	2·97				2 at.
Cu$_{31}$Sn$_8$.	Cubic, Cu$_5$Zn$_8$	T_d	17·91				416 at.

TABLE XLIV (continued)

Compound	System and Structure Type	Space Group	a	b	c	Ax. Ang.	Mols. per Unit Cell
Cu_2SnMn .	Cubic, b.c.	—	2·95				2 at.
	or cubic f.c. (double cell)	—	5·9				16 at.
Cu_3VS_4 . .	Cubic	O_h^5	10·750				8
CuZn . .	Cubic (random)	—	2·945				2 at.
	Cubic, CsCl						1
Cu_5Zn_8 (γ-brass)	Cubic	T_d^3	8·85				52 at.
ErB_6 . . .	Cubic	O_h^1	4·102				1
FeAs . .	Orthorhombic, pseudo-hexagonal, NiAs	D_{2h}^{16}	3·366	6·016	5·428		4
$FeAs_2$ . .	Orthorhombic	V_h^{12}	3·17	4·86	5·80		2
	Orthorhombic, Löllingite	D_{2h}^{12}	2·85	5·25	5·92		2
Fe_2As . .	Tetragonal	D_{4h}^7	3·627	·····	5·973		2
FeAsS . .	Monoclinic	C_{2h}^5	9·51	5·65	6·42	$\beta=90°$	8
FeB . . .	Orthorhombic	D_{2h}^{16}	4·053	5·495	2·946		4
Fe_2B . . .	Tetragonal	V_d^{11}	5·099	·····	4·240		4
$FeBe_2$ . .	Hexagonal, $MgZn_2$	D_{6h}^4	4·212	·····	6·834		4
$FeBe_5$ . .	Cubic, f.c. $MgCu_2$	D_{4h}^{18}	5·878				8
Fe_3C . .	Orthorhombic	D_{2h}^{16}	4·5144	5·0787	6·7297		4
$(Fe_2Mn)C$.	Orthorhombic	D_{2h}^{16}	4·50	5·04	6·73		4
Fe_7Mo_6 . .	Rhombohedral	D_{3d}^5	8·97			$\alpha=30°$ 38·6′	1
Fe_3Mo_3C .	Cubic	—	11·1				—
$Fe_{21}Mo_2C_6$.	Cubic, $Cr_{23}C_6$	O_h^5	~11·0				4
Fe_2N . .	Orthorhombic ?	D_{3d}^1	2·76	4·82	4·42		—
Fe_3N . .	Hexagonal	—	2·695	·····	4·362		—
Fe_4N . .	Cubic, f.c.	O_h^1	3·790				1
$(Fe,Ni,Co)_3P$	Tetragonal, b.c.	S_4^2	9·013	·····	4·424		8
$(Fe,Ni)_9S_8$.	Cubic, Co_9S_8	O_h^5	10·02				4
Fe_3NiAl_{10} .	Hexagonal, Al_5Co_2	D_{6h}^4	7·65	·····	7·61		28 at.
FeP . . .	Orthorhombic	D_{2h}^{16}	5·782	5·177	3·089		4
FeP_2. . .	Orthorhombic, FeS_2	V_h^{12}	2·725	4·975	5·657		2
Fe_2P. . .	Hexagonal	D_3^2	5·852	·····	3·453		3
Fe_3P. . .	Tetragonal	S_4^2	9·09	·····	4·45		8
FePt. . .	Cubic, f.c.	O_h^5	3·91				4 at.
FeS . . .	Hexagonal, NiAs	D_{6h}^4	3·43	·····	5·79		2

TABLE XLIV (continued)

Compound	System and Structure Type	Space Group	Lattice Constants				Mols. per Unit Cell
			a	b	c	Ax. Ang.	
FeS_2 . .	Cubic (pyrites)	T_h^6	5·404				4
	Orthorhombic (markasite)	V_h^{12}	3·35	4·40	5·35		2
$FeSb$ . .	Hexagonal, NiAs	D_{6h}^4	4·122	.....	5·163		2
$FeSb_2$ . .	Orthorhombic, FeS_2	V_h^{12}	3·19	5·82	6·52		2
$FeSbS$ . .	Monoclinic	C_{2h}^5	10·04	5·93	6·68	$\beta=90°$	8
$FeSe$ . .	Tetragonal, above 300°	D_{4h}^7	3·765	.....	5·518		2
	Hexagonal	D_{6h}^4	3·637	.....	5·958		2
$Fe_{11}Se_9$ . .	Monoclinic, pseudo-FeSe	—	6·247	3·581	5·809	$\beta= 90·98°$	—
$FeSi$ . . .	Cubic	T^4	4·480				4
$FeSi_2$ . .	Tetragonal	C_{4h}^1	2·687	.....	5·127		3
Fe_3Si . .	Cubic, Cu_2MnAl	O_h^5	2·82				2 at.
$FeSn$ . .	Hexagonal	—	5·292	.....	4·440		3
$FeSn_2$ . .	Hexagonal ?	—	5·317	.....	9·236		4
$FeTe$ . .	Hexagonal, NiAs	D_{6h}^4	3·800	.....	5·651		2
Fe_3Ti . .	Tetragonal	—	5·23	.....	8·21		4
FeV . . .	Cubic	—	2·89				—
Fe_2W . .	Hexagonal	—	4·727	.....	7·704		4
Fe_3W_2 . .	Rhombohedral, hex. cell	C_{3v}	4·738	.....	25·726		8
Fe_7W_6 . .	Rhombohedral	D_{3d}^5	9·02			$\alpha=30° 30·5'$	1
Fe_3W_3C .	Cubic	O_h^7	11·04				16
Fe_4W_2C .	Cubic, f.c.	—	11·04				16
$Fe_{21}W_2C_6$.	Cubic, $Cr_{23}C_6$	O_h^5	~11				4
Fe_3Zn_{10} .	Cubic, γ-brass	O_h^9	8·992				4
$GaAs$ . .	Cubic, zinc blende	T_d^2	5·63				4
GaP . .	Cubic, zinc blende	T_d^2	5·44				4
$GaSb$ . .	Cubic, zinc blende	T_d^2	6·09				4
GdB_6 . .	Cubic, CaB_6	O_h^1	4·12				1
GeS . . .	Orthorhombic	D_{2h}^{16}	4·29	10·42	3·64		4
GeS_2 . .	Orthorhombic	C_{2v}^{19}	11·66	6·86	22·34		24
HgS . .	Cubic, zinc blende	T_d^2	5·84				4
	Hexagonal, cinnabar	D_3^4	4·142		9·49		3
$HgSb_4S_7$.	Monoclinic	C_{2h}^5	15·14	3·98	21·60	$\beta= 104°$	4
$HgSe$ . .	Cubic, zinc blende	T_d^2	6·068				4

TABLE XLIV (*continued*)

Compound	System and Structure Type	Space Group	Lattice Constants				Mols. per Unit Cell
			a	b	c	Ax. Ang.	
HgTe . .	Cubic, zinc blende	T_d^2	6·440				4
Hg_5Tl_2 . .	Cubic, f.c.	—	4·67				—
InSb. . .	Cubic, zinc blende	T_d^2	6·45				4
KBi_2. . .	Cubic	O_h^7	9·501				8
$KFeS_2$ . .	Hexagonal	D_{3d}	13·041	.....	5·403		8
K_2S . . .	Cubic, CaF_2	O_h^5	7·35				4
K_2Se . .	Cubic	O_h^5	7·676				4
K_2Te . .	Cubic, zinc blende	O_h^5	8·152				4
LaB_6. . .	Cubic, CaB_6	O_h^1	4·145				1
LaC_2 . .	Tetragonal	D_{4h}^{17}	3·92	.....	6·55		2
$LaMg_3$ . .	Cubic	O_h^7	7·478				8
$LaPb_3$ . .	Cubic, f.c.	O_h^5	4·893				1
$LaSn_3$ . .	Cubic, f.c.	O_h^5	4·704				1
$LaTl_3$ . .	Hexagonal	—	3·45	.....	5·52		—
LiAg . .	Cubic, CsCl	O_h^1	3·168				1
LiAl . .	Cubic, CsCl	O_h^1	3·23				1
α-LiBi . .	Tetragonal, b.c.	—	3·361	.....	4·247		—
Li_3Bi . .	Cubic, f.c., BiF_3	O_h^5	6·708				4
LiGa . .	Cubic	O_h^7	6·195				8
LiHg . .	Cubic, CsCl	O_h^1	3·287				1
$LiHg_3$ . .	Hexagonal	—	6·240	.....	4·794		8
Li_3Hg . .	Cubic (CsCl)	—	6·548				16 at.
LiIn . .	Cubic, NaTl	O_h^7	6·786				8
Li_2S . . .	Cubic, CaF_2	O_h^5	5·70				4
Li_2Se . .	Cubic	O_h^5	5·94				4
Li_2Te . .	Cubic, CaF_2	O_h^5	6·47				4
LiTl. . .	Cubic, PdCu	O_h^1	3·42				1
LiZn . .	Cubic, NaTl	O_h^7	6·209				8
Li_2Zn_3 . .	Cubic ?	—	4·26				1
$LiZn_9$ . .	Hexagonal	—	2·782	.....	4·385		2
Li_7Zn_{18} . .	Hexagonal	—	4·362	.....	2·510		2·8
Mg_3As_2 . .	Cubic, Mn_2O_3	T_h^7	12·33				16
MgAu . .	Cubic, CsCl	O_h^1	3·259				1
Mg_3Bi_2 . .	Hexagonal, La_2O_3	D_{3d}^3	4·666	.....	7·401		1
MgCuAl .	Hexagonal, $MgZn_2$	D_{6h}^4	5·09	.....	8·35		4

TABLE XLIV (continued)

Compound	System and Structure Type	Space Group	a	b	c	Ax. Ang.	Mols. per Unit Cell
Mg_4CuAl_6 .	Cubic, b.c.	—	14·25				161 at.
Mg_2Ge . .	Cubic, CaF_2	O_h^5	6·378				4
$MgHg$ . .	Cubic, CsCl	O_h^1	3·442				1
$MgNi_2$ . .	Hexagonal	D_{6h}	5·26	.....	13·3		4
$MgNi$ . .	Hexagonal	—	4·87	.....	~16·0		8
$MgNiZn$.	Cubic, Cu_2Mg	D_{4h}^{18}	6·96				8
Mg_3P_2 . .	Cubic, Mn_2O_3	T_h^7	12·01				16
Mg_2Pb . .	Cubic, CaF_2	O_h^5	6·836				4
$MgPr$ . .	Cubic	T_1	3·883				1
Mg_3Pr . .	Cubic, NaTl	O_h^7	≈7·5				4
MgS . . .	Cubic, NaCl	O_h^5	5·19				4
Mg_3Sb_2 . .	Hexagonal, La_2O_3	D_{3d}^3	4·573	.....	7·229		1
$MgSe$ . .	Cubic, NaCl	O_h^5	5·45				4
Mg_2Si . .	Cubic, CaF_2	O_h^5	6·39				4
Mg_2Sn . .	Cubic, CaF_2	O_h^5	6·77				4
$MgTe$ . .	Hexagonal, wurtzite	C_{6v}^4	4·52	.....	7·33		2
$MgTl$ . .	Cubic, PdCu	O_h^1	3·628				1
$MgZn$ . .	Hexagonal	D_{6h}^4	10·66	.....	17·16		48
$MgZn_2$ . .	Hexagonal	D_{6h}^4	5·15	.....	8·48		4
$MgZn_5$ . .	Hexagonal	D_6^6	9·92	.....	16·48		16
$Mg_3Zn_3Al_2$.	Cubic, b.c.	—	14·16				161 at.
$Mg_3Zn_2Cu_2$ Al_2	Hexagonal	—	5·14	.....	8·41		—
$Mg_3Zn_2Cu_2$ Ni_2	Cubic	—	7·03				—
$MnAl_3$ . .	Orthorhombic	—	14·79	12·6	12·43		—
$MnAl_4$ . .	Hexagonal	—	28·35	.....	12·36		—
$MnAl_6$ . .	Orthorhombic	—	6·51	7·57	8·87		—
$MnAs$ . .	Orthorhombic, pseudo-NiAs	D_{2h}^{16}	6·38	5·63	3·62		4
MnB . .	Orthorhombic	D_{2h}^6	2·95	11·5	4·10		8
$MnBe_2$ . .	Hexagonal, $MgZn_2$	D_{6h}^4	4·231	.....	6·909		4
Mn_7C_3 . .	Hexagonal	C_{3v}^4	13·87	.....	4·53		8
$Mn_{23}C_6$ . .	Cubic, $Cr_{23}C_6$	O_h^5	~10				4
$MnCr_2S_4$ . .	Cubic	—	10·055				—

TABLE XLIV (*continued*)

Compound	System and Structure Type	Space Group	Lattice Constants				Mols. per Unit Cell
			a	b	c	Ax. Ang.	
MnNi . .	Tetragonal, f.c.	—	3·658	.....	3·540		—
MnP . .	Orthorhombic pseudo-NiAs	D_{2h}^{16}	5·905	5·249	3·167		4
MnS . .	α-cubic, NaCl, green	O_h^5	5·212				4
	β_1-cubic, zinc blende, red	T^2	5·600				4
	γ-hexagonal, wurtzite red	C_{6v}^4	3·976	.....	6·432		2
MnS₂ . .	Cubic, FeS₂	T_h^6	6·097				4
MnSb . .	Hexagonal, NiAs	D_{6h}^4	3·61	.....	5·03		2
Mn₂Sb . .	Tetragonal	D_{4h}^7	4·08	.....	6·56		2
MnSe . .	Cubic, NaCl	O_h^5	5·45				4
MnSi . .	Cubic, FeSi	T^4	4·548				4
MnSi₂ . .	Tetragonal	—	5·513	.....	17·422		16
Mn₃Si . .	Cubic, b.c.	O_h^9	2·85				2 at.
Mn₅Si₃ . .	Hexagonal	D_{6h}^3	6·898	.....	4·802		2
MnTe . .	Hexagonal, NiAs	D_{6h}^4	4·124	.....	6·698		2
MnTe₂ . .	Cubic	T_h^6	6·943				4
MnZn₃ . .	Cubic, γ-brass	T_d^3	9·1				52 at.
MnZn₇ . .	Hexagonal	—	2·750	.....	4·419		—
MoBe₂ . .	Hexagonal, MgZn₂	D_{6h}^4	4·434	.....	7·275		4
MoC . .	Hexagonal, c.p.	—	2·995	.....	4·723		—
Mo₂C . .	Hexagonal	—	2·997	.....	4·719		—
Mo₂Fe₃ . .	Hexagonal	D_{3d}	4·74	.....	25·63		8
MoS₂ . .	Hexagonal	D_{6h}^4	3·15	.....	12·30		2
MoSi₂ . .	Hexagonal	D_{4h}^{17}	3·200	.....	7·861		2
NaBi . .	Tetragonal	D_{4h}^1	3·46	.....	4·50		1
NaCd₂ . .	?	O_h					
NaCl . .	Cubic	O_h^5	5·6273	7 (18° C. pure)			4
	Cubic, rock-salt	O_h^5	5·6276	8			4
NaIn . .	Cubic, NaTl	T_d^2	7·297				8
Na₄Pb₇ . .	Cubic	—	4·873				4 at.
Na₁₅Pb₄ . .	Cubic, Cu₁₅Si₄	T_d^6	13·29				4
Na₁₅Sn₄ . .	Orthorhombic	—	9·79	22·78	5·56		—
Na₃₁Pb₈ . .	Cubic, f.c.	—	13·27				78 at.
Na₂S . .	Cubic, CaF₂	O_h^5	6·526				4
Na₂Se . .	Cubic, NaTl	O_h^7	6·809				8
Na₂Te . .	Cubic, NaTl	O_h^7	7·313				

TABLE XLIV (*continued*)

Compound	System and Structure Type	Space Group	Lattice Constants				Mols. per Unit Cell
			a	b	c	Ax. Ang.	
NaTl . .	Cubic	O_h^7	7·473				8
NbC. . .	Cubic, NaCl	O_h^5	4·40				4
NdAl . .	Cubic, CsCl	O_h^1	3·73				1
NdB$_6$ . .	Cubic, CaB$_6$	O_h^1	4·118				1
NdC$_2$ . .	Tetragonal, CaC$_2$	D_{4h}^{17}	3·90	.....	6·23		2
NiAs. . .	Hexagonal	D_{6h}^4	3·61	.....	5·03		2
NiAsS . .	Cubic	T^4	5·70				4
Ni$_2$B. . .	Tetragonal, b.c.	D_{4h}^{18}	4·980	.....	4·236		4
NiBe . .	Cubic, b.c.	—	2·603				1
Ni$_5$Be$_{21}$ . .	Cubic, γ-brass	—	7·56				2
NiS . . .	α, rhombohedral	C_{3v}^5	5·63			α= 116° 35′	3
	β, hexagonal, NiAs	D_{6h}^4	3·42	.....	5·30		2
NiS$_2$ . .	Cubic, FeS$_2$	T_h^6	5·74				4
Ni$_3$S$_4$ . .	Cubic, spinel, Al$_2$MgO	O_h^7	9·5				8
NiSb$_2$ . .	Orthorhombic	—	3·206	5·634	6·288		—
NiSb . .	Hexagonal, NiAs	D_{6h}^4	3·92	.....	5·11		2
Ni$_2$Sb . .	Tetragonal		5·785	.....	6·00		2
NiSbS . .	Cubic	T^4	5·90				4
Ni$_3$Sb . .	Cubic	—	6·054				4
NiSe. . .	Hexagonal, NiAs	D_{6h}^4	3·66	.....	5·33		2
NiSe$_2$ . .	Cubic, FeS$_2$	T_h^6	6·02				4
NiSi . .	Cubic, FeSi	T^4	4·437				4
NiSn . .	Hexagonal, NiAs	D_{6h}^4	4·081	.....	5·174		2
NiTe . .	Hexagonal, NiAs	D_{6h}^4	3·95	.....	5·36		2
Ni$_3$W$_3$C .	Cubic	—	11·15				—
NiZn . .	β$_1$-tetragonal, AuCu	—	2·754	.....	3·214		1
	β-cubic, CsCl, > 890°	O_h^1	2·9083				1
Ni$_5$Zn$_{21}$ . .	Cubic, γ-brass	T_d^3	8·904				2
OsS$_2$. . .	Cubic, FeS$_2$	T_h^6	5·6075				4
OsSe$_2$ . .	Cubic, FeS$_2$	T_h^6	5·933				4
OsTe$_2$ . .	Cubic, FeS$_2$	T_h^6	6·369				4
PbAs$_2$S$_4$. .	Orthorhombic	—	5·94	3·67	13·65		2
Pb$_2$Bi . .	Hexagonal, c.p.	D_{6h}^4	3·483	.....	5·78		2 at.
PbS . . .	Cubic, NaCl	O_h^5	5·93				4

TABLE XLIV (*continued*)

Compound	System and Structure Type	Space Group	Lattice Constants				Mols. per Unit Cell
			a	b	c	Ax. Ang.	
$6Pb(S,Tl)_2$.	$AuTl_2$ Tetragonal	—	12·5	. . . . .	30·25		8
$PbSb_2S_4$. . .	Orthorhombic	—	6·37	3·81	14·53		2
PbSe . .	Cubic, NaCl	O_h^5	6·14				4
$PbSnS_2$ . .	Orthorhombic, SnS	C_s	4·04	4·28	11·33		2
PbTe . .	Cubic, NaCl	O_h^5	6·44				4
$PdAs_2$ . .	Cubic, FeS_2	T_h^6	5·970				4
PdBe . .	Cubic, CsCl	O_h^1	2·813				1
$PdBe_5$ . .	Cubic, f.c.	T_d^2	5·982				4
Pd_2Cr_3 . .	Cubic, f.c.	O_h^5	3·8395				4 at.
PdSb . .	Hexagonal, NiAs	D_{6h}^4	4·070	. . . . .	5·582		2
$PdSb_2$ . .	Cubic, FeS_2	T_h^6	6·439				4
PdTe . .	Hexagonal, NiAs	D_{6h}^4	4·127	. . . . .	5·663		2
$PdTe_2$ . .	Hexagonal, CdI_2	D_{3d}^3	4·028	. . . . .	5·118		1
Pd_5Zn_{21} . .	Cubic, b.c. γ-brass	T_d^3	9·089				2
PrB_6 . . .	Cubic, CaB_6	O_h^1	4·121				1
PrC_2 . . .	Tetragonal, CaC_2	D_{4h}^{17}	3·85	. . . . .	6·38		2
$PrPb_3$ . .	Cubic, f.c.	O_h^5	4·857				1
$PrSn_3$ . .	Cubic	O_h^5	4·704				1
$PtAs_2$ . .	Cubic, FeS_2	T_h^6	5·92				4
Pt_5Be_{21} . .	Deformed γ-brass type	—	—				—
PtP_2. . .	Cubic, FeS_2	T_h^6	5·683				4
(Pt,Pd)S .	Tetragonal	C_{4h}^2	6·37	. . . . .	6·58		8
PtS . . .	Tetragonal	D_{4h}^9	3·47	. . . . .	6·10		2
PtS_2 . . .	Hexagonal, CdI_2	D_{3d}^3	3·537	. . . . .	5·019		1
PtSb. . .	Hexagonal, NiAs	D_{6h}^4	4·130	. . . . .	5·472		2
$PtSb_2$ . .	Cubic, FeS_2	T_h^6	6·428				4
$PtSe_2$ . .	Hexagonal, CdI_2	D_{3d}^3	3·724	. . . . .	5·062		1
PtSn. . .	Hexagonal, NiAs	D_{6h}^4	4·103	. . . . .	5·428		2
$PtTe_2$ . .	Hexagonal, CdI_2	D_{3d}^3	4·010	. . . . .	5·201		1
PtTl. . .	Hexagonal	D_{6h}	5·605	. . . . .	4·639		6
Pt_5Zn_{21} . .	Cubic, γ-brass	T_d^3	8·079				2
RbS_2 . .	Cubic, CaF_2	O_h^5	7·65				4
$ReBe_2$ . .	Hexagonal, MgZn	D_{6h}^4	4·345	. . . . .	7·087		4
RuS_2 . .	Cubic, FeS_2	T_h^6	5·57				4
$RuSe_2$ . .	Cubic, FeS_2	T_h^6	5·921				4

TABLE XLIV (*continued*)

Compound	System and Structure Type	Space Group	Lattice Constants				Mols. per Unit Cell
			a	b	c	Ax. Ang.	
$RuTe_2$ . .	Cubic, FeS_2	T_h^6	6·360				4
Sb_2S_3 . .	Orthorhombic	V_h^1	11·39	11·48	3·89		4
$SbTl$ . .	Cubic, $CsCl$	O_h^1	3·84				1
Sb_2Tl_7 . .	Cubic	O_h^9	11·59				6
SiC . . .	Hexagonal, Mod. I	C_{3v}^5	3·095	.....	37·95		15
	Mod. II	C_{6v}^4	3·0755	.....	15·08805		6
	Mod. III	C_{6v}^4	3·095	.....	10·09		4
	(zinc blende) Mod. IV	T_d^2	4·3503				4
SiS_2 . . .	Orthorhombic	D_{2h}^{26}	5·60	5·53	9·55		4
SnO_2 . . .	Tetragonal TiO_2	D_{4h}^{14}	4·72	.....	3·17		2
SnS . . .	Orthorhombic	D_{2h}^{16}	3·98	4·33	11·18		4
SnS_2 . . .	Hexagonal, CdI_2	D_{3d}^3	3·62	.....	5·85		1
$SnSb$ . .	Rhombohedral, pseudo-zinc blende	—	6·214			$\alpha = 89·38°$	4
$SnTe$ . .	Cubic, $NaCl$	O_h^5	6·28				4
SrB_6 . . .	Cubic, CaB_6	O_h^1	4·19				1
SrC_2 . . .	Tetragonal, CaC_2	D_{4h}^{17}	4·11	.....	6·68		2
$SrPb_3$ . .	Tetragonal	—	4·955	.....	5·025		1
SrS . .	Cubic, $NaCl$	O_h^5	6·01				4
$SrSe$ . .	Cubic, $NaCl$	O_h^5	6·23				4
$SrTe$ . .	Cubic, $NaCl$	O_h^5	6·65				4
$SrTl$ . .	Cubic, $CsCl$	O_h^1	4·024				1
TaC . .	Cubic, $NaCl$	O_h^5	4·446				4
Ta_2C . .	Hexagonal, c.p.	—	3·091	.....	4·93		1
ThB_6 . .	Cubic, CaB_6	O_h^1	4·32				1
ThC_2 . .	Tetragonal, CaC_2	D_{4h}^{17}	4·14	.....	5·28		2
$TiBe_2$ . .	Cubic, Cu_2Mg	D_{4h}^{18}	6·435				8
TiC . . .	Cubic, $NaCl$	O_h^5	4·320				4
TiS_2 . .	Hexagonal, CdI_2	D_{3d}^3	3·40	.....	5·69		1
$TiSe_2$ . .	Hexagonal, CdI_2	D_{3d}^3	3·53	.....	6·00		1
$TiTe_2$ . .	Hexagonal, CdI_2	D_{3d}^3	3·79	.....	6·45		1
$TlBi$ . .	Cubic, $CsCl$	O_h^1	3·98				1
VBe_2 . .	Hexagonal, $MgZn_2$	D_{6h}^4	4·385	.....	7·130		4
VC . . .	Cubic, $NaCl$	O_h^5	4·30				4
WC . . .	Hexagonal	—	2·894	.....	2·830		—

TABLE XLIV (*continued*)

Compound	System and Structure Type	Space Group	Lattice Constants				Mols. per Unit Cell
			a	b	c	Ax. Ang.	
W_2C . .	Rhombohedral, pseudo-cubic	D_{3d}^5	3·49	. . . . .	. . . . .	$\alpha = 84°\,0'$	I
	Hexagonal	—	2·986	. . . . .	4·712		—
WS_2 . .	Hexagonal, MoS_2	D_{6h}^4	3·18	. . . . .	12·5		2
WSi_2 . .	Tetragonal, $MoSi_2$	D_{4h}^{17}	3·212	. . . . .	7·880		2
WBe_2 . .	Hexagonal, $MgZn_2$	D_{6h}^4	4·437	. . . . .	7·274		4
W_2P . .	Hexagonal	—	6·18	. . . . .	6·78		—
YB_6 . . .	Cubic, CaB_6	O_h^1	4·07				I
YbB_6 . .	Cubic, CaB_6	O_h^1	4·13				I
$ZnAs_2$ . .	Orthorhombic	D_4^4 ?	7·72	7·99	36·28		32
Zn_3As_2 .	Tetragonal, Zn_3P_2	D_{4h}^{15}	8·316	. . . . .	11·76		8
Zn_2FeS_3 .	Cubic	—	5·415				—
ZnP_2 . .	Tetragonal	D_4^4	5·07	. . . . .	18·65		8
Zn_3P_2 . .	Tetragonal	D_{4h}^{15}	8·097	. . . . .	11·45		8
ZnS (zinc blende) .	Cubic	T_d^2	5·403				4
ZnS (wurtzite) . .	Hexagonal	C_{6v}^4	3·84	. . . . .	6·28		2
$ZnSb$ . .	Orthorhombic	—	6·17	8·27	3·94		4
$ZnSe$ . .	Cubic, zinc blende	T_d^2	5·66				4
$ZnTe$ . .	Cubic, zinc blende	T_d^2	6·09				4
ZrB_2 ? . .	Hexagonal	—	3·15	. . . . .	3·53		—
ZrC . . .	Cubic, NaCl	O_h^5	4·687				4
ZrS_2 . . .	Hexagonal, CdI_2	D_{3d}^3	3·68	. . . . .	5·85		I
$ZrSe_2$ . .	Hexagonal, CdI_2	D_{3d}^3	3·79	. . . . .	6·18		I
$ZrSi_2$ . .	Orthorhombic	D_{2h}^{17}	3·72	14·61	3·67		4
ZrW_2 . .	Cubic	O_h^7	7·61				8

X-RAY PROTECTION

Units of Intensity and Dosage. In crystallographic measurements, the intensity of radiation emitted by the tube or reflected from the crystal is expressed in c.g.s. units—that is, it is measured in ergs per square centimetre per second.

A different unit is employed in X-ray therapy. This is the International Unit of Quantity, or Röntgen (r), adopted at Stockholm in 1928, and is based upon intensity measurements made with an ionization chamber. The röntgen is defined as "the quantity of X-radiation which, when the secondary electrons are fully utilized and the wall effect of the chamber is avoided, produces in 1 c.c. of atmospheric air at 0° C. and 760 mm. of mercury pressure such a degree of conductivity that one electrostatic unit of charge is measured at saturation current". A suitable instrument for measuring the intensity is the Mecapion, described by E. J. H. Roth (*British Journal of Radiology*, **3**, 155, 1930).

X-rays have an adverse effect on the tissues of the body, and this effect is cumulative above a certain minimum dosage. A normally healthy person can tolerate quite safely an exposure to X-rays and radium γ-rays to an extent of one röntgen per working week of 35 hours, which corresponds roughly to a toleration dosage rate of 10^{-5} r per second. To effect these conditions, the operator must be protected from the direct beam and from scattered radiation by a suitable thickness of lead or other absorbing material. A table of protective thicknesses based upon the Recommendations of the British X-ray and Radium Protection Committee (6th revised report, 1943), is given opposite.

To ensure protection against scattered radiation, from a high voltage radiographic set, it is essential that the operator be stationed outside the X-ray room behind a protective wall, the lead equivalent of which will depend on circumstances. In the case of a single X-ray tube running up to 200 Kv. peak, the protective wall should have a lead equivalent of not less than 2 mm. Full protection must be provided in all directions where the *direct* beam may operate dangerously.

TABLE XLV

MINIMUM THICKNESS OF LEAD, PLASTER AND CONCRETE FOR PRIMARY PROTECTION

X-rays generated by Peak Voltages Not exceeding Kv.	Minimum Thicknesses in mm.		
	Lead	Barium Plaster * 3·2 grams/cc.	Concrete † 2·2 grams/cc.
75	1·0		
100	1·5		
125	2·0		
150	2·5	30	200
175	3·0		
200	4·0	60	275
250	6·0		
300	9·0	110	290
350	13·0		
400	17·0	150	350
500	26·0		
600	35·0	275	
700	44·0		
800	53·0	325	
900	62·0		
1000	70·0	350	
5 grams radium (0·5 mm. Pt Screen) at 50 cms. distance	12·5	60	90

* Barium Plaster.   2 parts coarse BaSO$_4$ + 2 parts fine BaSO$_4$ + 1 part cement.

† Concrete.   2 parts ballast + 2 parts sand + 1 part cement.

Symbol	Element	Atomic Number	Atomic Weight	Melting Point ° C.	Change Point ° C.	Boiling Point ° C.
Ag	Silver	47	107·880	960·5		1950
Al	Aluminium . .	13	26·97	659·7		1800
As	Arsenic . . .	33	74·91	500		615
Au	Gold	79	197·20	1063		2600
B	Boron. . . .	5	10·82	2300		2550
Ba	Barium . . .	56	137·36	850		1140
Be	Beryllium . .	4	9·02	1350	630–640	1500
Bi	Bismuth . . .	83	209·00	271·3		1450
C	Carbon . . .	6	12·010	> 3500		4200
Ca	Calcium . . .	20	40·08	810	α–β 300° β–γ 450°	1170
Cb	Columbium . .	41	92·91	1950		2900
Cd	Cadmium . .	48	112·41	320·9		767
Ce	Cerium . . .	58	140·13	640		1400
Co	Cobalt . . .	27	58·94	1480	450	3000
Cr	Chromium . .	24	52·01	1615		2200
Cs	Caesium . . .	55	132·91	28·5		670
Cu	Copper . . .	29	63·57	1083		2300
Fe	Iron	26	55·84	1535	α–γ 906 γ–δ 1403	3000
Ga	Gallium . . .	31	69·72	29·75		> 1600
Ge	Germanium . .	32	72·60	958·5		2700

I

ANTS

Lattice	Space Group	Lattice Type	Lattice Parameters				Density (X-ray)
			a	b	c	Ax. Ang.	
ubic, f.c.	O_h^5	A 1	4·07787				10·494
ubic, f.c.	O_h^5	A 1	4·04139				2·695
hombohedral	D_{3d}^{51}	A 7	4·135			$\alpha = 54° 7' 30''$	5·727
ubic, f.c.	O_h^5	A 1	4·07042				19·287
rthorhombic ?	—	—	17·86	8·93	10·13		2·310
etragonal ?	—	—	8·93	.....	5·06		2·310
ubic, b.c.	O_h^9	A 2	5·015				3·590
. hexagonal c.p.	D_{6h}^4	A 3	2·2680	.....	3·5942		1·857
. hexagonal	—	—	7·1	.....	10·8		1·89
hombohedral	D_{3d}^5	A 7	4·7364	.....		$\alpha = 57° 14\ 1\ 3''$	9·798
			4·53726	.....	11·8381 (hex. axes)		
cubic, f.c.	O_h^7	A 4	3·55965			Diamond	3·508
hexagonal	D_{6h}^4	A 9	2·456	.....	6·696	α-graphite	2·265
hombohedral	D_{3d}^3	—	2·456	.....	10·044	β-graphite (hex. axes)	
x-cubic, f.c.	O_h^5	A 1	5·560			20° C. (above 450°)	1·537
γ-hexagonal, c.p.	D_{6h}^4	A 3	3·94	.....	6·46		1·52
cubic, b.c.	O_h^9	A 2	3·2941				8·569
hexagonal, c.p.	D_{6h}^4	A 3	2·97311	.....	5·60694		8·637
x-hexagonal, c.p.	D_{6h}^4	A 3	3·65	.....	5·91		6·775
β-cubic, f.c.	O_h^5	A 1	5·143				6·792
x-hexagonal, c.p	D_{6h}^4	A 3	2·507	.....	4·072		8·766
β-cubic, f.c.	O_h^5	A 1	3·558 (700° C.)		3·545 (20° C.)		
α-cubic, b.c.	O_h^9	A 2	2·8786				7·188
β-hexagonal, c.p.	D_{6h}^4	A 3	2·717	.....	4·418		6·07
γ-cubic, b.c.	T_d^3	A 12	8·717				7·507
cubic, b.c.	O_h^9	A 2	6·05				1·98
cubic, f.c.	O_h^5	A 1	3·6080				8·923
α-cubic, b.c.	O_h^9	A 2	2·86046				7·868
γ-cubic, f.c.	O_h^5	A 1	3·564 (20° C.)		3·649 (950° C.)		7·58 (950°)
orthorhombic	V_h^{18}	A 11	4·5167	4·5107	7·6448		5·903
cubic, f.c.	O_h^7	A 4	5·647				5·316

Symbol	Element	Atomic Number	Atomic Weight	Melting Point ° C.	Change Point ° C.	Boiling Point ° C.
H	Hydrogen . .	1	1·0080	− 259·14		− 252·7
Hf	Hafnium . . .	72	178·6	1700		> 3200
Hg	Mercury . . .	80	200·61	− 38·87		356·9
I	Iodine . . .	53	126·92	113·5		184·35
In	Indium . . .	49	114·76	155		1450
Ir	Iridium . . .	77	193·1	2350		> 4800
K	Potassium . .	19	39·096	62·3		760
La	Lanthanum . .	57	138·92	826		1800
Li	Lithium . . .	3	6·940	186		>1220
Mg	Magnesium . .	12	24·32	651		1110
Mn	Manganese . .	25	54·93	1260	α to 742 β 742–1191 γ 1191 to m.p.	1900
Mo	Molybdenum .	42	95·95	2620		3700
N	Nitrogen . . .	7	14·008	− 209·86		− 195·8
Na	Sodium . . .	11	22·997	97·5		880
Nd	Neodymium . .	60	144·27	840		—
Ni	Nickel . . .	28	58·69	1455		2900
O	Oxygen . . .	8	16·000	− 218·4		− 183
Os	Osmium . . .	76	190·2	2700		5300
P	Phosphorus . .	15	30·98	44·1		280
Pb	Lead . . .	82	207·21	327·4		1620
Pd	Palladium . .	46	106·7	1553		2200
Pr	Praseodymium .	59	140·92	940		—
Pt	Platinum . . .	78	195·23	1773·5		4300
Rb	Rubidium . .	37	85·48	38·5		700
Re	Rhenium . . .	75	186·31	3000		—
Rh	Rhodium . .	45	102·91	1985		> 2500
Ru	Ruthenium . .	44	101·7	2450		> 2700

VI (*continued*)

Lattice	Space Group	Lattice Type	Lattice Parameters				Density (X-ray)
			a	b	c	Ax. Ang.	
hexagonal	?	?	3·75	.....	6·12		0·089 (2° abs.)
hexagonal	D_{3d}^5	A 11	3·200	.....	5·077		13·08
rhombohedral	D_{3d}^5	A 11	2·999			$\alpha = 70°\ 31·7'$ (227° abs.)	
orthorhombic	V_h^{18}	A 14	4·791	7·248	9·771		4·933
tetragonal	D_{4h}^{17}	A 6	4·585	.....	4·941		7·284
cubic, f.c.	O_h^5	A 1	3·8312				22·64
cubic, b.c.	O_h^9	A 2	5·333				0·850
α-hexagonal, c.p.	D_{6h}^4	A 3	3·754	.....	6·063		6·188
β-cubic, f.c.	O_h^5	A 1	5·296				6·165
cubic, b.c.	O_h^9	A 2	3·51				0·53
hexagonal, c.p.	D_{6h}^4	A 3	3·20300	.....	5·2002		1·736
α-cubic, b.c.	T_d^3	A 12	8·894				7·464
β-cubic	O_7	A 13	6·300				7·24
γ-tetragonal	D_{4h}^{17}	A 6	3·774	.....	3·526		7·21
cubic, b.c.	O_h^9	A 2	3·14103				10·217
cubic	T^4	—	5·66	(21° abs.)			1·02
cubic, b.c.	O_h^9	A 2	4·30				0·954
hexagonal, c.p.	D_{6h}^4	A 3	3·657	.....	5·880		6·984
α-hexagonal, c.p.	D_{6h}^4	A 3	2·49	.....	4·08		8·8
β-cubic, f.c.	O_h^5	A 1	3·51684				8·900
orthorhombic	—	—	5·50	3·82	3·44	(21° abs.)	1·46
rhombohedral	C_{3i}^2	—	6·19			$\alpha = 99·1°$ (33° abs.)	1·394
cubic	T_h^6	—	6·83			(48° abs.)	1·324
hexagonal, c.p.	D_{6h}^4	A 3	2·7304	.....	4·3099		22·69
cubic	—	—	7·17			(white)	2·22
orthorhombic	V_h^{18}	A 16	3·31	4·38	10·50	(black)	2·687
cubic, f.c.	O_h^5	A 1	4·9389				11·341
cubic, f.c.	O_h^5	A 1	3·8817				12·028
hexagonal, c.p.	D_{6h}^4	A 3	3·657	.....	5·924		6·77
cubic, f.c.	O_h^5	A 1	3·9158				21·438
cubic, b.c.	O_h^9	A 2	5·62	(100° abs.)			1·59
hexagonal, c.p.	D_{6h}^4	A 3	2·7553	.....	4·4493		20·996
cubic, f.c.	O_h^5	A 1	3·7956				12·418
hexagonal, c.p.	D_{6h}^4	A 3	2·6987	.....	4·2740		12·436

TABL

Symbol	Element	Atomic Number	Atomic Weight	Melting Point ° C.	Change Point ° C.	Boiling Point ° C.
S	Sulphur . . .	16	32·064	112·8 rhomb. 119·0 monocl.	95·5	444·6
Sb	Antimony . .	51	121·76	630·5		1380
Se	Selenium . . .	34	78·96	220		688
Si	Silicon . .	14	28·06	1420		2600
Sn	Tin	50	118·70	231·89	18	2260
Sr	Strontium . .	38	87·63	800		1150
Ta	Tantalum . .	73	180·88	2850		> 4100
Te	Tellurium . .	52	127·61	452		1390
Th	Thorium . . .	90	232·12	1845		> 3000
Ti	Titanium . .	22	47·90	1800		> 3000
Tl	Thallium . .	81	204·39	303·5	231	1650
U	Uranium . .	92	238·07	< 1850		—
V	Vanadium . .	23	50·95	1710		3000
W	Tungsten . . .	74	183·92	3370		5900
Zn	Zinc	30	65·38	419·47		907
Zr	Zirconium . .	40	91·22	1900	862	> 2900

I (*continued*)

Lattice	Space Group	Lattice Type	a	b	c	Ax. Ang.	Density (X-ray)
orthorhombic	V_h^{24}	A 17	10·48	12·92	24·55		2·04
monoclinic	C_{2h}^2	—					
monoclinic	C_{2h}^2	—	26·4	9·26	13·32	$\beta = 79° 15'$	2·00
rhombohedral	D_{3d}^5	A 7	4·49762			$\alpha = 57° 6' 27''$	6·688
hexagonal	D_{3d}^4	A 8	4·337	.....	4·944		4·845
monoclinic	C_{2h}^2	—	8·992	8·973	11·52	$\beta = 91° 34'$	4·48
monoclinic	C_{2h}^5	—	12·74	8·04	9·25	$\beta = 93° 4'$	4·40
cubic, f.c.	O_h^7	A 4	5·41982				2·325
α-cubic, f.c.	O_h^7	A 4	6·46				5·81
β-tetragonal	D_{4h}^{19}	A 5	5·81950	.....	3·17500		7·281
cubic, f.c.	O_h^5	A 1	6·075				2·577
cubic, b.c.	O_h^9	A 2	3·2959				16·654
hexagonal	D_3^4	A 8	4·445	.....	5·912		6·235
cubic, f.c.	O_h^5	A 1	5·077				11·695
hexagonal, c.p.	D_{6h}^4	A 3	2·953	.....	4·729		4·42
α-hexagonal, c.p.	D_{6h}^4	A 3	3·4496	.....	5·5137		11·84
β-cubic, b.c.	O_h^9	A 2	3·874	(262° C.)			
α-monoclinic	C_{2h}^3	—	2·829	4·887	3·308	$\beta = 64° 18'$	19·05
β-cubic, b.c.	O_h^9	A 2	3·43				19·45
cubic, b.c.	O_h^9	A 2	3·0338				6·015
α-cubic	O_h^3	A 15	5·038	(20° C.)			18·97
β-cubic, b.c.	O_h^9	A 2	3·15837	(25° C.)			19·261
hexagonal, c.p.	D_{6h}^4	A 3	2·65949	.....	4·93685		7·130
α-hexagonal, c.p.	D_{6h}^4	A 3	3·223	.....	5·123		6·525
β-cubic, b.c.	O_h^9	A 2	3·61		(867° C.)		6·39

SPACE-GROUP NOMENCLATURE

The space-group nomenclature used throughout the book is the classical one of Schoenflies. It is now being rapidly superseded by the more descriptive symbolism devised by Hermann and Mauguin. To facilitate changing from one nomenclature to the other, a synoptical table is appended.

The Hermann-Mauguin notation consists of a series of letters and numbers which describe the space-group symmetry in relation to the crystal axes a, b, c.

First comes a capital letter denoting the type of lattice. P denotes a simple or primitive lattice ; A, B, C lattices centred on faces (100), (010), and (001) respectively ; F is a lattice centred on all faces, I a body-centred lattice. R is a rhombohedral lattice ; C and H refer to hexagonal lattices.

The lattice symbol is followed by a number denoting the nature of the principal axis of the crystal. Thus $P4$ denotes a simple cell with a fourfold axis of rotation. If a bar is placed over the top of the number, it denotes an axis of rotary inversion, i.e. the structure is inverted through the centre after rotation through part of a turn. If there is a reflexion plane at right angles to the rotation axis, it is written as part of the symbol. Thus $P2/m$ denotes a simple cell with a twofold axis and a reflexion plane at right angles to it. Screw axes are indicated by suffices, e.g. 6_2 denotes an axis which rotates the structure through $\frac{1}{6}$ of a turn in a clockwise direction and translates it a distance $2c/6$.

A reflexion plane is denoted by the letter m. Glide planes involve a reflexion and a translation and are represented thus:

Translation			Symbol
$a/2$			a
$b/2$			b
$c/2$			c
$\dfrac{a+b}{2}$	$\dfrac{b+c}{2}$ or	$\dfrac{a+c}{2}$	n
$\dfrac{a+b}{4}$	$\dfrac{b+c}{4}$ or	$\dfrac{a+c}{4}$	d

Thus $Pnma$ is a frequently recurring orthorhombic space group. n denotes reflexion planes parallel to (100) involving a glide $\dfrac{b}{2} + \dfrac{c}{2}$.

Planes parallel to (010) are mirror planes m, while reflexion planes parallel to (001) involve a glide $\dfrac{a}{2}$ denoted by the final letter a.

For further information on this subject, the reader is referred to the *Internationale Tabellen zur Bestimmung von Kristallstrukturen*, to *The Crystalline State*, by W. L. Bragg, and to *X-ray Crystallography*, by M. J. Buerger.

TABLE XLVII
SPACE-GROUP NOMENCLATURES OF SCHOENFLIES AND OF MAUGUIN

	Schoen-flies	Mauguin Normalized	Mauguin Other Orientations		Schoen-flies	Mauguin Normalized	Mauguin Other Orientations
I	C_1^1	$P1$	$A1, B1, C1, F1, I1 \ldots$	28	C_{2v}^{13}	Ccc	$\ldots$
				29	C_{2v}^{14}	Amm	Bmm
2	C_i^1, S_2^1	$P\bar{1}$	$A\bar{1}, B\bar{1}, C\bar{1}, F\bar{1}, I\bar{1} \ldots$	30	C_{2v}^{15}	Abm	Bma
				31	C_{2v}^{16}	Ama	Bbm
				32	C_{2v}^{17}	Aba	Bba
3	C_{1h}^1, C_s^1	Pm	Bm	33	C_{2v}^{18}	Fmm	$\ldots$
4	C_{1h}^2, C_s^2	Pc	Pa, Pn, Ba, Bc, Bd	34	C_{2v}^{19}	Fdd	$\ldots$
5	C_{1h}^3, C_s^3	Cm	Am, Im, Fm	35	C_{2v}^{20}	Imm	$\ldots$
6	C_{1h}^4, C_s^4	Cc	Aa, Ia, Fd	36	C_{2v}^{21}	Iba	$\ldots$
				37	C_{2v}^{22}	Ima	Ibm
7	C_2^1	$P2$	$B2$				
8	C_2^2	$P2_1$	$B2_1$	38	V^1, D_2^1	$P222$	$\ldots$
9	C_2^3	$C2$	$A2, I2, F2$	39	V^2, D_2^2	$P222_1$	$P2_122 ; P22_12$
10	C_{2h}^1	$P2/m$	$B2/m$	40	V^3, D_2^3	$P2_12_12$	$P22_12_1; P2_122_1$
11	C_{2h}^2	$P2_1/m$	$B2_1/m$	41	V^4, D_2^4	$P2_12_12_1$	
12	C_{2h}^3	$C2/m$	$A2/m, \quad I2/m, F2/m$	42	V^5, D_2^5	$C222_1$	$A2_122; B22_12$
				43	V^6, D_2^6	$C222$	$A222; B222$
13	C_{2h}^4	$P2/c$	$P2/a, P2/n, B2/a, B2/c, B2/d$	44	V^7, D_2^7	$F222$	$\ldots$
				45	V^8, D_2^8	$I222$	$\ldots$
14	C_{2h}^5	$P2_1/c$	$P2_1/a, \quad P2_1/n, B2_1/a, \quad B2_1/c, B2_1/d$	46	V^9, D_2^9	$I2_12_12_1$	$\ldots$
				47	V_h^1, D_{2h}^1	$Pmmm$	$\ldots$
				48	V_h^2, D_{2h}^2	$Pnnn$	$\ldots$
15	C_{2h}^6	$C2/c$	$A2/a, I2/a, I2/c, F2/d$	49	V_h^3, D_{2h}^3	$Pccm$	$Pbmb; Pmaa$
				50	V_h^4, D_{2h}^4	$Pban$	$Pcna; Pncb$
				51	V_h^5, D_{2h}^5	$Pmma$	$Pmmb; \quad Pmam; Pmcm; \quad Pbmm; Pcmm$
16	C_{2v}^1	Pmm	$\ldots$				
17	C_{2v}^2	Pmc	Pcm	52	V_h^6, D_{2h}^6	$Pnna$	$Pnnb; \quad Pnan; Pncn; \quad Pbnn; Pcnn$
18	C_{2v}^3	Pcc	$\ldots$				
19	C_{2v}^4	Pma	Pbm	53	V_h^7, D_{2h}^7	$Pmna$	$Pnmb; \quad Pman; Pncm; \quad Pbmn; Pcnm$
20	C_{2v}^5	Pca	Pbc				
21	C_{2v}^6	Pnc	Pcn				
22	C_{2v}^7	Pmn	Pnm				
23	C_{2v}^8	Pba	$\ldots$	54	V_h^8, D_{2h}^8	$Pcca$	$Pccb; \quad Pbab; Pbcb; \quad Pbaa; Pcaa$
24	C_{2v}^9	Pna	Pbn				
25	C_{2v}^{10}	Pnn	$\ldots$				
26	C_{2v}^{11}	Cmm	$\ldots$	55	V_h^9, D_{2h}^9	$Pbam$	$Pcma; Pmcb$
27	C_{2v}^{12}	Cmc	Ccm				

TABLE XLVII (continued)

	Schoenflies	Mauguin Normalized	Mauguin Other Orientations
56	V_h^{10}, D_{2h}^{10}	Pccn	Pbnb; Pnaa
57	V_h^{11}, D_{2h}^{11}	Pbcm	Pbma; Pcam; Pcmb; Pmab; Pmca
58	V_h^{12}, D_{2h}^{12}	Pnnm	Pnmn; Pmnn
59	V_h^{13}, D_{2h}^{13}	Pmmn	Pmnm; Pnmm
60	V_h^{14}, D_{2h}^{14}	Pbcn	Pbna; Pcan; Pcnb; Pnab; Pnca
61	V_h^{15}, D_{2h}^{15}	Pbca	Pcab
62	V_h^{16}, D_{2h}^{16}	Pnma	Pnam; Pbnm; Pcmn; Pmnb; Pmcn
63	V_h^{17}, D_{2h}^{17}	Cmcm	Ccmm; Amma; Amam; Bmmb; Bbmm
64	V_h^{18}, D_{2h}^{18}	Cmca	Ccma; Abma; Abam; Bmab; Bbam
65	V_h^{19}, D_{2h}^{19}	Cmmm	Ammm; Bmmm
66	V_h^{20}, D_{2h}^{20}	Cccm	Amaa; Bbmb
67	V_h^{21}, D_{2h}^{21}	Cmma	Abmm; Bmam
68	V_h^{22}, D_{2h}^{22}	Ccca	Abaa; Bbab
69	V_h^{23}, D_{2h}^{23}	Fmmm	...
70	V_h^{24}, D_{2h}^{24}	Fddd	...
71	V_h^{25}, D_{2h}^{25}	Immm	...
72	V_h^{26}, D_{2h}^{26}	Ibam	Icma; Imcb
73	V_h^{27}, D_{2h}^{27}	Ibca	...
74	V_h^{28}, D_{2h}^{28}	Imma	Imcm; Ibmm
75	S_4^1	$P\bar{4}$	$C\bar{4}$
76	S_4^2	$I\bar{4}$	$F\bar{4}$
77	V_d^1, D_{2d}^1	$P\bar{4}2m$	$C\bar{4}m2$
78	V_d^2, D_{2d}^2	$P\bar{4}2c$	$C\bar{4}c2$
79	V_d^3, D_{2d}^3	$P\bar{4}2_1m$	$C\bar{4}m2_1$
80	V_d^4, D_{2d}^4	$P\bar{4}2_1c$	$C\bar{4}c2_1$
81	V_d^5, D_{2d}^5	$C\bar{4}2m$	$P\bar{4}m2$
82	V_d^6, D_{2d}^6	$C\bar{4}2c$	$P\bar{4}c2$
83	V_d^7, D_{2d}^7	$C\bar{4}2b$	$P\bar{4}b2$
84	V_d^8, D_{2d}^8	$C\bar{4}2n$	$P\bar{4}n2$
85	V_d^9, D_{2d}^9	$F\bar{4}2m$	$I\bar{4}m2$
86	V_d^{10}, D_{2d}^{10}	$F\bar{4}2c$	$I\bar{4}c2$
87	V_d^{11}, D_{2d}^{11}	$I\bar{4}2m$	$F\bar{4}m2$
88	V_d^{12}, D_{2d}^{12}	$I\bar{4}2d$	$F\bar{4}d2$
89	C_4^1	$P4$	$C4$
90	C_4^2	$P4_1$	$C4_1$
91	C_4^3	$P4_2$	$C4_2$
92	C_4^4	$P4_3$	$C4_3$
93	C_4^5	$I4$	$F4$
94	C_4^6	$I4_1$	$F4_1$

	Schoenflies	Mauguin Normalized	Mauguin Other Orientations
95	C_{4h}^1	$P4/m$	$C4/m$
96	C_{4h}^2	$P4_2/m$	$C4_2/m$
97	C_{4h}^3	$P4/n$	$C4/a$
98	C_{4h}^4	$P4_2/n$	$C4_2/a$
99	C_{4h}^5	$I4/m$	$F4/m$
100	C_{4h}^6	$I4_1/a$	$F4_1/d$
101	C_{4v}^1	$P4mm$	$C4mm$
102	C_{4v}^2	$P4bm$	$C4mb$
103	C_{4v}^3	$P4cm$	$C4mc$
104	C_{4v}^4	$P4nm$	$C4mn$
105	C_{4v}^5	$P4cc$	$C4cc$
106	C_{4v}^6	$P4nc$	$C4cn$
107	C_{4v}^7	$P4mc$	$C4cm$
108	C_{4v}^8	$P4bc$	$C4cb$
109	C_{4v}^9	$I4mm$	$F4mm$
110	C_{4v}^{10}	$I4cm$	$F4mc$
111	C_{4v}^{11}	$I4md$	$F4dm$
112	C_{4v}^{12}	$I4cd$	$F4dc$
113	D_4^1	$P42$	$C422$
114	D_4^2	$P42_1$	$C422_1$
115	D_4^3	$P4_12$	$C4_122$
116	D_4^4	$P4_12_1$	$C4_122_1$
117	D_4^5	$P4_22$	$C4_222$
118	D_4^6	$P4_22_1$	$C4_222_1$
119	D_4^7	$P4_32$	$C4_322$
120	D_4^8	$P4_32_1$	$C4_322_1$
121	D_4^9	$I42$	$F42$
122	D_4^{10}	$I4_12$	$F4_12$
123	D_{4h}^1	$P4/mmm$	$C4/mmm$
124	D_{4h}^2	$P4/mcc$	$C4/mcc$
125	D_{4h}^3	$P4/nbm$	$C4/amb$
126	D_{4h}^4	$P4/nnc$	$C4/acn$
127	D_{4h}^5	$P4/mbm$	$C4/mmb$
128	D_{4h}^6	$P4/mnc$	$C4/mcn$
129	D_{4h}^7	$P4/nmm$	$C4/amm$
130	D_{4h}^8	$P4/ncc$	$C4/acc$
131	D_{4h}^9	$P4/mmc$	$C4/mcm$
132	D_{4h}^{10}	$P4/mcm$	$C4/mmc$
133	D_{4h}^{11}	$P4/nbc$	$C4/acb$
134	D_{4h}^{12}	$P4/nnm$	$C4/amn$
135	D_{4h}^{13}	$P4/mbc$	$C4/mcb$
136	D_{4h}^{14}	$P4/mnm$	$C4/mmn$
137	D_{4h}^{15}	$P4/nmc$	$C4/acm$
138	D_{4h}^{16}	$P4/ncm$	$C4/amc$
139	D_{4h}^{17}	$I4/mmm$	$F4/mmm$
140	D_{4h}^{18}	$I4/mcm$	$F4/mmc$
141	D_{4h}^{19}	$I4/amd$	$F4/ddm$
142	D_{4h}^{20}	$I4/acd$	$F4/ddc$
143	C_3^1	$C3$	$H3$

TABLE XLVII (*continued*)

	Schoenflies	Mauguin Normalized	Mauguin Other Orientations		Schoenflies	Mauguin Normalized	Mauguin Other Orientations
144	C_3^2	$C3_1$	$H3_1$	185	D_6^1	$C62$	$H62$
145	C_3^3	$C3_2$	$H3_2$	186	D_6^2	$C6_12$	$H6_12$
146	C_3^4	$R3$	...	187	D_6^3	$C6_52$	$H6_52$
				188	D_6^4	$C6_22$	$H6_22$
147	C_{3i}^1, S_6^1	$C\bar{3}$	$H\bar{3}$	189	D_6^5	$C6_42$	$H6_42$
148	C_{3i}^2, S_6^2	$R\bar{3}$	...	190	D_6^6	$C6_32$	$H6_32$
149	C_{3v}^1	$C3m$	$H31m$	191	D_{6h}^1	$C6/mmm$	$H6/mmm$
150	C_{3v}^2	$H3m$	$C31m$	192	D_{6h}^2	$C6/mcc$	$H6/mcc$
151	C_{3v}^3	$C3c$	$H31c$	193	D_{6h}^3	$C6/mcm$	$H6/mmc$
152	C_{3v}^4	$H3c$	$C31c$	194	D_{6h}^4	$C6/mmc$	$H6/mcm$
153	C_{3v}^5	$R3m$	...	195	T^1	$P23$	...
154	C_{3v}^6	$R3c$	...	196	T^2	$F23$	...
				197	T^3	$I23$	
155	D_3^1	$H32$	$C312$	198	T^4	$P2_13$	...
156	D_3^2	$C32$	$H312$	199	T^5	$I2_13$	...
157	D_3^3	$H3_12$	$C3_112$				
158	D_3^4	$C3_12$	$H3_112$	200	T_h^1	$Pm3$	...
159	D_3^5	$H3_22$	$C3_212$	201	T_h^2	$Pn3$	...
160	D_3^6	$C3_22$	$H3_212$	202	T_h^3	$Fm3$	...
161	D_3^7	$R32$	...	203	T_h^4	$Fd3$	...
				204	T_h^5	$Im3$	...
162	D_{3d}^1	$H\bar{3}m$	$C\bar{3}1m$	205	T_h^6	$Pa3$	...
163	D_{3d}^2	$H\bar{3}c$	$C\bar{3}1c$	206	T_h^7	$Ia3$	...
164	D_{3d}^3	$C\bar{3}m$	$H\bar{3}1m$				
165	D_{3d}^4	$C\bar{3}c$	$H\bar{3}1c$	207	T_d^1	$P\bar{4}3m$	...
166	D_{3d}^5	$R\bar{3}m$	...	208	T_d^2	$F\bar{4}3m$	...
167	D_{3d}^6	$R\bar{3}c$	...	209	T_d^3	$I\bar{4}3m$	...
				210	T_d^4	$P\bar{4}3n$	...
168	C_{3h}^1	$C\bar{6}$	$H\bar{6}$	211	T_d^5	$F\bar{4}3c$	...
				212	T_d^6	$I\bar{4}3d$	...
169	D_{3h}^1	$C\bar{6}m$	$H\bar{6}2m$	213	O^1	$P43$	...
170	D_{3h}^2	$C\bar{6}c$	$H\bar{6}2c$	214	O^2	$P4_23$	...
171	D_{3h}^3	$H\bar{6}m$	$C\bar{6}2m$	215	O^3	$F43$	...
172	D_{3h}^4	$H\bar{6}c$	$C\bar{6}2c$	216	O^4	$F4_13$	...
				217	O^5	$I43$	...
173	C_6^1	$C6$	$H6$	218	O^6	$P4_33$	...
174	C_6^2	$C6_1$	$H6_1$	219	O^7	$P4_13$	...
175	C_6^3	$C6_5$	$H6_5$	220	O^8	$I4_13$	...
176	C_6^4	$C6_2$	$H6_2$				
177	C_6^5	$C6_4$	$H6_4$	221	O_h^1	$Pm3m$	...
178	C_6^6	$C6_3$	$H6_3$	222	O_h^2	$Pn3n$	...
				223	O_h^3	$Pm3n$	...
179	C_{6h}^1	$C6/m$	$H6/m$	224	O_h^4	$Pn3m$	...
180	C_{6h}^2	$C6_3/m$	$H6_3/m$	225	O_h^5	$Fm3m$	...
				226	O_h^6	$Fm3c$	...
181	C_{6v}^1	$C6mm$	$H6mm$	227	O_h^7	$Fd3m$	...
182	C_{6v}^2	$C6cc$	$H6cc$	228	O_h^8	$Fd3c$	...
183	C_{6v}^3	$C6cm$	$H6mc$	229	O_h^9	$Im3m$	...
184	C_{6v}^4	$C6mc$	$H6cm$	230	O_h^{10}	$Ia3d$	...

INDEX